Y0-AGO-291

Report Writing

FOURTH EDITION

PRENTICE-HALL INTERNATIONAL, INC., *London*
PRENTICE-HALL OF AUSTRALIA, PTY., LTD., *Sydney*
PRENTICE-HALL OF CANADA, LTD., *Toronto*
PRENTICE-HALL OF INDIA (PRIVATE), LTD., *New Delhi*
PRENTICE-HALL OF JAPAN, INC., *Tokyo*

Report Writing

FOURTH EDITION

Harold F. Graves
Professor Emeritus of English Composition
The Pennsylvania State University

Lyne S. S. Hoffman
Professor of Technical Writing
The Pennsylvania State University

PRENTICE-HALL, INC.   ENGLEWOOD CLIFFS, N.J.

Current printing (last digit):
12 11 10 9 8 7 6 5 4 3

Library of Congress Catalog Card No.: 65-11494
Printed in the United States of America
[77367-C]

Preface

ANY textbook entering a fourth edition has one basic problem. What, if anything, of the original conception of the book remains pertinent to our day? And, on the other hand, what is so out-of-date that it must be discarded and forgotten?

In revising, we were surprised to find that much of the original preface is still applicable today. We repeat some of it:

Nowadays reports play a large part in public and corporate affairs. An increasing number of men and women must know how to write them. When no standard form is available, it is often difficult to develop a logical arrangement for a report and to present clearly and emphatically the facts and ideas which it must contain. This book, which applies certain principles of composition and rhetoric to the special field of the report, is intended to be helpful to those writers who are either inexperienced or less effective than they would like to be.

The report writer must meet several requirements. He must be "audience-minded"; that is, he must write with an appreciation of his reader's point of view. He must be clear and accurate. He must have the ability to determine what to include and how to arrange it. In this book the authors have tried to hold in mind these common demands and to point out reasonable and effective methods of meeting them.

The materials of the text are so arranged that the student may advance progressively from the simple problems to the more complex. The business letter is chosen as the proper approach, both because it demands somewhat less skill in organization than many longer forms and because its relationship to all report writing is so close. The student's practice begins with the writing of letters and short compositions, in which he can find interest because of their obvious relationship to the practical reports of business and industry. With this foundation laid, he is prepared to attack the more complicated problems.

Certainly the number of reports and report writers has increased fantastically since 1929, but what may have seemed new then seems only too obvious today. That the principles laid down in the first edition have been found pragmatic is evidenced by the continuous adoption of *Report Writing* in classrooms, in government, and in industry, here and abroad. (It is noteworthy, too, that the Third Edition was recently reproduced in

Braille.) The *principles* emphasized in the Fourth Edition are therefore not essentially different from those emphasized in the First.

Yet important changes were necessary. Illustrations and exercises had lost their timeliness and had to be replaced. Moreover, it seemed necessary to *test* every apparent requirement of report writing by a thorough survey of current practices and by an inquiry among those persons who actually read today's reports. The two authors had accumulated some seventy years of experience in university classrooms and in reading actual reports, but what did the men who read modern reports expect— and especially, what did they find wanting in the reports they had to read?

Our survey yielded more than two hundred replies from persons professionally concerned with the effectiveness of reports. Consensus: too many reports, even now, are badly organized, too wordy, and too inconsiderate of the reader. We quote some of their answers in Chapter 1.

We have made one major change in organization of the text. A *Handbook* at the end of the book now covers details of "mechanics": abbreviations, punctuation, usage, spelling, and the handling of numbers.

The authors are indebted to countless persons and organizations for material and for constructive suggestions, but particularly to the following:

Mr. William R. Cushman	American Potash & Chemical Corporation
Mr. R. W. Mumford	American Potash & Chemical Corporation
Editors	American Standards Association
Mr. Michael Baker	The Baker Engineers
Dr. Michael Cannon	Cannon Instrument Company
Mr. Richard McFalls	Cluett Peabody
Dr. Bernard R. Jones	The Ethyl Corporation
Mr. Brooke Alexander	*Fortune* Magazine
Mr. T. O. Richards	General Motors Corporation
Mr. Ralph A. Richardson	General Motors Corporation
Dr. R. E. Birch	Harbison-Walker Refractories Company
Dr. R. S. George	Hercules Powder Company
Mr. Philip Freed	HRB-Singer, Inc.
Mr. L. P. Reilly	HRB-Singer, Inc.
Dr. G. D. Byrkit	The Mathieson Alkali Works, Inc.
Dr. Hugh Odishaw	National Academy of Sciences
Mr. B. S. Converse	New York Central System
Dr. John A. Hipple	Philips Laboratories
Prof. Edward J. Nichols	The Pennsylvania State University
Dean Lawrence Perez	The Pennsylvania State University
Mr. Jack Guthrie	The Sun Oil Company
Dr. Harold Perrine	The Sun Oil Company
Dr. W. E. Kuhn	The Texas Company
Mr. Osborne H. Graves	Tennessee Valley Authority
Prof. Joseph Vaughan	University of Virginia
Mr. Gilbert Remey	United Eastern Coal Corporation

Contents

CHAPTER 1

The Demand for Reports   1

What is a report? Who writes reports? Who reads reports? What makes a good report writer? Guiding principles. Assignments.

CHAPTER 2

Letter and Memorandum   9

The letter of inquiry. Answering an inquiry. The letter of instructions. The letter report. Notes on form and style. Summary. Exercises.

CHAPTER 3

The Style of a Good Report   26

Unity. Clarity. Economy. Readability. Accuracy. The paragraph. The sentence. Sentence unity. Sentence clarity. Sentence economy. Sentence readability. Sentence accuracy. Mechanical considerations. Abbreviation. Capitalization. Hyphenation. Spelling. Numbers. Punctuation. Exercises.

CHAPTER 4

Collecting Data   60

Analyzing the problem. Potential sources of information. Evidence from reading. Direct observation and experiment. Sampling. Interview and questionnaire. Applications of logic. Recording the data—note-taking. A final checklist. Exercises.

CHAPTER 5

Planning the Report   77

General thesis and support. Length and form. Periodic report plans. Progress report plans. Investigative report plans. Plans for proposals and recommendation reports. Representative report outlines. Assignments. Exercises.

CHAPTER 6

Preparing the Manuscript: Rhetorical Elements   92

Prefaces and introductions. Letter of transmittal. Cover letters. The introduction. Summaries. Epitome. Abstract. Conclusions and recommendations. Introductory summary. Terminal summary. Summaries of evidence. Definitions. Interpretation of data. Summary and simplification. Evaluating the data. Logical inferences. Assignments. Exercises.

CHAPTER 7
Preparing the Manuscript: Format   119

Importance of appearance. The report binder. The title page. Table of contents. The summary. Introduction. Conclusions and recommendations. The main text. Terminal summary. Appendices. Bibliography and references. Documentation—acknowledging the contributions of others. Footnotes. Endnotes. Compromise method. Paper. Standards for margins and spacing. Page numbering. Submitting the manuscript to the printer. Types of mechanical aids. Tables. Figures. Size of mechanical aids. Placement of mechanical aids.

Specimen Reports   153

1. RECOMMENDATION REPORT: *The Feasibility of the Use of Radioisotopes to Measure Catalyst Circulation Rates in the Catalytic Cracking Unit of the Sungei Gerong Refinery.*
2. CONSTRUCTION PROGRESS REPORT: *Wilson Lock, Tennessee Valley Authority, Construction Progress.*
3. MONTHLY REPORT—RESEARCH AND DEVELOPMENT: *American Potash & Chemical Corporation.*
4. ONE-PAGE STATUS REPORT: *Department of the Army.*
5. RECOMMENDATION REPORT: *New York Central System.*
6. INVESTIGATIVE REPORT: *U.S. Bureau of Mines.*

The Handbook Section   211

1. *Abbreviations.* 2. *Capitalization.* 3. *Compounding and Hyphenation.* 4. *Spelling.* 5. *Preferred Usage (Glossary).* 6. *The Handling of Numbers.* 7. *Punctuation.* 8. *Letter Form.*

APPENDIX A
The Letter of Application   265

What the reader looks for. What you have to offer. The letter itself. The contract. Evidence. Close. The data sheet.

APPENDIX B
Bibliography of Abstracts and Indexes   275

Index   281

Report Writing

FOURTH EDITION

CHAPTER 1

The Demand for Reports

ONE characteristic of our highly organized society is the emphasis it gives to reports. As corporations grow and government agencies multiply, the quantity of private and public reports reaches staggering proportions. By what other means can one specialist know what other specialists are doing? How else can the responsible executive get the information he needs to reach important decisions? How else can records be kept for future reference? Reports often tend to breed more reports, and the executive who complains about "too many reports" has a point. Perhaps we do have too many of them. That is why a really *good* report—one that says something the reader wants to know and says it right—gets so much recognition. The man who can write *good* reports stands out from all the rest. He wins respect, he gets attention, and usually he goes up the ladder.

When employers of recent college graduates complain that the new man "can't write a report," just what do they mean? Here are some representative answers:

"They don't know what to include and what to leave out."

"They waste our time. They can't boil it down. They're wordy. They don't seem to know what to put first, what next, and what last."

"They can't write simple, readable English. They want to exhibit all the gobbledygook they've been learning in college."

"They either leave out all supporting evidence—just state opinions without any backing—or they fill pages with ill-digested, uninterpreted raw data. One is just as bad as the other."

"They don't seem to know why they're writing a report in the first place. They have no sense of purpose—why a reader might want to know something and how they might tell him what he wants to know."

1

These complaints suggest possible remedies. The young graduate going into any business, industry, or public agency deserves some fair answers.

WHAT IS A REPORT?

Every report is expected to communicate useful information. Information is more than vague ideas, feelings, opinions, and prejudices; it is verifiable fact or at least the conclusions of recognized specialists. The information in a report may come from a variety of sources: direct observation and experience, tests and experiments, surveys involving interviews or questionnaires, unpublished records or reports, and published materials. What makes such information *useful* is the kind of conclusions or recommendations that it leads to. Primarily, information in a report is not introduced to amuse, to entertain, or even to educate. It is always intended to have a specific use for its reader: to facilitate work he is doing or to help him make important decisions.

The report has a limited audience. It is directed to an individual or group to whom the writer feels a definite responsibility. The assistant engineer reports on tests that his chief had directed him to make; his superior reports to another superior higher up; the president of the corporation reports to stockholders; the President of the United States occasionally reports to the American citizens whom he represents. Every real report is aimed at some specific audience to whom the writer feels responsible.

The tone and emphasis of every report are expository rather than persuasive. Of course the good report is both interesting and convincing to its readers, but it is not salesmanship or propaganda. Because of his strong sense of responsibility, the good report writer avoids exaggeration, card-stacking, and emotional appeals. He aims for accuracy and applies tests of logic to his inferences. His report is essentially objective; that is, it relies on verifiable evidence and subordinates personal feelings.

Reports certainly differ in aim. Some are by-products of routine activities, covering only what has been done and what will be done; these reports emphasize progress or status. Others present the end results of investigations (tests, experiments, surveys, research); their aim is to support conclusions and recommendations.

Reports differ in length, and therefore in form, because length naturally influences form. Routine daily reports are often made by check marks on a printed questionnaire. Somewhat less routine reports of minor matters may appear as memos or brief letters. More important matters are discussed in longer reports with title page, table of contents, and other features characteristic of the formal report. Length and form depend upon the importance of the problem and the size of the audience.

WHO WRITES REPORTS?

In our society it is no exaggeration to say that almost everyone whose job calls for more than a high school education becomes a report writer. Everyone who works for a corporation or government agency is a good prospect, and the more responsible his job, the more likelihood that report writing will become an important aspect of it.

Nearly all specialists must become report writers. Accountants, engineers, architects, chemists, foresters, research scientists, and specialists in transportation, traffic control, site planning, and personnel problems usually discover that their reports represent the greater part of the work they have done. Without good reports their work may be wasted.

Most executives find reports a necessary element in their work. They must regularly report to other executives or to stockholders. They must especially learn (1) how to read and digest reports of subordinates, and (2) how to summarize and put into readable form the quantities of information that lead to their decisions.

The demand for efficient reports has become so clear that many large corporations have established editorial departments to supervise the production of reports. Specialists in report writing advise, instruct, edit, and—when necessary—actually write the reports that specialists and administrators must submit. The editorial experts usually have broad scientific or technical education as well as the ability to organize and to write.

Anyone with knowledge of report writing obviously has an advantage over others in the same kind of job who lack this knowledge. He can save time and money. If his own reports must be edited by others, he knows what improvements can help and what changes can hurt. He knows what must be included and what may usefully be left out.

Every good report writer has something to say. No report can be better than the information and interpretation which go into it. Unfortunately, those who *probably* have something to say and *probably* know what it signifies are not always able to communicate their knowledge and wisdom to readers who might profit by it. The good report writer *can* communicate useful information in a way that his reader understands and appreciates.

Good report writers, quite naturally, are in demand.

WHO READS REPORTS?

No real report is directed to the general reader. A person who reads a report is a special reader expecting something of specific importance. The title of the report (the subject line or the opening paragraph in the short report) ought to let any reader know whether he wants to go further. Nobody is likely to read beyond that point unless the problem for discussion promises something useful.

Many reports must consider both *primary* and *secondary* readers. The primary reader is the person to whom the report is specifically addressed, the individual named on the title page or at the head of a memorandum: "To John Griffin, Branch Manager." Secondary readers are persons who may need to refer to this report at a later time. The primary reader is commonly serving in some executive capacity; he needs a clear summary of conclusions that will help him reach administrative decisions. Secondary readers may include technical specialists who want specific technical details. Sometimes secondary readers are called upon to advise the primary reader regarding the conclusions or recommendations in the report. They study the evidence and the reasoning and say, "Yes, these conclusions are sound," or "No, such conclusions are not justified." The report writer must therefore write for *two* audiences: he must make himself entirely clear to the executive, often a layman, and he must substantiate his conclusions with sufficient technical evidence to satisfy the technical specialist.

Some reports, of course, go immediately to specialists in the writer's own field, perhaps to his immediate superior in a technical department or to colleagues working on similar problems. The reader may use such reports as a basis for decision (to carry on further tests or to stop them, to make recommendations for or against production) or as a guide in further research. These readers understand the writer's technical terminology without translation or definition.

Other reports go first to readers who are not familiar with the writer's special field and do not have the technical education required to understand the common language of chemists, metallurgists, psychiatrists, or anthropologists. One obvious requirement of a good report writer is to learn how to translate his special terminology, when necessary, into language his reader will understand.

"Who will read my report?" is a question you must answer before you answer several other questions:

"How long should it be?" Does your reader consider the problem a major one or a very minor one? Does he want full details or a brief summary? Will a memo or a letter be enough, or should you employ a formal report? Does your reader want full explanations of methods and complete statistical evidence, or will he be satisfied with general statements which are subject to verification if necessary? You must know your reader to answer these questions well.

"What kind of language is appropriate?" Can you use normal technical terminology, or must you translate into everyday language? How much must you define? Does your reader expect a personal, informal style or an objective, formal report?

Readers certainly differ. A report which satisfies one may prove inadequate for another, but at least we may generalize to this extent: Every reader is looking for something useful to him—he wants to get it as easily as possible, and he wants to be rid of this report and free to go on to something else. The less time a reader is forced to devote to your report, the happier you will make him.

WHAT MAKES A GOOD REPORT WRITER?

Good report writers are made through their own effort. Of course general intelligence always counts, but anyone capable of handling a job where report writing seriously matters can learn how to write reports as easily as he learns the other requirements of his job. The good report writer develops the following characteristics:

1. The good report writer can analyze a problem. He can state it clearly. He can discover pertinent issues and define them. Thus he is prepared to look for relevant evidence. He knows what to include in a report and what to leave out.
2. The good report writer has the energy, curiosity, and diligence to dig out the information he needs.
3. He has good judgment. He can evaluate sources and evidence, distinguish the relevant from the irrelevant, separate the sound from the unsound. He recognizes significant relationships and reasons logically to a conclusion.
4. He is objective. He can keep prejudices and preconceptions under control.
5. He is able to understand his reader's point of view.
6. He can economize. He learns to condense and to summarize. He can say much in few words.
7. He is accurate. He checks and rechecks his figures, checks and rechecks his words. He means what he says—and everybody can count on his statements.

GUIDING PRINCIPLES

This book presents numerous rules for report writing, many suggestions and bits of advice, and some do's and don't's for writers. Let us start, however, with *first* principles. All the specific rules you learn later are only means of achieving success with these:

1. Know your purpose. Before you write, decide exactly what you want your report to do.
2. Meet your reader's needs. What questions does he want answered? Have you answered them? The reader always comes first.

3. Make your reader like your report. Prove that your report is worth his time. Make it physically attractive. Make it interesting *to him*.
4. Be accurate, honest, and objective.
5. Save your reader's time. You can do that by adopting the best form and format for your purpose, placing good summaries in the right places, including clear tables and charts that dramatize or simplify, and *especially* by writing a clean and simple prose that eliminates deadwood and gobbledygook.
6. Make it clear. Everything you write need not be clear to everybody, but it must be entirely clear to those who need to read it.

Assignments

A course in report writing can be most profitable when you start early to seek subjects and occasions for major reports which will be completed at a later time. With long-range objectives in view, you can find more that seems practical and interesting in your short assignments and more that seems applicable in your study of the text.

For long reports, find subjects that you already know something about (from experience or study) but that demand further investigation.

Decide upon an *audience*—a reader or readers who can use the information you expect to provide.

Decide on a clear *purpose:*

To report progress on a project.

To report the activities and condition of an organization, such as a department of a company.

To report the results of an investigation (inspection, survey, test, or experiment).

To propose or recommend, and to defend your recommendations.

With such a start, you can find suggestions in the following chapters that will apply to *your* major assignments.

The following general topics may suggest possibilities. Of course your own subjects must be more specific.

1. For a periodic report (monthly, quarterly, or annual), providing a record of accomplishments for the period and a comparison with similar periods of the past:

A college society or fraternity	A college department
A town, borough, or village	A finance committee
A labor union	A small corporation
A personnel department	A sales manager
A safety program	A cost department
A production department	A health officer

2. For a progress report, covering the progress made in a project not yet completed:

A dam, water system, road, or building under construction

A housing development or urban renewal program

The erection and equipment of an addition to a plant
The conversion of a plant to a new product
A pilot plant or extended laboratory experiment
An extensive research project

3. For an investigative report, covering facts discovered through observation, experiment, interrogation, or reading:

Inspection, calling for description, evaluation, and explanation:

A heating system	A timber cruise of a small tract
A traffic problem	Fire-protection equipment
Safety measures	A sewage-disposal plant
A harbor or naval base	An airport
A commercial garage	An office filing system
A geological study of a small area	A park or playground
A water-supply system	

A comparison of values:

Different road materials	Different types of cameras
Two heating systems	Types of building insulation
Different group-insurance plans	Air-conditioning systems
Different fuels	New machinery for a factory
Computers	Accounting procedures
Different safety devices	

A search for causes:

Varying living costs in different towns
Differences in price of similar items
A strike (or strikes)
Decrease or increase in profits
Distribution of students in different courses
Factors leading to success or failure in certain jobs
An increase or decrease in sales
Trouble with a machine or instrument
Increase or decrease in workers' productivity
A voting pattern in county, city, or state

4. For a recommendation report which reaches a decision, advocates an action, and presents supporting evidence:

Plans:

Reorganization of office	Reorganization of a plant
A real-estate development	A recreational area
A safety program	An accounting system
A public-relations program	An advertising program

A plan for improving interoffice
   communications

Advisability of action:

Purchasing new trucks	Installing new machinery
Installing parking meters	Building a new hospital
Appropriation for an airport	Buying a store, farm, or factory
Buying electronic equipment	Approving a city bond issue

Selection of sites:

A restaurant	A shopping center
A golf course	A bypass
A branch office	A new plant
A motel	A service station

5. For a search of the literature which integrates, summarizes, and interprets published information on some technical or scientific problem of current interest (see the bibliography, Appendix B):

Newly discovered synthetics

Peaceful uses of nuclear energy

New drugs and the new treatments of certain diseases

Electronic devices

New uses for known materials

Theories of zoning

Theories of local taxation

Effects of automation

CHAPTER 2

Letter

and

Memorandum

THE short report, with which our study naturally begins, appears most often in the form of business correspondence, as a letter or memorandum. The prospective report writer who understands the conventions and standards of good letters and memorandums has the best possible start.

Business correspondence, like the modern report, has undergone significant changes in the past quarter-century. "Natural" English replaces trite business jargon. Directness, economy, and simplicity characterize the style. The "You-Attitude"—emphasizing the reader's interests and needs first—results in more effective communications. All these changes affect the report writer.

The letter and the memorandum concern the report writer in other ways. A letter may propose an investigation or assign a study. A memorandum may authorize an important report. A letter of transmittal may serve as the preface of a long report. Cover letters frequently accompany copies of a report that go to several readers. Even the long report, using a form that seems far different from the usual letter, ordinarily results from or is supplemented by these shorter forms.

So the study of report writing begins most effectively with a study of certain kinds of simple correspondence: the letter of inquiry and answer to an inquiry, then the letter of instructions and the short report that follows it.

THE LETTER OF INQUIRY

The letter of inquiry is a request for information. Sometimes it may be preliminary to sending an order or signing a contract, and in such circumstances the reader will profit directly from the reply he makes. The kind of inquiry we shall study, however, is one where the reward for answering is at best intangible or remote. The writer really asks a favor. Figures 1 and 2 illustrate the characteristics of such a letter.

The following characteristics of the letter of inquiry deserve attention:
1. The first paragraph (the "contact") states the business of the letter and indicates a good reason for the request.

HALLIDAY CHEMICAL COMPANY

Beaverton
Oregon

January 15, 1965

Mr. Amos Levitt, Head
Testing and Instrument Division
Crossly Salt Products Corporation
Farwell, New York

Dear Mr. Levitt:

We are contemplating replacing present recording flow meters with Johnston equipment. We understand that after considerable investigation you have already made this change. Will you tell us something of your experience?

Would you be willing to let us know why you chose the Johnston meters and how satisfactory they have proved since their installation? We are expecially interested in answers to the following questions:

1. How much maintenance do these meters require?

2. How much is their accuracy affected by changes in the temperature of the liquid?

3. What kind of replacement and parts service do you get?

We will appreciate any information you can send us, and we look forward to the opportunity of returning the favor.

Very truly yours

HALLIDAY CHEMICAL COMPANY

Abbott Laurence

Abbott Laurence
Purchasing Agent

AL:kvc

FIGURE 1. LETTER OF INQUIRY.

BREWSTER PRODUCTS, INC.

200 Rock Mills Road
Brewster, Connecticut

February 26, 1965

Professor Alden T. Mann, Head
Department of English
De Soto University
University Station 2, Missouri

Dear Professor Mann:

As a former student of yours in Business Writing, I am appealing to you for some specific help in preparing a "Style Sheet" for our company correspondence. No doubt you have noted changes since I took your course nearly a decade ago.

One of my problems is to select the most appropriate letter form for our use. The textbooks I have consulted leave me in some doubt about the following points:

1. Which form—block, modified block, indented, military, or some other—is most approved today?

2. What punctuation is required? What optional?

3. In the salutation is it courteous to address a stranger by name, or should one use "Dear Sir," or "My dear Sir"?

4. Is it proper to itemize questions as I am doing here?

5. Where should the "Attention" line be placed?

6. Is it good practice to include a "Subject" line? If so, where is it best placed?

I shall much appreciate your advice on these points—and on any others you think may be troublesome.

Respectfully yours

Samuel F. Grunau
Samuel F. Grunau
Executive Assistant

SFG:wak

FIGURE 2. LETTER OF INQUIRY.

11

2. The inquiry itself is arranged and phrased to make answering easy:
   (a) If several specific questions are asked, each question appears in a separate paragraph.
   (b) If each question deserves separate emphasis, the questions may be numbered, indented, or set apart by a different spacing scheme.
3. The inquiry is courteous and tactful. When possible, it offers a service in return, or at least shows a willingness to serve.
4. The whole letter is as brief as the writer can effectively make it.

ANSWERING AN INQUIRY

The answer to the usual letter of inquiry is a type of short report. To be sure, the writer may actually owe his reader nothing; he is not subordinate or responsible to him except as good public relations may dictate. Nevertheless, if he intends to answer at all, he will do his best to provide the information requested. The scope of his answer, if not fixed by the letter of inquiry, is at least implied.

Figures 3 and 4, then, are in the form of simple reports. In each case the letter either supplies the information requested or directs attention to other possible sources.

Consider the plan of such an answer to a letter of inquiry:
1. The first paragraph refers to the inquiry and states the subject and aim of the letter.
2. In either the first or second paragraph, especially if the letter is of some length, the writer may summarize very briefly what follows.
3. Each question receives a separate answer. If the questions were originally numbered, the answers should be numbered the same way. Paragraphing helps emphasize the different topics.
4. The final paragraph shows a courteous willingness to add further information if it is needed.

THE LETTER OF INSTRUCTIONS

The letter of instructions—from superior to subordinate, client to specialist, employer to employee—deserves considerable attention, because such a letter defines the purpose and scope of investigations leading to a report. It gives the report writer his assignment.

Though the relationship of writer to reader is somewhat different, the letter of instructions resembles a letter of inquiry in purpose and plan. To be sure, this letter is less a request than a demand, but modern management adopts a friendlier tone than that of the old-fashioned autocratic boss. Commands no longer sound like commands, but rather like

CROSSLY SALT PRODUCTS CORPORATION

FARWELL, NEW YORK

January 23, 1965

Mr. Abbott Laurence
Purchasing Agent
Halliday Chemical Company
Beaverton, Oregon

Dear Mr. Laurence:

I am glad to send you what information we have regarding our Johnston flow meters.

We chose the Johnston meter for several reasons:

1.   Though the original cost is higher, the instrument is more fully guaranteed than other flow meters.

2.   Original cost includes installation and recalibration by Johnston engineers.

3.   The recorder can be placed at a considerable distance from the meter body and orifice plate without time lag. As you know, this proves especially important in closely controlled processes where one or two men must be in constant touch with many elements.

4.   Actual flow tests satisfied us that the Johnston meter was never less than 99 per cent accurate over a considerable range of flows, densities, and temperatures. I enclose a copy of the report made from these tests.

The meters, without exception, have proved completely satisfactory since we installed them. We have seldom had any difficulty at all with the recorders or meter bodies. Periodically the mercury has become dirty and required cleaning. In some of the lines carrying heavy solutions of salt we have had to remove and clean the orifice plates once a month. About the only other maintenance costs resulted from routine tests and calibrations of the recorders.

We have had little occasion to order replacements or parts. The few times we did need such service it has been very prompt.

I hope that this information is what you need. If I can be of further assistance, let me know.

Sincerely yours

Amos Levitt

Amos Levitt, Head
Testing Division

AL:bra
Enclosure

FIGURE 3. ANSWER TO INQUIRY.

13

DESOTO UNIVERSITY
Department of English
University Station 2, Missouri

March 1, 1965

Mr. Samuel F. Grunau, Executive Assistant
Brewster Products, Inc.
200 Rock Mills Road
Brewster, Connecticut

Dear Mr. Grunau: Subject: Suggestions for style sheet

I am glad to offer a few suggestions about business correspondence as your
letter of February 26 requested. Practice varies, but I am sure you can prepare
a style sheet that will help make Brewster Products correspondence modern and
efficient.

1. The two letter forms most in use today are the block (which you used) and the
full block (which this letter illustrates). Both use single-spacing with double
spaces between paragraphs and elements. Neither indents paragraphs except for
some special emphasis. The difference is that the full block starts most elements
at the left margin, including heading, complimentary close, and signature; your
letter, representing more conservative and traditional practice, brings heading
and date line, close, and signature near to the right-hand margin. The full block
is naturally a time-saver for typists and is gaining popularity.

There are other styles, of course, including the so-called NOMA, which eliminates
salutation and complimentary close entirely. But I suggest that you adopt a form
that is neither old-fashioned nor radical. The one you used and the one I am using
are both good.

2. Punctuation for heading, inside address, and envelope raises no problem these
days. We all use "open" punctuation: no commas or periods at the ends of lines.
The colon after the salutation is generally retained, though it may disappear within
a decade. The comma after "Sincerely" or "Yours truly" may as well disappear
right now, since I doubt that anybody will seriously miss it.

Internal punctuation of course follows conventional practice; for example, comma
between city and state, day and year. Incidentally, the "zip" number follows the
state name without parentheses: "New York, N.Y. 11011"

FIGURE 4. ANSWER TO INQUIRY.

3. The trend is to make salutations personal—to address even a stranger by his name. Why not? And the trend is also to use the friendlier "Sincerely" or "Cordially" rather than the more formal "Yours very truly," and "Respectfully yours."

4. It certainly is efficient to itemize questions and answers as you and I have done. Some authorities prefer a separate letter for each subject discussed. You may prefer that rule for your own memos, but it seems wasteful for most outside correspondence. Itemization seems a good solution.

5. The Attention line, when you use one, appears on the left margin directly above the salutation (with double spacing to set it off as a separate element). The salutation, however, must correspond to the address on the envelope and the inside address. For example, If I had addressed "Brewster Products, Inc." and added "Attention Mr. Grunau," my salutation would have been "Gentlemen," and not "Dear Mr. Grunau."

My preference is to eliminate the Attention line and address the individual directly.

6. The Subject line is increasing in popularity. It is efficient for quick reference. It belongs where I have placed it— on the same line with the salutation; and it should be underscored. Its use does not eliminate need for clear statement of the purpose of the letter in the opening paragraph.

I am pleased to be of this small assistance, and shall be equally pleased to answer any further questions that may come up. Good luck with your style sheet.

Sincerely yours

Alden T. Mann

Alden T. Mann, Head
Department of English

ATM:pr

FIGURE 4 (*cont.*). SECOND PAGE OF ANSWER TO INQUIRY.

suggestions or requests. Hence a good letter of instructions reads very much like a letter of inquiry.

Very commonly the letter of instructions uses the form of a *memorandum;* because it represents internal or interoffice correspondence, the memorandum generally omits the inside address, the salutation, the complimentary close, and often the signature.

Here is an illustration:

TO: B. N. Lendrim, Engineering Dept.   DATE: Jan. 7, 1964

FROM: Len Larson, Vice-President

SUBJECT: Request for study of soda-ash hazard

The Mojave Hospital reports show a constant increase in the number of cases of soda-ash burns treated. Several of these cases have been expensive to the company in loss of employee time as well as money.

Will you investigate and report with recommendations as soon as possible?

This memo of instructions leaves all methods of investigation to the reader. He must use his own judgment in deciding how much time to devote to the assignment and what kind of report to submit. He understands the reason for his investigation and its importance, but he also recognizes that his superior is counting on his reliability and good sense and gives him full responsibility.

The memorandum in Figure 5 is more specific in defining the scope of the study called for, and hence the scope of the report that must follow.

The length of a letter of instructions depends upon several things. Frequently the writer himself is unfamiliar with all requirements of a necessary investigation; he lacks the technical knowledge that he expects of the one he assigns to do the job. He knows the broad problems that must be solved, but he leaves details to the discretion of the specialist. In other situations the writer addresses a subordinate or assistant who needs considerable guidance; he may explain in some detail the questions he wants answered and may even suggest methods to use. Length, then, depends upon how much faith the executive writer has in the ability of his reader to undertake an assignment independently and upon how much of a specialist the writer is himself.

THE LETTER REPORT

When the information demanded in a report requires no more than two or three pages, it is often written as an ordinary letter or memoran-

FEDON & MARCON

Home Office

To: Bower Kneen
       Area Investigator

Date: 21 October 1964

From: Ansel Kirkpatrick

Subject: File G1954-63
Gainsal Bldg.

Mr. Gainsal informs us he has made the improvements we suggested and requests a premium reduction to the standard rate.

Will you check out the following:

    1. Installation of an approved sprinkler system (our specification SP42.1 or better) throughout the building. It should include even the third-floor apartments and storage rooms.

    2. Construction of a firewall (block or brick) around the furnace.

    3. Improved housekeeping inside and out. No storage of waste flammables.

    4. Provision of closed metal Dumpster receptacles for trash disposal.

Since Mr. Gainsal's current policy expires in December, we should have your report as soon as possible.

FIGURE 5. MEMORANDUM OF INSTRUCTIONS.

dum. The similarity between an answer to inquiry and a short report will be evident from a study of the following examples.

The memorandum in Figure 6, though written in response to very general instructions, follows a logical plan:

1. The first paragraph states the authorization for the report and its subject.
2. The second paragraph provides a summary of conclusions.
3. Underlined subtitles introduce each separate recommendation. Reasons for each recommendation appear as supporting statements in the same paragraph.

The short report that follows is a *preliminary* report, one to be followed by a longer report with full details. A preliminary report may merely report progress, or, as in this example, it may provide a summary of the longer report to come.

BENJAMIN DILLIARD, INC.

MEMORANDUM

TO: Karl Fixter, Vice-President   DATE: March 2, 1965

FROM: Ed Wasson, Employee Services Dept.

SUBJECT: Proposed group-insurance plan

It is now possible to recommend the best group-insurance plan for all our employees. It is the one offered by Pine Grove Mutual, providing better coverage at lower rates than any of the other plans we studied.

Participation is voluntary, but at least 75 per cent of all employees must vote to accept the plan before it can go into effect. We must set May 1 as the deadline.

Coverage includes benefits in case of sickness, nonoccupational accidents, total and permanent disability, and death. Face amount payable at death will range from $2000 to $10,000, depending upon annual income. Each employee will pay $7.40 per thousand, per year, deductible from wages monthly. Costs to the company will depend partially upon future experience with the plan, but our immediate cost for the first year is set at $8000 to $10,000, depending upon the percentage of employees who vote to accept it. If experience the first year is as good as we anticipate, our cost in later years will be lower.

Several other insurance companies promise dividends in future years that might eventually reduce our costs, but a guaranteed low premium seems a wiser choice. Pine Grove Mutual's rates are lower than any of the others and the benefits are somewhat more liberal.

Full details from Pine Grove Mutual will be in your hands within a week.

KENT & DENNIS

Interoffice Communication

TO: Len Larsen, Vice-President   DATE: Jan. 14, 1965

FROM: B. N. Lendrim

SUBJECT: Recommendations for reducing caustic burns

I have completed the investigation you requested in a memo of Jan. 7 regarding the number of hospital cases of caustic burns suffered by employees of the Soda Products Plant.

Most of these burns might be prevented by enforcing rules already prescribed by the Safety Committee. I am convinced that 90% of the burns could be eliminated by putting the following recommendations into effect:

1. Employees. The 12 men especially susceptible to soda-ash irritation should be transferred to jobs where they will not be subject to caustic dust.

2. Clothing. Men should not be allowed to work unless fully protected by dustproof clothing, or more accurately, dust-resistant clothing. This would mean gloves, caps, long sleeves, and high heavy leather shoes. The Safety Committee's present rule regarding clothing is too general.

3. Showers. All the men should be required to take showers after each shift. If this rule is to be effective, a shower room must be provided and the men allowed to use it on company time.

4. Cuts, etc. No one with even a small uncovered cut or abrasion should be allowed in the plant. Very serious infections can result from such carelessness. Foremen should be told emphatically to check on this.

5. Hours. I recommend 6-hr shifts for all men working in the Soda Products Plant. The usual 8-hr shift is too long for work in this environment. The evaporating units and rotary dryers make the place very uncomfortable for men properly clothed even in winter. In summer it is practically unbearable. The hottest and dustiest place in the plant is the dryer room, and men there might change off with men in the burkeite yard or on the Dorr thickener. Installation of some induced-draft ventilators is desirable. The 6-hr shift is feasible, and it will be at least a partial solution.

6. Auxiliary conveyors. An auxiliary conveyor should be installed to eliminate one serious hazard. Many of the more serious cases of soda-ash burn—almost all of those where lungs and throat are affected— result from a breakdown in the conveying system. Such breakdowns are unavoidable despite the micromax-thermocouple control of the dryers, because sometimes the filter cake feeding the dryer is too damp, forms lumps, and clogs the conveyors. The dryers cannot be stopped without losing several hours' production; consequently, there is nowhere for the soda ash to go except on the dryer-room floor. An auxiliary conveyor is therefore imperative.

FIGURE 6. LETTER REPORT.

Another kind of short report may be labeled the *proposal*. Proposals are of various kinds and of various lengths. The letter of instructions is one kind: the writer assigns or "proposes" a job to be done. Another kind originates with the person or agency that wants to undertake an investigation: the writer explains what he proposes to do or have done. Sometimes the proposal may be sufficiently clear and well defended in a letter or memorandum; sometimes it calls for a report of considerable length.

The following memorandum illustrates the proposal that may originate with a consultant:

INDUSTRIAL RESEARCH, INC.

Cambridge, Illinois

September 18, 1964

TO: MILLSAPS MACHINE COMPANY

After preliminary studies we are ready with the following proposal for an investigation of means of improving your operations:

OFFICE PROCEDURES: We shall look for possible economies in communications, filing, accounting; and possible reorganization of office space.

PERSONNEL POLICIES: We propose a study of methods of hiring and training workers with the hope of improving quality of personnel and reducing labor turnover.

PLANT EQUIPMENT: We suggest a thorough investigation of machinery and equipment to determine its efficiency in comparison with possible replacements. We believe that a number of newly introduced processes would prove beneficial to you.

PLANT LAYOUT: Since even the best equipment may prove inefficient if the general plant layout is inefficient, we propose a study of the whole manufacturing process to determine what kind of reorganization is advisable.

We estimate that this investigation can be completed at a cost of about $16,000.

INDUSTRIAL RESEARCH, INC.

R. E. Krauss

R. E. Krauss

CHARLES L. BARKER

Landscape Architect
Carragut, Indiana

June 23, 1964

Mr. Brent F. Southley
114 West Ninth Avenue
Glen Forge, Illinois

Dear Mr. Southley:

This letter confirms the oral understanding reached in our conference of June 21, at which you and Mrs. Southley, Mr. L. A. Swift, representing Loomis Construction Company, and I were present.

Plans and specifications were read and approved in part as follows:

It was agreed that the Loomis proposal be accepted for all roads shown on the plans and as specified, except the connecting service road shown on the plans as Road "E." Mr. Swift agreed to deduct $1780 from his proposal for the omission, leaving a total of $8800.

Mr. Aldrich was authorized to order the necessary flagstone for the paths shown on the plans, to be delivered at the nearest freight station at $750, and to be laid by the Loomis Construction Company for the sum of $550.

Grading was authorized according to plans and specifications at rates named in Mr. Swift's proposal:

"A"	$1150
"B"	900
"C"	2800
"D"	3600

The contract is to be prepared at once by the Landscape Architect, signed by the Loomis Construction Company, and then sent to you for your approval and signature.

Very truly yours

Charles L. Barker

Charles L. Barker

FIGURE 7. LETTER OF CONFIRMATION.

The letter in Figure 7 represents what is known as a "confirmation report." It supplies no new information, but serves as a written record of a verbal agreement or of information previously communicated orally. Such letters often follow a conference or meeting.

Every report, long or short, should present what is important to the reader and eliminate everything else. Failure to cut out the irrelevant is a common weakness in many a novice's reports. A report on a meeting could start like this:

> As you directed in your memo of August 7, I attended the meeting of the Association of Automation Control in Stamford for three days last week.
>
> Because of bad weather, the flight I had intended to take was canceled and that meant rail travel for much of the way. I missed the first half-day of meetings and several addresses by prominent men, but the rest of my stay was pleasant and rewarding.
>
> At a luncheon Thursday noon I met a number of other young members of the Association and we exchanged ideas. The main address by Douglas Davenport was interesting, but of little concern to us here.

But the executive who sent this writer to that meeting has no interest in any of these matters. What he wants are ideas from the meeting that apply to his job and his company. The report writer might better begin:

> Here is a summary of the pertinent meetings of the Association of Automation Control in Stamford last week. You will note from the attached program numerous other papers and talks that I consider of little importance to us.
>
> 1. In a paper on "Retraining for Automation," George Sparks pointed out. . . .

NOTES ON FORM AND STYLE

The form of every letter and memorandum ought to fit the purpose and situation; it should seem appropriate to the reader who receives it. Certain conventions are important because they save everybody time and they permit concentration on the message rather than on the writer's idiosyncrasies. Style is equally important. If it is direct, economical, and generally pleasing, the reader naturally responds more favorably than to something abstruse, rambling, or disorganized.

Conventions regarding paper, margins, spacing, and typing appear in the Handbook Section at the end of this book. Mechanics involving headings, inside address, salutation, complimentary close, signature, supplement, page numbering and the like are considered in the same section. The letters and memorandums in this chapter, however, represent acceptable current practice.

The right style of your letters and memorandums will generally be the one that "comes naturally" when you think of them as your own personal communications to your readers. If you consider first what your reader needs and what you have to tell him, appropriate language should follow. Your purpose is never to exhibit yourself, but to deliver an effective message.

Avoid trite, stereotyped, overworked expressions. Avoid outdated phrases associated with old-fashioned business letters: *in line with your request, may I acknowledge, it is with regret that, in reference to yours of recent date, I wish to advise you that*.

Eliminate deadwood. Do not waste the reader's time with needless words and phrases. Revise and prune letters until you have learned how to make your writing economical.

Finally, aim for simplicity. It is possible to be both courteous and intelligent and to present important information and sound judgments in everyday language.

SUMMARY

A good letter or memorandum:

Makes object and scope clear at once—in the first paragraph.

Summarizes early.

Separates the important elements distinctly by paragraphing, by indenting, or even by numbering significant points.

Uses a direct, simple, natural, readable style.

Adapts to its reader and always considers his interests first.

Exercises

1. Write a letter of inquiry and the answer to it. Choose one of the following situations:

   (a) A friend writes for specific information about the kind of work you are doing.

   (b) An employer writes to a job applicant's previous employer.

   (c) A department store writes to a bank requesting information about the credit standing of a man who wishes to open a charge account.

   (d) You write to a professional man or to a company for help in preparing a report.

   (e) A farmer writes to the agricultural experiment station in his state asking for advice about crop rotation in his area or for information about what stock to purchase.

   (f) A young man entering the insurance business writes to his uncle, who is district manager of a large insurance company, asking for advice and suggestions.

2. Write a letter of instructions and a letter report answering it.

   (a) The business manager of a college newspaper asks an assistant to discover why several prominent local stores do not advertise in the paper.

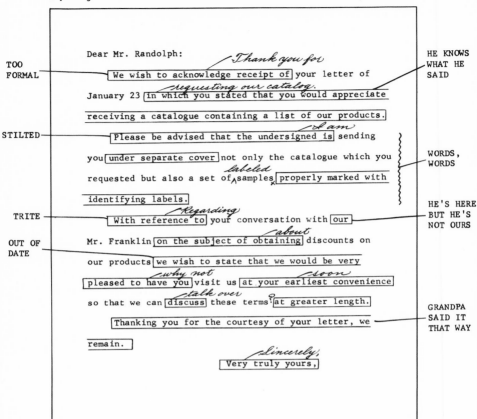

AVOID THESE
(They're Moss-Covered)

Attached please find
According to our records
And oblige
At an early date
At hand
Attached hereto
As per your request
Beg to advise
Contents carefully noted
Esteemed favor
In due course
In the amount of
In reply wish to state
Please be advised
Recent date
Referring to the matter
Thanking you in advance
The undersigned

The writer
Under even date
Under separate cover
Under date of
We remain
With reference to
We desire to acknowledge
We are in receipt of
We would like to be advised

CHECK LIST
For Letter Writers

Does the letter get under way
 quickly?
Is it friendly in tone?
Does it answer all questions?
Is it logically arranged?
Is it easy to understand?
If I were the reader, how would
 I react to it?

LETTER STYLE (Courtesy of the Sun Oil Company).

(b) An employer asks an assistant to investigate the character and ability of a young man who has applied for a position.

(c) A fire insurance company asks one of its agents for a report on the risk involved in insuring a local store.

(d) A client writes to his architect asking why a certain requested change in the plans is not feasible.

(e) The general manager of a chain store writes to a local manager asking him to explain the abnormal turnover of personnel in the local store.

(f) A dean writes to the undergraduate leader in a certain activity asking for a report on the number of students engaged in this activity, the time they devote to it, and the proportion who continue to participate in it.

3. Write for your instructor a *proposal* of a major report to be submitted at a later date: the subject, the audience, and the possible sources of evidence.

4. Rewrite the following letters:

A short progress report:

Dear Mr. Fullerton:

I got to Dennis Monday. Started my investigation next morning promptly at about nine o'clock. I shall proceed to conduct the necessary interviews as efficiently and promptly as conditions permit. The possibilities of locating your proposed branch in this town seem less promising than was deemed probable at the time orders were issued to me to come to Dennis for the investigation. Two real-estate agencies have been interviewed by me at length. It was reported by both agencies that locations in the central business district are at this time unavailable. It is my intention to study the prospects of locations which are from three to six blocks north of Marvin Avenue, which presently includes nearly all of the central business establishments. It is conceivable that one or more such locations might serve, though, according to my present information, the prospects are not bright. There is a possibility that my investigation may be concluded before the 24th of March. Final report will be submitted when study is completed.

Answer to an inquiry about an applicant:

Dear Mr. Sullivent:

I regret to inform you that I don't know the man you ask about quite so well as your letter indicates he believes I do, although he was employed by us in the capacity of assistant to our Personnel Director for a period of approximately 8 months. In making inquiries among those who knew this Mr. Horace Krunch while he was in our employ, there are no serious adverse comments about him. On the other hand, Mr. Krunch severed his connection with us before any question of his promotion or advancement was brought to my attention. Mr. Stovers, our Personnel Director, says the man was diligent, courteous, imaginative, and generally liked by employees. Trusting this will be of value to you, I remain

Yours truly

CHAPTER 3

The

Style

of a

Good

Report

THE reader is the final judge of a good report. If he gets facts and ideas from it that he can use, the report is successful; if he gets them easily and agreeably, it is excellent. He seldom takes the trouble to consider *why* one report is better than others. The *why* is the writer's business.

The writer with nothing useful to tell his reader can never produce a good report. No report can be worth more than what is in it. Format and style are only the means of communicating something potentially useful in itself. If they are effective, the reader scarcely pays any attention to them at all. It is when they are not effective that they stand out so glaringly. The writer's problem, then, is how to direct his reader's attention to the substance of his report —to *what* he says, not *how* he says it.

The style of report writing, therefore, should be unobtrusive. It should never direct attention to itself. It should be guided always by a concern for the reader's interests. Words, sentences, and paragraphs are to be the *means* to a good report; they are not an end in themselves.

Every rule concerning style must somehow point out a way to communicate with your reader. Here are a few general principles:

1. *Aim for unity.* Your report should have one central purpose and everything in it should help achieve that purpose. Each section, each paragraph, each sentence must serve that end. The sentence must be a tiny unit in a larger paragraph in an even larger section of a coherent whole.

2. *Aim for clarity.* Language must be entirely clear to its readers. All distortions and ambiguities are abhorrent.

3. *Aim for economy.* No reader has time for anything that is not really relevant. You will need complete supporting data and fully reasoned exposition of most of your judgments, but you can never afford to include any real *waste.* You must learn to cut out the deadwood.

4. *Aim for readability.* Problems may be complex, analysis may be profound, but the language of a report should never be more difficult to understand than the subject absolutely demands. Mere language should never stand in the way of interpretation. Simplicity is a major aim of every good report. No reader wants to give time to translating what could be put into simple terms.

5. *Aim for accuracy.* Accuracy is obviously the most indispensable quality of good report writing. The facts must be accurately stated; the words must fit the facts.

This chapter concerns general problems of style that nearly all report writers have to consider. Specific rules governing the style of reports are discussed in the Handbook Section at the end of this book. When you have a specific problem, that is the place to turn.

Unity

A unified report expresses and supports a single thesis. The whole report demonstrates a central purpose; each section, paragraph, and sentence has a clear function in advancing that purpose.

Unity of the whole report is achieved, first, by including all that seems necessary to develop the central thesis and excluding everything else. When in doubt, relegate details to an appendix.

Unity also depends upon clear distinction between major and minor points. Just as the complex sentence subordinates the less important ideas by placing them in subordinate clauses, so the unified report subordinates secondary points by placing them in less prominent positions. Generally, the good report places the most important matters (those that *must not be missed*) at the beginning and the least important ones at the end.

Besides the position of certain sections, *space* may demonstrate comparative importance. Usually the more important topics require more thorough discussion than secondary topics.

Unity in reports is further promoted by consistency in *tone*. The short, informal report calls for an informal or personal style. The long formal report, especially one addressed to technical readers, should adopt an objective, impersonal style. But in any case, the style should be consistent: mixing formal with colloquial expressions or shifting from passive to active voice or from third person to second has a disturbing effect.

Clarity

Clarity is even more indispensable to effective style. What the reader does not understand he cannot use. If he gets the wrong meaning, the result may be worse than if he gets no meaning whatever.

Clarity depends to a great extent on the experience and intelligence of the reader. What is clear to one reader may be meaningless jargon to another. The writer's first consideration, then, is to determine the kind of readers who will read his report. Experts in a technical field understand the terminology commonly used in that field. A report addressed to such readers should use the specialized language they know; attempts to paraphrase or popularize would impair clarity, not improve it. A second class of readers includes the generally educated nonspecialists. They know something of science, economics, government; they read and understand *Scientific American* and the financial pages of their newspapers. Many major executives belong in this category. Reports addressed to these readers must translate the specialized language of the experts, but not language which is common among the generally educated. A third class of readers may lack even basic scientific, mathematical, and economic education. Reports to them must be as simple and nontechnical as the *Reader's Digest*. Reports to a mixed audience of specialists, executives, and laymen present a difficult challenge to the writer. The language must be relatively nontechnical, but accurate. The report must include enough solid evidence to satisfy the critical specialist, yet must not overwhelm the general reader with its technical complexity.

Definitions may be one aid to clarity, but a large number of definitions of technical terms will not always make the subject clearer. One need for defining occurs when the report gives common terms a restricted meaning. A report on "temporary employees" must define what is meant by *temporary*.

Preciseness is an important element in clarity, because inaccurate statements can lead to serious misunderstanding. The report that says "inclusive of managerial personnel" when the writer means *ex*clusive may cause real confusion. An "economical system" is not at all the same as an "economic system."

Many factors lead to clarity—or away from it. More than clear diction is involved: sound sentence structure, intelligent punctuation, good usage, and coherent paragraphs all play an important part. Moreover, unity, clarity, and accuracy are interdependent. Above all else, the report writer must have full command of his subject. He must be thoroughly familiar with the problem, sure of his conclusion, and prepared to support his judgments with ample evidence and reasoning. If he has such control of his subject, vagueness and uncertainty will disappear.

Economy

In a report, economy means *conciseness*. It means that everything included—all the sections, all the data, all the paragraphs, and even all the words—serves a real purpose. Economy means "no waste."

Of course, economy is necessarily related to both unity and clarity. A truly unified report must be economical almost by definition. Clarity affects economy in the same way that economy influences clarity. In making your report entirely clear, you eliminate waste.

One way to be economical is to throw out masses of detail that you can be fairly sure your reader will not read. This applies especially to details of methods used in your investigation if these details are recognized as common to such investigations. Masses of raw data seldom belong in a report, but whatever data seem necessary "for the record" may be relegated to the appendix.

If you find your sentences growing abnormally long, it is time to look at them closely for deadwood. Long sentences are sometimes careless sentences that the writer has been too lazy to prune. (See pages 42-49.) If your sentences are abnormally short, this also may be a sign of waste. Perhaps you are repeating words more than you need to, or perhaps you use too many pronouns.

Avoid stereotyped phrases. Expressions like *in the field of, along this line, due to the fact that, in the case of,* and *with a view to* can get to be a bad habit. Often they become excess baggage. (For other examples, see pages 45-46.)

Readability

Readability means "reading ease." It seems rather ironical that experts in communication who advise editors and corporation executives on ways to make writing simple should themselves revert to a word like *readability.* Nevertheless their contributions have been useful. Their aim is to eliminate gobbledygook, the business cliché, deadwood, and excess verbiage—everything, in fact, that stands in the way of clear, direct, and interesting writing. In their view, the best writing, even the most profound, is reasonably simple, as simple as the thought in it can possibly be expressed.

Since World War II various experts in readability have won considerable recognition. Best known are Rudolph Flesch, author of *The Art of Readable Writing,* and Robert Gunning, author of *The Technique of Clear Writing.* Both are communications consultants to corporations and publishers. Both have publicized their formulas for measuring "reading ease" of any piece of written prose. It is possible, they say, to take sample sections from any report, apply the formula, and thereby learn how clear and understandable the report will be to readers of a given educational level. For example, scores from Gunning's "Fog Index" represent equivalent grades of schooling for the *average* reader. A score of 9.3 by this index indicates that a reader of average intelligence with a year or two of high school could comprehend the report being evaluated. A score of 16.6 indicates that only a reader with something more than a college degree could cope with it.

Both Flesch and Gunning emphasize that the "reading-ease" score should always be considerably lower than the reader's actual grade in school. The *Atlantic Monthly,* not generally considered beneath the college graduate's notice, has an average Fog Index score of about 12 (high school graduate). The point both of these men make is that writing should be entirely clear without forcing the reader to his limit.

One important discovery of these experts has special interest for writers of business and technical reports. They found that in some large corporations the ordinary business letter and memo were harder to read than either the *Atlantic* or the *Wall Street Journal.* They also found Department of Agriculture bulletins intended for dirt farmers that would be difficult for Ph.D.'s. Such writing is inexcusably ill-adapted to its readers.

The formulas of Flesch and Gunning actually measure only two factors in reading difficulty: sentence length and the number of syllables. Long sentences and "big words" do *tend* to make writing harder to understand. The formulas, however, are not intended to become guides for clear writing; they may indicate that the writing needs simplification, but they do not show exactly how to write more effectively.

What are the rules that really count?

1. Keep sentences moderately short—but *vary the length.* A series of short, choppy sentences may make reading difficult, because major ideas are not distinguished from subordinate ideas. A good long sentence may be followed by a good short sentence. If the *average* sentence length in a report is more than twenty words, take a good look at the sentences; some are probably too long. If the *average* length is below twelve words, take a good look too.

2. Choose the common, familiar, everyday word when you can; but remember that it is more important to find the precise word than to accept a synonym that is vague or inaccurate.

3. Use active verbs whenever possible. Use the passive voice only when you need to place emphasis on *what was done* or when you aim to make the exposition entirely impersonal.

4. Be specific. Be concrete. Names, exact dates, precise figures, and concrete details are usually easy to read. Of course, *too much* detail may call for attention the reader does not want to give; but it is possible to avoid vague and abstract writing without overdoing concreteness.

5. Eliminate words you can do without. Economy is a major factor in reading ease.

6. Remember the principles of unity. Unity of the whole report is built upon unity of paragraphs and sentences, and the result is easier reading.

Accuracy

Though obvious, the importance of accuracy can hardly be over-emphasized. Without accuracy your writing is worthless. Look at it this way. You can produce on paper five different levels of efficiency:

1. Writing that your reader can't *mis*understand. [He can't miss your meaning.]
2. Writing he can understand. [But he may have to work at it.]
3. Writing he may either understand or misunderstand. [He's guessing; you're gambling.]
4. Writing he can't understand. [He gets nothing.]
5. Writing he misunderstands. [He gets worse than nothing.]

Plainly you can afford to turn out only the first level. To achieve this level, you must employ the principles already discussed under unity, clarity, economy, and readability; for complete accuracy you must combine all four to produce a quality inherent in each—proper scale, proportion, emphasis; in other words, you must keep unimportant things unimportant and important things important. If you are a responsible writer, you will apply this thinking not only to what you say but also to how you say it. You will exercise restraint.

By *restraint* we mean an absence of exaggeration and overstatement. Proper restraint results from the report writer's sense of responsibility to his reader and from his desire to maintain an objective attitude. Most of us use expressions in everyday conversations that would be highly inappropriate in reports. We may refer casually to "all the graft in City Hall," "illiterate stenographers," "machines that do all the work." If pressed for evidence, we would have to admit that we had none. Although these expressions are irresponsible, they are not really intended to be taken seriously. In a report, however, there is no place for careless epithets or snap judgments.

Thoughtlessly exaggerated phrasing unfortunately does appear in reports. A writer refers to "an ideal site" he has found, when he knows it cannot possibly be that good; a "very promising" site would seem more likely, and the statements about it more convincing.

The formal conclusions and recommendations of a report need special attention. When they are exaggerated statements, the report that fails to support them will seem weaker than it really is. When they are restrained and carefully phrased, the supporting evidence seems correspondingly more convincing.

The careful writer *qualifies* his judgments when necessary:

> Though the evidence from the survey is inconclusive, it suggests interesting possibilities.
>
> These data lead to several tentative conclusions.
>
> These preliminary tests lead to four reasonable conclusions.
>
> Experience of the past year may not be altogether typical, yet it does suggest a need for reconsidering the plan.

Critics of scientific writing have objected to the "hedging" they find there. Scientists, they say, never say anything flatly, always qualify everything. Similar criticism might be directed at many report writers. It is possible to *over*qualify. Even the technical specialist should be willing to state unequivocally what he knows to be fact. Such statements as the following are absurd:

> On the basis of data before us, it seems probable that sick-time leaves last year were approximately 21.2% higher than they were in the previous year.
>
> Past experience suggests that we should anticipate a lower mortality rate among employees in the 20–30 age group than in the 50–60 age group.

The well-known engineering firm of Arthur D. Little, Inc. says this about hedging: *"May, might, could,* and *should* should suffice to make any statement conditional." And the Company illustrates the point this way:

If ADL *knows* it *will* work	it WILL work
If ADL *feels reasonably sure* it will work	it SHOULD work
If ADL *thinks* it will work	it MAY work
If ADL *isn't sure* it will work	it MIGHT work
If ADL *wants more time to study it*	it COULD work
If ADL *knows* it *won't* work	it WON'T work

The rule is to distinguish certainties from strong probabilities and probabilities from possibilities. Proper restraint in a report demands that such distinctions be made clear.

THE PARAGRAPH

Paragraphs are more important units in a good report than they are in more informal writing. They are more than convenient breaks for breathing time. Good paragraphing in the report facilitates rapid reading; it serves the purposes of unity and clarity.

The following rules apply:

1. Fit the length of your paragraphs to your purpose and your readers:

In a very long report, very short paragraphs not only produce a choppy, disjointed effect; they make reading harder. On the other hand, very long paragraphs demand more concentration and sometimes give inadequate emphasis to important points.

Use short paragraphs for special emphasis. A series of short paragraphs, perhaps with extra indentions, will give separate emphasis to separate facts or ideas.

Use separate paragraphs for separate conclusions and separate recommendations. Each deserves such attention.

Generally break up a preliminary summary or abstract into paragraphs that give emphasis to separate points in the report.

Use comparatively long paragraphs to develop complex explanations.

2. Place a clear, summarizing topic sentence first in each long paragraph.

Your reader may skim through rapidly. If he does, his eye naturally falls on these summarizing statements.

The topic sentence should epitomize the paragraph:

"The first and greatest obstacle was lack of utilities."
[Paragraph following that topic sentence then points out utilities that were lacking.]
"Several tests have shown that iodine is most effective. . . ."
[Paragraphs report these tests and their results.]
"Another aspect of street parking is its influence on traffic accidents."
[Paragraph gives evidence of such accidents.]

Whenever possible, include significant information in your topic sentence. The busy reader will appreciate it.

3. For paragraph unity, stick to your topic sentence. Exclude everything from the paragraph not clearly related to the thesis of the topic sentence. If you must digress, make a separate paragraph for the digression. If another important point comes to mind, put it in another paragraph. But whenever you alter your plan after writing a topic sentence, be sure you revise or rewrite that topic sentence so that it accurately summarizes the paragraph it introduces.

4. Plan each paragraph to follow a clear pattern. Everything in the paragraph must be a development of the topic sentence, and everything must appear in an intelligible order. Here are a few possible plans for paragraph development:

(a) The general statement (topic sentence) is followed by *examples* to support it. The most impressive example is put first.

(b) The general statement is followed by *divisions*. Each division has a sentence or group of sentences in order. Each division is clearly pointed out by a transitional term such as "second," "next," or "another."

(c) The first statement is *reiterated* for clarity and emphasis.

(d) If the general statement presents a *contrast,* the paragraph presents more specific evidence of this contrast. Each sentence may use the pattern: "A is . . . , but B is . . ." Or the first half may present facts about "A" and the second half the contrasting facts about "B."

(e) If the general statement emphasizes a *comparison,* the pattern is the same as that used for contrast, except that it stresses similarities rather than differences.

(f) The topic sentence may summarize a process or event. The paragraph then gives details in chronological order.

5. To make transition clear from one paragraph to the next, transitional words and phrases may introduce the topic sentence of the next paragraph:

To reduce these dangers . . .

Such experience, then,

A second method . . .

In spite of these apparent . . .

THE SENTENCE

In business and technical writing nothing serves the reader better than good sentences; nothing frustrates him more than bad ones. But what makes a sentence good or bad? In the space available here, any answer is an oversimplification. The principal qualities, however, are those considered earlier in this chapter: (1) unity, (2) clarity, (3) economy, (4) readability, and (5) accuracy. No sharp line can be drawn between any two: their functions overlap. Consider these principles as they apply to the sentence.*

Sentence Unity

Common sense tells us that if a sentence is to have unity it must:

1. Include everything necessary to develop its meaning [completeness].

* For economy in reference, the illustrative sentences in this section are numbered consecutively #1, #2, etc. and their revisions R1, R2, etc.

2. Exclude everything else [relevance].

3. Distinguish clearly between major and minor elements [emphasis].

4. Maintain uniformity in tone and treatment [consistency].

When your sentences fail to meet these requirements, your readers must either make the proper adjustments themselves or get a partial or distorted version of your message. The following sentence violates three of these requirements:

> #1 Soot, a black, combustible form of carbon, collects in the glazed terra-cotta flue liners so that you should have someone clean your chimney regularly to prevent flue fires.
>
> R1 To prevent flue fires, have your chimney cleaned every two years.

The reader of this sentence probably already knows (or doesn't care) what soot is and what the chimney is lined with—but he does want to know what "regularly" means. Note that the revision gives him a simple, straightforward statement of what to do and why, and that it corrects a serious mistake in emphasis (the important idea had been subordinated in a *so that* clause).

Similarly, the author of the next sentence has buried his important idea in a subordinate clause and forced a nonessential into the role of principal actor:

> #2 A comparison of this stock with Kuwait crude shows that the yield and quality of the gasoline from the two crudes is approximately the same.
>
> R2 The yield and quality of gasoline from this stock are about the same as those from Kuwait crude.
>
> *or* This stock and Kuwait crude yield about the same quantity and quality of gasoline.

By such careless selection of subject and verb (*faulty predication*), an author wastes words and distorts values. Note how the effect in the following cause-and-effect relationship is thoughtlessly relegated to a minor, participial position:

> #3 We can replace the still-plating installation with a barrel-plating unit, thereby slashing labor costs.
>
> R3 We can slash labor costs by replacing this still-plating installation with a barrel-plating unit.
>
> *or* By replacing this still-plating installation with a barrel-plating unit, we can slash labor costs.
> [This revision illustrates a *periodic sentence,* one in which strong emphasis is secured by putting the important idea at the end, next to the period.]

The following sentence illustrates the reverse error, improper coordination, here the use of *and* to connect two unequal ideas:

> #4 The warehouse was built in 1910 and it is perfectly sound.
>
> R4 The warehouse, though built in 1910, is perfectly sound.

One construction particularly to be avoided is the "escalator" sentence, one in which the main clause is followed by a modifying phrase or clause (often a relative clause), which is itself followed by a modifying phrase or clause (again likely to be a relative clause), one of whose elements may be modified by yet another phrase or clause. Ignoring detail, we can diagram that last self-exemplifying horror of a sentence like this:

> Main clause
> > 1st rel. clause
> > > 2nd rel. clause
> > > > 3rd rel. clause

Such a sentence violates *climactic order,* the principle that places the important element last, where the reader will remember it. Here is an example:

> #5 Heater temperature is recorded continuously by a B&S monitor mounted on the panel which forms the east wall of the control lab located on the filter bay of the evaporator unit.

And another, from a job description:

> #6 When time permits I do elementary glass blowing to help in the building of a vacuum system to obtain data for sorption displacement tests required in making surface area and porosity measurements.

You cannot—and should not—always use climactic order. But never abuse it. Never leave your reader out on that remotest twig, the tail-end modifier.

What *can* you do? Probably you can spare your reader the details:

> R5 A B&S monitor continuously records the heater temperature.
>
> R6 When time permits, I do elementary glass blowing.

If the location of the instrument in #5 or the ultimate use of the glass is important in #6, use a second sentence.

What was said on page 27 about unity in tone applies, of course, to the sentence. You would hardly use, for example, the formal *cannot* in one part of a sentence, the informal *can't* in another. The same thinking applies to inconsistency in (a) number, (b) person, (c) tense, (d) voice, and (e) mood. For consistency in grammatical rank and form see *parallel structure,* pages 52-53.

> (a) #7 The State is sending their engineers.
> >   R7 The State is sending its engineers.
>
> (b) #8 When one wants to study, you go to the library.
> >   R8 When you want to study, you go to the library.
>
> (c) #9 The process next increased the density of the sludge and begins to break down the Glauber salt.

R9   The process next increased the density of the sludge and
      began. . . .

(d) #10   The chain was attached to the axle and then we pulled. . . .

R10   We attached the chain to the axle and then pulled. . . .

(e) #11   Calibrate the meters first and then they should be returned
      to service.

R11   Calibrate the meters and return them to service.

You can violate grammatical completeness if you employ "tele-graphic" style—that is, if you omit verbs, nouns, or articles from your sentences. Sentences like the following *might be* adequate for field or laboratory notes, but only a careless writer would use them in anything written for others:

#12   Just completed preliminary investigation.

#13   Object investigation determine efficiency boilers.

#14   Was found impossible finish excavation this week.

Without knowing more than these fragments tell us, we can only guess they should read:

R12   We have just completed our preliminary investigation.

R13   The object of the investigation is to determine boiler efficiency.

R14   It was found impossible to finish the excavation this week [or
      "We found it impossible. . . ."]

Your reader can comprehend a complete statement more quickly and more easily than a partial one. To omit an article, a connective, a subject, or a verb may save a little time for the writer; it saves none for the reader.

Sentence Clarity

For sentence effectiveness, only accuracy is more important than clarity—and complete accuracy is impossible without clarity. Yet no principle is more generally violated, even by experienced writers. Here is an example:

#15   The x-ray was identified as the one taken during the operation
      by the radiologist.

The writer knew what this sentence was supposed to mean; the reader had to guess. Did the radiologist *identify* the x-ray? Did he take it? Did he do both? Whatever the actual meaning, it must be pinned down:

R15a   The radiologist identified the x-ray as the one taken during the
       operation.

R15b   The x-ray was identified as the one the radiologist had taken
       during the operation.

R15c   The radiologist identified the x-ray as the one he himself had
       taken during the operation.

Note that the clarification results from changing the passive voice to active, a change that eliminates the trouble-making phrase *by the radiologist.* For the first two situations we could get nearly the same result by inserting *by the radiologist* immediately after *identified* or *taken,* whichever it should modify. This single example illustrates two major threats to sentence clarity: the passive voice and careless word order.

Passive voice: The passive voice should be reserved for sentences in which the actor is unknown or is less important to the meaning than the object of his action:

#16   Sevor was murdered. [Murderer unknown.]

#17   Morrison was trapped in the cave-in. [The cave-in is less important to the meaning than Morrison.]

#18   The passive voice should be reserved. . . . [*Passive voice* is the central subject of the entire paragraph, and therefore more important than an "editorial we" or imperative "you."]

Many writers have long preferred the passive voice in report writing for the very reason that it emphasizes facts (not the person who obtained them) and actions (not the person who performed them):

#19   Construction was begun.

#20   The process was found unsatisfactory.

#21   The engine was tested in the cryogenic lab.

#22   Better operation was obtained by adding lithium concentrates.

These can be rewritten to avoid both the passive voice and the subjective "I" or "we":

R19   Work crews began the construction.

R20   The process proved unsatisfactory.

R21   Engine tests, conducted in the cryogenic lab, . . .

R22   The addition of lithium concentrates produced a better operation.

There is little doubt that the passive voice often impairs clarity. Its very virtue can be its liability. When it removes the real subject from the sentence (or relegates it to phrasal rank, for example, *by the radiologist* in #15), it also creates a vacuum. Modifiers abhor a vacuum and promptly attach themselves to the wrong element. Result: one kind of dangling modifier. Examples:

#23   By postponing construction, a heavy expense will be avoided.

#24   Realizing they were overheating, the men were ordered by the shift foreman to take the pumps off the line.

#25   Some difficulty was encountered by the formation of ice on the wing tips.

If there is a trend in business writing and technical writing, it is away from the passive. But as a writer you must decide for yourself which treatment expresses your idea more accurately.

Careless modifiers: Dangling modifiers, together with their cousins, misplaced modifiers, constitute a threat to clarity (and sometimes to solemnity as well):

#26 Wired for direct current only, the foreman could not use the old switch.

#27 After testing the first-effect heaters, three were found defective.

#28 With this theory in mind, a monkey was inoculated with the serum.

#29 When revolving at 1500 rpm, the engineer noticed. . . .

These four sentences begin with danglers, phrases which either modify the wrong thing or have nothing at all to modify. (Note that two of them use the passive voice in the main clause.) Because English grammar requires that opening phrases such as these modify the first noun to follow them, the reader first gets the impression that the foreman was wired, the heaters tested themselves, the monkey theorized, and the engineer revolved. To revise such sentences, the writer must provide a subject for the opening phrase (making it a clause), correct the subject of the main clause, or recast the entire sentence:

R26a Since the old switch was wired for direct current only, the foreman could not use it.

R26b Wired for direct current only, the old switch was unsuitable.

R26c The foreman could not use the old switch; it was wired for direct current only.

R27 Our tests of the first-effect heaters revealed three of them defective.

R28 With this theory in mind, we inoculated a monkey with serum.

R29 When the shaft reached 1500 rpm, the engineer noticed. . . .

Similarly, misplaced or carelessly placed modifiers cause confusion:

#30 The company guaranteed when the experiment was completed it would return the deposit.

This sentence could mean that the guarantee was given either before the experiment was completed or possibly before it was even begun. If so, it should have been arranged like this:

R30a The company guaranteed it would return the deposit after the experiment was completed [or, "on completion of the experiment"].

The sentence could also mean that the guarantee was not given until after the experiment was completed:

R30b When the experiment was completed, the company guaranteed to return the deposit.

The next example illustrates the need for care in placing prepositional phrases (as did #15):

> #31   The bits sent for examination by your company exhibit little wear.

Interchanging the phrases clarifies the meaning:

> R31   The bits your company sent for examination exhibit little wear.

A final example needs no comment:

> R32   Tantalus was placed in water up to his chin, which receded when he tried to drink it.

Careless reference: Most confusion in reference originates with a pronoun. Understandably so. For, unlike the noun, the pronoun is not a true symbol: it does not *directly* represent a person, place, or thing. The pronoun represents another symbol, a noun. Thus a pronoun is meaningless to the reader until he associates it with that noun (its antecedent); then he must associate the noun with whatever *it* represents. If the reader cannot find the antecedent, or if he finds more than one antecedent, he is confused. For example:

> #33   They operated the filters until they were worn out. [Who or what was worn out, operators or filters?]
>
> #34   The brine was added to the mother liquor when it reached 150°F. [When brine or liquor reached 150°F?]
>
> #35   The agitating system on the Door thickener is defective and it must be replaced. [The system or the entire thickener?]
>
> #36   The project must be abandoned because of the drouth, which means a substantial loss in time and materials.
>
> #37   The project must be abandoned, because of the drouth. This means a substantial loss in time and materials.

In #36 and #37 no noun antecedent exists. The reader must therefore supply one for himself, a step he should not be forced to take, and one which will delay (and sometimes prevent) his comprehension. It is worth pointing out that conversion to a participial construction is not much help:

> #38   The project must be abandoned because of the drouth, meaning a substantial loss in time and materials.

The participle (always an adjective) now has no specific noun to modify and becomes a dangling modifier. Among the possible revisions for #36, #37, and #38:

> R38a   The fact that the project must be abandoned because of the drouth means a substantial loss in time and materials. [A noun clause is provided as a subject for *means,* and no pronoun is required.]

R38b The project must be abandoned because of the drouth. Such a step means. . . . [or, "This action means. . . ." A single noun subject is provided for *means*.]

R38c The project must be abandoned because of the drouth, an action representing a substantial loss in time and materials. [An appositive sums up the previous idea and provides a clear subject for the following expression.]

The demonstrative pronoun *this* generally makes an unsatisfactory subject or object:

#39 Persons owning common stock vote for the directors. This is not usually significant, however, unless. . . .

#40 Occasionally we can purchase used equipment. This lowers our capital costs.

#41 Because the car had just been inspected, they knew this was not likely to be the cause of the accident.

#42 We suggest that you cut your order in half and pay cash for it. This will entitle you to our 2% discount.

Probably the simplest way to eliminate the problem is to change *this* from a demonstrative pronoun to a demonstrative adjective followed by a summary noun:

R39 Persons owning common stock vote for the directors. *This privilege* is not. . . . [*Privilege* does a reasonably good job of summarizing the entire idea expressed in the first clause.]

Often no satisfactory summary noun comes to mind, and we must recast the sentence:

R40 Occasionally we can lower our capital costs by buying used equipment.

R41 Because the car had just been inspected, its condition was not thought likely. . . . [or, "they did not believe its condition. . . ."]

R42 We suggest that you cut your order in half and pay cash for it. You will then be entitled to our 2% discount.

Similarly the relative pronoun *which* is too often used to refer to the idea expressed by an entire clause:

#43 The results were unreliable, which was partly due to the method used.

#44 In this process we can reduce the pressure, which will enable us to use the existing pipe line.

#45 The building is uninsulated, which would permit a fire to spread rapidly.

We could make a sentence of each clause and replace *which* with *this,* but such a change is merely the substitution of one loose construction for another. This similarity is our cue: we can revise as we did the previous group of sentences:

R43   Partly because of the method used, the results were unreliable.

R44a   In this process we can reduce the pressure, a reduction enabling us to use the existing pipe line.

R44b   Because this process permits us to reduce the pressure, we can use the existing pipe line. [Better emphasis than R44a]

R45   Because the building is uninsulated, a fire could spread rapidly.

Miscellaneous abuses of clarity: Uncritical writers produce ambiguity and incoherence in such abundance and such variety as to defy classification. Even the careful writer must develop his ability for self-criticism to the point where his words mean exactly the same thing to his reader as they mean to him. The authors of the following sentences sloughed this part of their job:

#46   The presence of red and yellow stop signs is not conducive to safe driving. [*Both* red signs and yellow signs or a single, two-color sign?]

#47   You can't devote too much time to fundamentals. [Does this mean that you cannot afford to spend much time on fundamentals or that it is impossible to spend too much time on fundamentals?]

#48   The selective logging method is most commonly practiced in Pennsylvania. [Does this mean that selective logging is the commonest method in Pennsylvania, or that it is more common in Pennsylvania than anywhere else?]

#49   In welding the steel plate can be held in position by a gantry. [Here punctuation is vital to the meaning (see page 246). Without a comma after *welding,* it is likely that the reader will misread this sentence until he gets to the verb *can be held.* Then he must go back to correct the writer's mistake.]

#50   The loss of the anthracite market for space heating has been to competitive fuels. [This is a "good" example of faulty predication (see page 35). The result is a wordy and confusing sentence. When the proper predicate is selected, the sentence reads:

R50   The anthracite industry has lost the space-heating market to competitive fuels.]

To eliminate errors like these—all of them, incidentally, from professional writing—you must assume that a sentence may have a different meaning for your reader than it does for you. Then you must check out each clause, each phrase, each word, each comma. No less rigorous procedure is good enough.

Sentence Economy

Economy (or conciseness) is essential to the four other sentence qualities, particularly clarity. You achieve economy by reducing complexity, by shortening, by cutting out. If you cut judiciously, you not only reduce the possibility of error, but also lessen the demand on the reader's time and concentration. Examine the following sentence:

> #51   However, in the event that you have any further questions or require any additional information on the subject, have no hesitation in calling on me at your earliest convenience.

Now, evaluate the ideas and the words used to express them:

However	[Probably unnecessary.]
in the event that	[Wordy for *if*.]
have any further questions or require any additional information	[Either alternative does the job.]
on the subject	[Obvious.]
have no hesitation	[The real verb is *hesitate;* make the verb a working verb.]
at your earliest convenience	[Trite, outdated, and inferred anyway.]

So we can reduce 30 words to 10:

> R51   For further information please don't hesitate to call on me.

Though the original sentence was extracted from an actual business letter, such drastic reduction is seldom possible. But *some* waste clutters most writing, and any reduction is pure gain.

If you are like most writers (and in this respect you should be), you will obtain economy when you revise. When you polish your rough draft, strike out the deadwood first, then reword. For example:

> STEP 1.   As you requested in ~~our recent meeting of about~~ August ~~12, 1963,~~ I have prepared a paper ~~which reports~~ concerning ~~the details of the investigation that I made of the subject of~~ radiology ~~as it is~~ linked with the new discoveries in ~~the field of~~ atomic energy. ~~I have prepared this paper or report~~ in a ~~not too technical~~ style ~~which should be of a~~ simple enough ~~nature to be understood by~~ the ~~average~~ layman ~~in the street.~~

The deletion leaves for final revision only 28 of the original 78 words:

> As you requested in August, I have prepared a paper concerning radiology linked with the new discoveries in atomic energy in a style simple enough [for] the layman.

Unless we know the exact circumstances we can only split hairs about the appropriateness of the deletions and retentions. Certainly, the worst deadwood has been pruned out and something akin to the real tree structure shows through. Probably the sentence should finally look something like this:

> STEP 2.   As you requested in August, I have prepared, in simple language, a report on the effect of atomic energy upon the future of medicine. [24 words.]

Most such waste results from thoughtlessness, together with a reluctance to examine what you have written. Nothing will replace the willingness to apply common-sense criticism to your work. Some of the following suggestions may help:

1. Avoid faulty predication; prefer the verb to the noun in expressions like these; use a *working* verb:

make allowance for	allow for
make a calibration	calibrate
make a calculation	calculate
make an inquiry	inquire
make a judgment	judge
make an adjustment	adjust
make provision for	provide for
make an investigation	investigate
give instruction to	instruct
give consideration to	consider
give encouragement to	encourage
have an investigation	investigate
conduct an investigation	investigate
come to a conclusion	conclude
reach a conclusion	conclude
draw a conclusion	conclude
take into consideration	consider
undertake the removal of	remove
have a necessity for	need
perform a measurement	measure
numerals are used to identify	numerals identify
if vibration of the pinion occurs	if the pinion vibrates
helps in the production of	helps produce
may result in damage to	may damage
produce a reduction in cost	reduces cost
have no hesitation	don't hesitate
is in the process of correlation	is being correlated
is indicative of the fact that	indicates that

NOTE: Even this abortive list should make one point obvious: beware of do-nothing, do-everything verbs like *make, have, come, take.* You need them often enough; don't use them in place of a meaningful verb.

2. Eliminate redundancy (words doing a job already done):

visible to the eye	visible
sufficient enough	sufficient
rectangular in shape	rectangular
160 cubic feet in volume	160 cubic feet
in the form of a square	square
red in color	red
10 P.M. in the evening	10 P.M.
the month of December	December
horizontally level	level

first originated	originated
consensus of opinion	consensus
my personal opinion	my opinion
surrounded on all sides	surrounded
mesh together	mesh
combine together	combine
fellow classmate	classmate
enclosed herewith	enclosed
attached hereto	attached

One particular form of redundancy shows up frequently in expressions involving *and so on* or its abbreviation, *etc.:*

#52   . . . modern materials, such as glass, steel, aluminum, etc.

#53   . . . some examples are Nylon, Dacron, Orlon, etc.

#54   [worst of all] . . . for example, iodine, fluorine, and etc.

When you use *such as* or *some examples,* or *among them* you do the job; the *and so on* (or *etc.*) at the end is redundant.

Furthermore, use *etc.* only when you know what it stands for and are sure your reader will know too. Too often we throw *etc.* into a list as a hedge against omitting something we might have overlooked.

3.   Similarly, do not qualify words needing no qualification:

maximum possible	maximum
minimum possible	minimum
complete monopoly	monopoly
entirely completed	completed
absolutely essential	essential
most unique	unique
most correct	correct
most exact	exact

Also be frugal in using *very, most,* or other superlatives in expressions already indicating extremes. (See *restraint,* pages 31-32).

4.   Use the infinitive of purpose (especially to avoid the passive):

for the purpose of learning	to learn
advisable that a study be made	advisable to study
in order that sufficient information be obtained	to obtain sufficient information

5.   Reduce predication; that is, reduce grammatical rank or complexity by changing clauses to phrases, phrases to single words.

Reducing phrases: Many phrases, particularly adverbial and prepositional phrases, have single-word equivalents:

in a satisfactory manner	satisfactorily
without making any noise	noiselessly
most of the time	usually

in the same way	similarly
leaving out of consideration	disregarding
in spite of the fact that	although
in the near future	soon
at the present time *	now
in order to	to
due to the fact that	because
in the event that	if
during the time that	while
in the amount of	for
in the neighborhood of	about
resulting in death	fatal
lacking in substance	insubstantial
a large number of	many
a small number of	few

Reducing clauses: You often can and often should reduce relative clauses to participial phrases or to appositive constructions:

#55	Clause:	. . . the latch which is used on these doors.
R55	Participial Phrase:	. . . the latch used on these doors.
#56	Clause:	. . . the company that owns this patent.
R56	Participial Phrase:	. . . the company owning this patent.
#57	Clause:	. . . pulping, which is the process for removing lignin from wood.
R57	Appositive:	. . . pulping, the process for removing. . . .
#58	Clause:	Dr. Hipple, who is a well-known physicist. . . .
R58	Appositive:	Dr. Hipple, a well-known physicist. . . .

Compounding adjectives: You can often reduce complexity by converting a following adjective clause to a preceding compound adjective. (For rules of hyphenation, see pages 223-25.)

#59	Clause:	The tunnel, which was 750 feet long, was....
R59	Compound:	The 750-foot tunnel was. . . .
#60	Clause:	The evaporator unit, which consists of three evaporators in tandem, . . .
R60	Compound:	The triple-effect evaporator unit. . . .

WARNING: You can overdo this kind of compacting. If you insert too many compound modifiers ahead of a noun, your reader will have difficulty in distinguishing the noun from its modifiers. His difficulty will be a major one if you fail to punctuate properly. The following expressions would be confusing even with the proper commas and hyphens:

single cylinder caterpillar oil test engine
furfural extracted hydrocracked virgin bottoms

* Usually the present tense of the verb will do this job without help.

rare gas shield arc welding process
just arrived experimental stabilized heavy motor alkylate
bituminous plant mix surface course
pilot miscible phase displacement operation
positive impeller type displacement blower
high voltage three conductor oil filled cable installation

6. For economy as well as emphasis, avoid multiple hedging. Accuracy requires some qualification, perhaps, but don't overdo it:

#61 I believe the evidence gathered in this investigation seems to indicate that it appears feasible to dispose of atomic waste in the salt formations of the State of Kansas [29 words].

R61 The investigation indicates that it is feasible to dispose of atomic waste in the Kansas salt formations [17 words].

The revision eliminates the excessive caution, yet retains scientific restraint.

Some hedges to avoid:

It will be readily agreed that. . . .
It is interesting to note that. . . .
It would seem reasonable to believe that. . . .
It might be suggested that. . . .
It seems to be indicated that. . . .
There has been considerable speculation that. . . .
There seems to be evidence that. . . .
That data appear to indicate that. . . .
Results seem to indicate that. . . .

7. Avoid worthless alternatives. The alternatives in the following expressions perform no useful function:

purpose of this report or paper
any possible help or assistance
investigate or research the problem
the value and importance of this effort
waste of power or energy

Retain the more exact or more concrete alternative, or use your thesaurus to find a more precise replacement.

8. Save words—and avoid annoying repetition—by compounding, collecting, and enumerating. In the following sentence you would instinctively make one subject and one verb serve both adjectives:

#62 The crane is too big and the crane is too expensive.
R62 The crane is too big and too expensive.

The same revision would improve a two-sentence version of the same concept:

#63 Such a big crane is not necessary. Furthermore it costs too much.

You should apply this principle to more complicated expressions containing either repetition of phrasing or similarity of idea. For example:

#64 To obtain facts as accurately as possible is of prime importance. The arrangement and evaluation of the facts are equally essential to the effectiveness of a research report. This much is obvious, but it must be remembered that accuracy of expression is just as important.

R64 Accuracy is essential to the effectiveness of a research report, not only in obtaining, evaluating, and arranging the facts, but also in expressing them.

In addition to cutting 45 words to 25, we have centered the expression around its principal concept—accuracy.

Enumeration is a practical method for obtaining economy, clarity, and emphasis simultaneously. You will find it especially useful in any kind of informative writing. Here are two examples you have seen before, the first linear, the second vertical:

#65 The principal qualities of a good sentence are (1) unity, (2) clarity, (3) economy, (4) readability, and (5) accuracy.

#66 To have unity, a sentence must:
Include everything necessary to develop its meaning.
Exclude everything else.
Distinguish clearly between major and minor elements.
Maintain uniformity in tone and treatment.

The linear treatment saves space; the vertical provides greater emphasis and greater clarity. Both methods, of course, save words and prevent repetition. In #65, for example, enumeration saves repeating "one of the principal qualities of a good sentence is." In reports, you will find enumeration almost indispensable for itemizing conclusions and recommendations.

Observe how the colon itself saves words. You should never write, for example:

#67 A report writer could divide his problem into five steps. These are:
1. Gathering material.
2. Evaluating material.
3. Organizing material.
4. Writing.
5. Revising and editing.

Instead, place the colon after *steps* and delete *These are*.

WARNING: Enumerated items, like members of a series, must conform to the rules of parallel structure. (See pages 52-53.) In example #67 all are gerunds, in #65 all are nouns, and in #66 all are sentence completions.

9. Use ellipsis (the deliberate omission of a word or words your reader can instinctively supply for himself) to avoid repetition:

#68 The smaller the particles are, the better the separation is.

R68 The smaller the particles, the better the separation.

#69 The wax plant is almost ten years old. The ammonia plant is only three years old.

R69 The wax plant is almost ten years old, the ammonia only three.

#70 This is the process that we use.

R70 This is the process we use.

#71 Some motors require regular oiling; other motors don't require regular oiling.

R71 Some motors require regular oiling; others don't.

#72 The tank was lined with rubber on the inside and covered with Durabell on the exterior.

R72 The inside of the tank is covered with rubber, the outside with Durabell.

#73 I believe the structure is a good risk. However, if a few changes are made it could be considered an excellent insurance risk.

R73 I believe the structure is a good risk—with a few improvements, an excellent one.

Sentence Readability

The ease with which your reader comprehends your sentences depends on your success in weaving unity, clarity, and economy into them. More specifically, readability depends to a large degree on sentence length and word choice.

To summarize our earlier discussion of readability, we repeat:

1. If your *average* sentence length is less than 12 words, check your subordination and coordination. Be sure that your sentences are not unnecessarily choppy, that you do not force your reader to supply missing relationships, and that you have not made minor ideas into major ones.

2. If your average sentence length is greater than 20 words, check your reader adaptation and sentence unity. Be sure that your sentence structure is not so intricate that it defies reader comprehension, that you haven't included extraneous or worthless detail, that you have only one major idea per sentence (more only if properly coordinated), and that you have not made major ideas into minor ones.

3. Vary your sentence length. Neither Gunning nor Flesch nor the authors of this book would recommend holding sentence length to *any* constant number of words. All agree that an average length exceeding 15 or 20 words could very well con-

stitute a threat to reader comprehension. The concept of *average* is vital here, for an average sentence length of 20 words, or even 15, permits variety, and variety sustains emphasis and thwarts monotony.

4. Prefer the common word to the uncommon if they are equally precise.

5. Prefer the specific and concrete to the general. General concepts are inescapable in all writing, of course, but when you must use them always consider the possibility of specific or concrete illustration.

The last sentence, itself a generalization, needs to be specifically and concretely illustrated:

General: Switzerland is a small country.

  This atomic power plant can generate a tremendous amount of electricity.

Specific: Switzerland has an area of 15,940 square miles.

  This atomic power plant can generate 400,000 kva.

Concrete: Switzerland is about a third of the size of New York State.

  This atomic power plant can generate enough electricity to supply metropolitan Cleveland.

Combination: Switzerland is a small country of 15,940 square miles, about one-third the area of New York State.

  This atomic power plant can generate a tremendous 400,000 kva, enough electricity to supply metropolitan Cleveland.

Though writing is often criticized for being too general, it can be equally vague to some readers when it is too specific. In the examples above, the specific terms *15,940 square miles* and *400,000 kva* would be meaningless to most readers. The general terms *small* and *tremendous* would be more meaningful, and the concrete terms much more so. If your statements are intended for laymen (stockholders and taxpayers, for instance), you must try to make your facts vivid.

Many other things contribute to sentence readability or to the lack of it, but we shall touch only briefly upon the most important points: sentence variety, sentence direction, and parallel structure.

Sentence variety: We have already pointed out that you should vary the length of your sentences. You should also vary their structure. How? Here are a few suggestions:

1. Vary sentence openings. Use different constructions and above all different words. Particularly avoid *frequent* opening with *This, I, It, There is,* and *There are.*

2. Vary clausal sentence types (simple, complex, compound, and compound-complex). For easy reading prefer the simple and the two-clause complex sentences, but occasionally use a compound sentence or possibly even a compound-complex one to express your thought most effectively.

3. Be wary of a succession of compound sentences.

4. Vary sentence emphasis. If you make *all* your sentences periodic, you lose emphasis instead of gaining it.

5. Occasionally—but only occasionally—juggle the normal grammatical sequence of subject-verb-object:

   #74   This operation we performed at once.

6. Consult a textbook on composition, or, better yet, study for yourself the kinds of sentences authors in your field are writing.

The opening paragraph from Herbert Solow's "How NSF Got Lost in Mohol" will illustrate the variety used by a modern writer in both sentence length and sentence structure. Published in *Fortune* (May 1963), it is, of course, aimed at an above-average reader group. Note the different sentence beginnings, the range of sentence length (13 low; 33 high; 20 average), and the variety in sentence structure—though none of the nine sentences is compound and only one contains more than two clauses (four are simple sentences, five are complex).

Dr. Vannevar Bush realized during World War II that science and government were not likely ever again to part company. He saw that the demands of national missions would evoke ever more complex and costlier basic research tools, such as cyclotrons, reactors, computers, and, beyond them, giant radiotelescopes and instrument-laden outer-space vehicles. The financing of basic research by government on a scale without precedent would be unavoidable. What worried Dr. Bush was how the fragile hothouse flower of basic science could absorb government nourishment yet be sheltered against the inclement atmosphere of agency bureaucracy. So, when Congress set up the National Science Foundation in 1950, it was placed under a protective limitation. NSF was not to perform but "to initiate and support basic scientific research." This it now does at the rate of over $300 million a year. Uniquely among government agencies, NSF was to be *in* government but not altogether *of* it, a federal agency responsive to the creative suggestions of the general scientific community. Thus it was hoped to maintain that special quality of spontaneity that is the well-spring of basic research.

Sentence direction: The reader expects to travel from sentence beginning to sentence end. Unfortunately, though the accomplished writer will let him make the trip with little interruption, too many thoughtless writers slow, stop, or even reverse him. Earlier sections discussed the worst reader obstacles: misplaced modifiers, danglers, faulty predication, and ambiguous reference. We list here some other specific, and frequent, offenders:

1. *There is, there are* (*there* plus *to be*). Use this construction sparingly. It promotes wordiness, indirection, faulty predication, and errors in agreement. Reserve it for constructions that are awkward without it:

   #75   There are three reasons.
   #76   He realized there would be trouble.

Avoid it in sentences like the following:

   #77   There are five motors in the borax plant that should be replaced.
   R77   Five motors in the borax plant should be replaced.

   #78   There are a pinion gear and an eccentric cam missing.
   R78   A pinion gear and an eccentric cam are missing.

2. The indefinite or "preparatory" *it*. The rules for *there is* apply almost exactly to this use of *it:*

   #79   It would be appreciated if you would analyze the enclosed samples.
   R79   Please analyze the enclosed samples.

   #80   It is imperative that sufficient time be allowed.
   R80   Sufficient time must be allowed. [*or* "Allow sufficient time."]

   #81   It is quite possible that the impact may. . . .
   R81   The impact may. . . .

3. Throwbacks. Built into the following words is the requirement that the reader think *back* to something. Use them only when you must—and then only when their referent is clear and close. Never use the asterisked items.

above	latter	aforementioned *
said (adj.)*	former	abovementioned *
last	respectively	second-to-last

   #82   The circulation of sea water and distilled water is accomplished by a brine pump and a condensate pump respectively.
   R82   A brine pump circulates the sea water and a condensate pump the distilled water.

4. *And/or.* In expressing the existence of three possibilities this device saves words but probably not reader time.

Parallel structure: When two or more related ideas are similar in meaning, make them similar in form. The result is parallel structure. Violations of parallelism usually flank a coordinating conjunction, most often *and* (or its replacement in a series, the comma). As the following examples demonstrate, failure to use parallelism results in waste and incoherence:

#83   This engine has the disadvantages of being too heavy, costing too much, has a slow speed, and starts too hard.

R83   This engine is too heavy, too slow, too hard to start, and too expensive.

#84   Our attention should be fixed on the basic causes of the disease rather than to concentrate on symptoms and ways to suppress it.

R84   We should concentrate on the causes of the disease, not on its symptoms or preventatives.

#85   The initial costs of steel supports are expensive, but previous records have shown them to be cheaper in the end.

R85   Records show that steel supports cost more in the beginning but less in the end.

Avoid also the opposite sin, faulty coordination. Particularly, do not use *and* or its equivalent to equate concepts that are not equal or to compare concepts that are not comparable:

#86   . . . apples, pears, and fruit.

#87   Pitchblende is found chiefly within the U.S. and no geologist knows how much ore there may be in the world.

#88   The two small generators were inadequate and we purchased a larger one.

#89   It is dangerous to have a leaky muffler and one should be careful to ventilate his car.

#90   The employment of unskilled workers, aliens, and loafing is not tolerated. [A two-way violation!]

In summary, remember that parallelism is part of the principle of *consistency*. Treat similar things similarly. You will find parallelism useful—and necessary—in all manner of series and enumerations, from a simple sentence list to a table of contents or a system of headings.

Sentence Accuracy

Common sense and a working knowledge of the principles laid down under unity, clarity, and economy will promote accuracy in the sentence or anywhere else. But more important is an active awareness of responsibility. We need only remind the report writer, whether student or professional, that he is responsible not only for *what* he sets down on paper but also for *how*. In writing, he gets no second chance.

MECHANICAL CONSIDERATIONS

Mechanical considerations, primarily concerned with proper *form* rather than function, are treated in depth in the Handbook Section, pages 211-63. There you will find quick answers to specific questions about abbreviations, capitalization, hyphenation, spelling, usage, numbers, and punctuation. The following brief sections provide only the general perspective that the report writer should apply to these problems.

Abbreviation

Abbreviations, even in reports, should be used sparingly. The best business and professional writers try to maintain dignity of expression; thus they regard too-frequent shortcuts as likely to give an impression of slovenliness. Nevertheless, in many routine reports, especially those that are definitely technical, the writer is allowed to use abbreviations more freely than he is in general composition. Recognized abbreviations often save as much time for the reader as for the writer. When a reader is known to be in the habit of thinking in abbreviations, the writer should employ them.

In general, however, the report writer will do well to use few abbreviations rather than many; when he has any doubt, it is always safe to write the terms in full. Take no chances. Be sure that the meaning is clear to the reader, and that the report appears carefully written and "professional."

Rules for abbreviating are given on pages 213-14; they are followed by the American Standards Association list of *Abbreviations for Scientific and Engineering Terms*.

Capitalization

Some writers capitalize important words indiscriminately and without justification. Wholesale capitalization cannot be defended. It costs money, wastes time, and confuses the reader. Capitalization is treated in detail on pages 221-23.

Hyphenation

The condensation of report-writing style often results in confusion unless the writer adopts artificial methods to make his meaning clear. One often-abused characteristic of report writing is the abundant use of compound words (see page 46). Despite the objections of some critics to such condensed expressions as business and technical writers employ, these compounds cannot be very severely condemned. *An iron-furnace* is surely better form than *furnace for smelting iron ore; fuel-saving device* better than *device designed to save fuel.*

Save words, of course, when the meaning can be made as clear with compounded elements, but observe the rules discussed on pages 223-25.

Spelling

Most readers recognize someone else's misspelling. They are attracted to the error and distracted from the message. The result is a drop in communicating efficiency—and a loss of respect for the writer. Do not let this happen to you. If you have either a general or a specific problem in spelling, consult pages 226-28.

Usage

For treatment of problems in grammar and diction (word choice), see pages 229-37.

Numbers

In technical and business writing of all kinds, figures are used freely. Usually they are preferred to spelled-out numbers. See pages 238-41 for a complete discussion on the handling of numbers.

Punctuation

Punctuation, as every writer knows, is intended primarily to make the sense more evident to the reader. Too much punctuation, therefore, is fully as bad a fault as too little, and inconsistent punctuation often leads to a reader's confusion. The best practice is to punctuate only where you can see a sound reason for doing so.

Bad punctuation often accompanies complex and involved sentence structure. The solution may be to employ simpler sentences rather than to attempt correct punctuation of constructions that are needlessly difficult. A long, rambling, and incoherent sentence is difficult to punctuate. If the sentence is unified and clear, punctuating is seldom troublesome.

Punctuation is treated comprehensively on pages 242-53. Note in your study the three problems in punctuation that prove most troublesome to writers:

1. How to distinguish a restrictive from a nonrestrictive element (see section 7.4.1.3, pages 246-47). Proper use of this rule is important to meaning.
2. Whether to use a comma between the last two items of a series (see note under section 7.4.1.5, page 248).
3. When to separate qualifying adjectives by commas (see Section 7.4.1.6, page 248).

Exercises

A. Rewrite the following sentences:

1. The tests were conducted by the Western Laboratories for the purpose of determining if improvements as to quality might be obtained in the various materials which were tested.
2. Due to fluctuations in price levels it cannot be definitely decided at this time that the projected production of these instruments will result in the anticipated profits.

3. One factor that has high significance in management is office personnel possessed of initiative, reliability, and stability.

4. It is impossible to make a final prediction as too many intangibles enter the scene.

5. The results of the survey indicate that there is considerable dissatisfaction among some of our customers with the cables.

6. Viewing the program objectively it may be said that there are serious defects which might in future years lead to either a diminution of investments or they could have the effect of creating labor trouble.

7. The residential zone is located on high ground and with excellent accessibility to markets, although recreational facilities are limited.

8. Should the company, as in the past year, proceed with construction and maintenance advancements designed to modernize the whole process of production, it can be anticipated that in a short time we can lead the field.

9. As the rate of depreciation increased more than that of investment, it can be deduced that steps must be taken to maintain our position through an increase in the budget for maintenance.

10. That the alloy meets specifications adequately can be seen by a comparison of the two accompanying charts, one of which depicts the specifications while the other the results of tests just completed.

11. In the survey that was recently conducted by the Personnel Division it was discovered that there is a serious failure of interlevel communication between management and personnel of lower levels due to an inadequate definition of the function of a successful personnel relations policy.

12. It should be pointed out that, as these instruments have not been made familiar to all essential personnel as yet to provide an adequate appraisal of their potential, any final conclusion regarding them would be premature.

13. Three factors must be taken into consideration by the department, the first cost, whether or not the tabulators do what is claimed for them by the manufacturer, and we must also attempt to find out what if anything can be saved over and above the use of present methods.

14. 1962 was the best year, as in that year there were a smaller percentage of total costs assigned to maintenance, however, the final figures would be misleading.

15. The rubber companies are certain they can produce tires with the same rapidity as automobiles.

16. The entire bottom of the pond is covered with a dense growth of vegetation.

17. If the table on page 14 is consulted, it will be seen that there has been a steady decline in efficiency.

18. There were many variables which were not controlled and no attempt was made to do otherwise.

19. While the population has been increasing the water supply has been decreasing since there are more people using the existing facilities.

20. Fatal accidents can result from head-on collisions that are severe enough to cause death.

21. It is advisable to use a barrier.

22. To determine what the causes of the scaling were the experiments outlined below were utilized. These were conducted as follows.

23. The purpose of this booklet is to explain how to put two compound generators in parallel operation.

24. Deposits of hard sulfur rock are occasionally encountered in rise drilling and dip drilling which constitutes an abnormal condition that cannot be anticipated, consequently weighted averages were chosen without taking into consideration this condition.

25. The next item you should consider concerns the cooling of the engine.

26. In addition to the protection provided by the extinguishers, the building is located only two miles from the local fire department, which has a unique record.

27. The capture of these fines [coal size] in preparation and recovery of impounded tonnages is one step in the conservation of the natural resource as well as an economic aid to local industry.

28. The foam is neither hygroscopic nor when it comes into contact with water does it decompose so the foam will return to its original condition when it is removed from the water and dried.

29. The importance of production, type, and pedigree in a herd of breeding cattle is of the utmost significance.

30. Higher education helps women face national and international problems as well as men.

31. If an employee is injured in connection with his work, however slight, it should be reported immediately.

32. One spark plug deposit also contained aluminum silicate, indicating a reaction between the deposit and the ceramic, which may be partly responsible for the adhesion.

33. Another reason why your bill has increased over the passed year is because you have added several electric appliances to your home that you did not have in the past.

34. It has been generally recognized that the limiting factor of significance in extending the scope of isotope utilization is man's imagination.

35. We might further mention that we would be glad to furnish any one of these Whistles on a trial basis to the extent that if the smaller size was not adequate enough, it could be returned in lieu of the purchase of a larger size depending upon actual operation and suitability of your requirements for signal distance and audibility.

36. Many people develop bad habits when they are learning to drive which they continue to use during the rest of their driving days.

37. The scrap turnings are from all kinds of metal which would seem to make standardization of scrap impossible.
38. A chemical analysis was run in our laboratories and the technicians found that the paint was properly mixed.
39. It has been our experience that during the month of December most of our customers electrical bills are higher than other months.
40. Heat is supplied by a coal fired stoker furnace which is of large enough capacity to supply steam to the clothes presses as well as heating the building.
41. In general the wiring in the house is quite poor, there being but one outlet in the dormitory style rooms on the second and third floors, resulting in an octupus of tangled wires and blown fuses.
42. One pound of ammonia nitrate mixture is required per foot of a 2-inch diameter hole, two and a half pounds of ammonia nitrate mixture is required per foot of a 3-inch diameter hole and ten pounds per foot of ammonia nitrate is required in a 6-inch diameter hole.

B. Rewrite the following paragraphs:

1. The author of one book that bears on this problem is Chief Psychologist at Hillside Hospital and Assistant Clinical Professor of Psychology at Adelphi College. For purposes of illustrating the dynamics of psychological testing, he selected all the cases referred for appraisal in a single month at Hillside Hospital. Here he reproduces all the data together with interpretive diagnostic formulations. Dr. Gurvitz has a more scientifically objective viewpoint than most recent books in the field demonstrate. His interpretations of personality dynamics are based solidly on test data rather than unsupported speculations. His *Dynamics of Psychological Testing* is the source of evidence for the following analysis.

2. During the Thirties Lou R. Maxon built up his big Detroit advertising agency. He became one of the highest-income men in the country by emphasizing something that other agencies did not emphasize. This was a small agency. Larger agencies avoided the kind of thing Maxon was doing. What he did was make direct mail an integral part of a well-rounded promotional effort. Since that time larger agencies have recognized the soundness of this idea. Larger agencies are taking it on. Maxon's own agency grew phenomenally.

3. Although the Research Department has nearly 200 professionals, these all report to Dr. Krose. Dr. Krose has had wide research experience and is well known in his field. It seems fortunate that the company has him in this vital position. It is vital because basic scientific research can mean profits in the end. It is short-sighted to appropriate funds only for directly practical applied research as many companies do. Without basic research no applied research can exist. Of course it is expensive, and a large proportion of the research brings no immediate profit to the company. In the end, however, fundamental scientific research, which Dr. Krose directs, can provide the basis for the most revolutionary and practical discoveries we can hope for.

4. Many of the agents are located at great distances from the home office. Often they have most useful information to contribute which might be of utmost importance to the company, yet important losses have occurred because they did not so communicate. Heretofore we have had no official system of getting information from our agents. It would help considerably if we had such a system. Regular monthly reports are recommended from each agent as a means of correcting this deficiency. Were we to require such reports from every agent, the company might avoid losses and be much better prepared for unusual developments. It is therefore recommended that every agent be instructed to submit a report once a month, preferably before the 15th of each month. Of course exceptional circumstances in a given district might require some postponement, but in general a monthly report should be required.

5. It has been the constant endeavor of the consultants to serve the company broadly not alone along the lines of improvements in efficiency of management, eliminating duplications and wastes, but equally in the creation of an improved relationship within the organization between the various departments, and a higher degree of morale. Now the task of reorganization of the three departments, Accounting, Transportation, and Sales—which has occupied the attention of the consultants for a period of seven months, is concluded. The recommendations for each of these three departments are included in the report.

6. The confidence of businessmen was demonstrated during the past year by their planning for more expansion than it was possible to be realized with the materials and the credit that were immediately available. Such factors as the rise in population, increased family income and higher living standards in recent years, together with the upsurge of consumer buying that had been evidenced for some time, all necessitated more productive capacity to supply the growing needs which consumers were feeling. It was in an effort to meet such demands that businessmen embarked on a program of plant expansion last year which during the coming year is estimated at somewhat more than 22% above amounts expended for plant expansion in any of the past five years. Thus the plans inaugurated last year may be predicted to culminate this year in increased expenditures for plant expansion which businessmen last year were unable to find the means of bringing to full fruition.

CHAPTER 4

Collecting

Data

Two kinds of bad reports disturb executive readers. One kind is overloaded with facts—perhaps pages of statistical tables, graphs, charts, and diagrams—but does no interpreting; it dumps masses of material into the reader's lap without pointing out what it all means. The essential data may all be there, but the reader is forced to write the report; and because readers are always busy men, they are never happy doing work that somebody else was supposed to do for them. The second kind of bad report is easy enough to read: it simplifies, summarizes, generalizes beautifully. The only trouble is that the reader can find no evidence to support any of the conclusions.

The reader of a report, then, expects both facts (evidence, data) and interpretations of the facts. Not all the facts you collect will be useful, and not all are relevant. But the facts that *are* directly relevant become your *data*. All facts that lead toward a significant conclusion, or qualify such a conclusion, become important evidence. Such factual evidence is what we mean by *data*.

ANALYZING THE PROBLEM

The purpose and scope of the report determine the kind and quantity of data needed. What facts will be pertinent? The answer comes from an intelligent analysis of the problem the report is intended to discuss. Sometimes a letter of instructions spells out exactly what a report is to cover. At other times the writer must set his own boundary lines. Two steps properly precede the search for relevant data:

1. Find the central problem and state it. Precisely what main question is the report to answer?
2. Find and state all subordinate questions that must be answered in order to arrive at a reasonable answer to the central problem.

Reports differ so widely that no formula can fit them all. Critical study of the organization of actual reports can prove useful, but ultimately each writer must develop his own plan. A few examples will show some possibilities:

PROBLEM:

Why should the company appropriate $20,000 for further tests to determine the feasibility of new materials? [Problem for a *proposal* report.]

CONTROLLING FACTORS:

1. What problems led to earlier tests?
2. What tentative conclusions are warranted on the basis of tests performed so far?
   2.1 Probable cost
   2.2 Probable durability
   2.3 Probable flexibility
   2.4 Probable economy
3. What further tests are sufficiently promising?
   3.1 Durability tests
   3.2 Economy tests

PROBLEM:

What progress on construction deserves reporting for the month of February?

PHASES OF THE WORK

1. Work through January 31 [previously reported]
2. Delivery of materials
3. Exterior
4. Interior
5. Personnel
6. Costs
7. Next steps

PROBLEM:

Which site should be recommended for the new plant?

LIMITATIONS:

Reasons for limiting investigation to three towns.

CONTROLLING FACTORS:

1. Accessibility
   1.1 To raw materials—what facilities?
   1.2 To markets—what facilities?
2. Costs
   2.1 Land
   2.2 Grading
   2.3 Improvements
   2.4 Construction
3. Labor
   3.1 Available skilled labor
   3.2 Available semiskilled and unskilled labor
   3.3 Prevailing wages
   3.4 Union activities
4. Living conditions for personnel
   4.1 Available housing
   4.2 Community facilities for recreation, etc.

5. Community influences
   5.1 Restrictive ordinances
   5.2 Taxes
   5.3 Police protection
   5.4 Insurance rates
   5.5 Sanitation

Such outlines clearly indicate what supporting data are necessary. The reason for such an analysis *before* the search for data starts is obvious.

POTENTIAL SOURCES OF INFORMATION

Next consider the potential sources of useful evidence. These are the general areas from which the data in reports may come:

1. Unpublished records in company files or elsewhere: related correspondence, earlier reports on the same subject or in the same series, contracts, specifications, memos and formal reports from assistants or other departments.
2. Previous observation and experience: what the writer recalls from his own past that may be useful here, or what he has already written in earlier reports.
3. Publications: books, publications of government agencies or foundations, annual reports of corporations, bulletins, professional journals—occasionally even newspapers and general magazines.
4. New observation or experiment: inspections, controlled tests, experimental studies under the writer's direction.
5. Interrogations: interviews or questionnaires, correspondence with specialists, group discussions.

Every report writer must master his own techniques for obtaining the data he requires. The marketing specialist obviously learns quite different methods of investigation from those required by the automotive engineer. This chapter, without pretending to tell either specialist or administrator the requirements of his own job, discusses some general principles for gathering and recording data.

Evidence from Reading

The reading that provides material for a report may have one of several functions:

1. It may provide essential background. A review of the literature on a particular subject summarizes work previously reported and may lead to additional work in the same area. Reading may prevent duplication of investigations already made. It helps the writer point out what is new in his report—what he is adding to previous findings.
2. Reading may produce facts to supplement evidence from experi-

ment, inspection, or survey. It may provide a significant part of the necessary data in the report.

3. Reading the reports of assistants or colleagues may provide the report writer with the substance of an administrative report. Most of the data in the executive's report come from more detailed reports of specialists and assistants.

Reading may consist largely of the examination of what is in the company's files and the company library, or it may require considerable time in a public or university library. Learning to use the files of a company or department need not take long. Finding what we want in a large library is more complex, but numerous indexes are available as guides, and reference librarians can usually help.

The first step in library investigation is to prepare a *working bibliography*—a list of potential sources. The preliminary analysis provides a list of topics to be covered or questions to be answered. Now, from appropriate indexes, it is possible to list all the references that may produce the necessary evidence.

Already familiar to many writers are such general indexes as the library card catalog, *The Readers' Guide to Periodical Literature* and the *New York Times Index*. There are many more, many of them specialized (*Accountants' Index, Agricultural Index, Nuclear Science Abstracts*)—so many, in fact, that an annotated bibliography of indexes is provided on pages 275-80.

Three indexes deserve special emphasis:

1. *Chemical Abstracts* indexes and summarizes (in English) every article concerned with chemistry or chemicals appearing in over 8000 periodicals.

2. The *Public Affairs Information Service* (PAIS) indexes nearly a thousand periodicals, books, pamphlets, and government documents for problems related to business, finance, sociology, and government.

3. The often-overlooked *Monthly Catalog of U.S. Government Publications* indexes the voluminous literature published by the Federal agencies, authorities, bureaus, commissions, and departments. Books, bulletins, pamphlets, and bibliographies on every conceivable subject are included. No researcher, whatever his subject, can afford to neglect this source. The following examples suggest the wide range of this index:

   A Study of Small Business in the Electronic Industry (229 pp.)
   Experimental Statistics (504 pp.)
   Crystal Chemistry of Beryllium (30 pp.)
   A Consumer's Guide to USDA [U.S. Dept. of Agriculture] *Services* (49 pp.)

Neurosurgery, Vol. III (705 pp.)

Navigation Dictionary (253 pp.)

Geology of the Dodgeville and Mineral Point Quadrangles, Wisconsin (77 pp.)

Weather Science Study Kit (16 publications)

Reasonable diligence in the library will acquaint the researcher with countless other sources of useful information. Only a few of the better known can be mentioned here:

1. *The Statistical Abstract of the United States* includes a wide variety of economic, political, and sociological data selected from the Department of Commerce *Census Volumes.*

2. *The Minerals Yearbook* includes comprehensive information on the producers, processors, and users of metals, minerals, and fuels.

3. Moody's *Manuals (Transportation, Industrial, Public Utility, Municipal and Government,* and *Bank and Finance)* supply comprehensive information on the history, business, property, officers, sales, and financial status of corporations and governments throughout the world.

4. *The Thomas Register of American Manufacturers* gives financial information, classified by product, for every industry in the United States.

5. *Sweet's Catalogs* constitute a classified collection of manufacturers' catalogs.

A working bibliography prepared from indexes and other reference works directs the writer to the most promising sources; it gives him some view of the extent of his task.

Taking efficient notes is necessary for effective research. (We discuss note-taking at the end of this chapter.) Not everything you read, however, is worth recording in notes. So far as possible, it is better to understand, assimilate, and remember the most important ideas; take notes only on specific figures, proper names, complex details, and statements that must be precise.

Direct Observation and Experiment

Primary investigation means direct first-hand acquaintance with relevant facts. It includes simple observations: inspection of safety devices in a plant, equipment in a department, sections of a city pavement, or motors in a fleet of trucks. It also includes experiments or tests in which the investigator manipulates one factor at a time to provide a "control" (for example, under identical driving conditions he tests two different cars or two different gasolines). Certain sciences, like astronomy, rely principally upon observation; others, like chemistry, rely upon experiment.

In all primary investigations an objective approach is fundamental. An objective approach subordinates personal feelings and preconceptions; it centers attention on facts. The investigator usually does start with a kind of hypothesis or preliminary guess, but the purpose of his investigations is not to *prove* his hypothesis but to *test* it. He must check facts against his preconceptions, always ready to revise his hypothesis when the facts demand it. His reputation as investigator depends upon his accuracy, his diligence, and his ability to apply the techniques recognized in his own field. Each field—engineering, biology, transportation, marketing, or hotel administration—has its own techniques.

Details of method are important, even when the final report says little about them. The responsible report writer can always explain and defend his methods when asked to do so. If he makes a traffic count at a busy intersection, he knows exactly where, when, how, and why—as well as what it revealed. He always has the data essential to support his conclusions.

Sampling

Most important conclusions in a report are based, at least in part, on a kind of *sampling*—that is, a representative *part* is assumed to possess characteristics of a *whole*. Tests on one motor are used to provide information about all motors of the same kind under similar conditions. A properly selected sample of ore from a mine represents the ore in that mine. A few hundred typical steelworkers can be questioned to learn something about steelworkers generally. Because it is seldom possible to obtain *all* the information about any problem, we must usually make our generalizations from a limited number of facts. That is why the way we choose a sample becomes so important.

The first question in sampling concerns the whole that the sample is to represent. What total area? What period of time? What limitations of persons or things, methods or processes? A market survey of potential customers in the Chicago area must first define *Chicago area:* the geographic boundaries to be considered, the part of the total population to be counted. It may include "all adults within a hundred-mile radius" or only "men with incomes over $10,000 living within the city limits." Tests of "compact cars" must start with a decision about what makes, years, and models of cars are to be considered. It is not possible to obtain a representative sample without knowing first what it is supposed to represent.

We have two possible sampling methods, the *random* method and the *weighted* or *stratified* method. A random sample is not what the word implies to uninitiated laymen. It is not a careless, haphazard selection, but one in which every significant element *has an equal chance to appear*.

It usually takes considerable care to obtain such a sample. The weighted or stratified sample, used by the Gallup Poll, is arbitrarily selected to include correct proportions of segments of the whole that the investigator considers significant.

You should first consider possible ways to obtain a good random sample. It cannot be done by questioning persons on a street corner, because all persons *not* on that street corner are automatically excluded; nor can it be done by testing production for an hour on Monday, because that automatically excludes production at all other hours and other days. But from a complete list of the population to be investigated, say 20,000 employees, it is possible to select 200 *by lot* that would constitute a true random sample of the 20,000. In the true random sample *nothing must influence the selection but chance.*

When feasible, random sampling is the most reliable method, but for many situations it is not feasible. The weighted sample can be highly reliable too. Experts in sampling soils, ores, streams, and "publics" have developed sound techniques for obtaining representative samples. Public opinion polls, for example, start with statistics concerning various characteristics of the public to be sampled: the percentage in various income groups, the percentage of urban and rural dwellers, the percentage in various age groups, and so on. Then the sample is chosen to include the exact proportion in each category considered important.

In the weighted sample, the investigator makes an arbitrary choice of the factors to be weighed. A sample of voters taken from the telephone directory automatically eliminates everybody not having a telephone—most of whom would be in the lowest income bracket. If income seems a significant factor in voting tendencies, then *income* must be properly weighted in the sample.

A survey of employee attitudes toward a company's group-insurance program selected a sample with the following weights (because these were the *actual* percentages on record in company files):

AGE:
Under 30 (25%), 31-45 (60%), over 45 (15%)

YEARS WITH COMPANY:
Less than 5 (30%), 5-15 (40%), over 15 (30%)

OCCUPATION:
Administrative (5%), clerical (15%), skilled labor (50%), unskilled labor (30%)

ANNUAL INCOME:
Under $5000 (25%); $5000-$8000 (50%); $8000-$10,000 (13%); over $10,000 (12%)

How large a sample is necessary for a sound generalization? If the whole population or universe is homogeneous or standardized, as with manufactured products like this year's Oldsmobile, a very small sample will do. If the whole is heterogeneous, like office workers or the streams of Ohio, a much larger sample is necessary. But the mere size of the sample is never so important as the manner in which it is selected. A truly random sample of about 250 workers could represent a million such workers in an opinion poll calling for a yes-or-no answer; the margin of error would be less than 5 per cent. A good sample of a hundred is always better than a carelessly selected sample of thousands.

No sample is perfect. Every sample contains some possible margin of error. It is possible to reduce the margin of error by getting a larger sample, but to cut the margin of error in half it is necessary to get a sample four times as large. In market research a 10 per cent margin of error is frequently good enough. In national polls intended to predict presidential election results, an error of 2 per cent may prove altogether too great.

The raw data obtained in sampling are important only so far as they can be reasonably projected to the whole which they represent. The reader of a report has little interest in the raw data—that "37 skilled workers in our sample plan to retire next year," or that "17 clerical workers took over a month of sick leave last year." Projected, the conclusion may be that "we can expect over 3500 skilled workers to retire next year." Because there must be a margin of error, the projection should never be stated as a precise figure; it is always an *approximation:* "about 5200," "almost 20,000," "nearly a thousand."

All the generalizations we make about past, present, and future must result from at least a rough kind of sampling. The requirement in report writing is to find samples that are really *representative*—fair cross sections that do not ignore important exceptions.

Interview and Questionnaire

Interrogation (asking significant questions of persons likely to have the answers) is one important source of data for reports. It may take the form of a letter of inquiry, which we discussed in Chapter 2. It may employ direct interview, telephone calls, or questionnaire. The resulting answers may provide suggestions for further investigation, expert opinion, or factual evidence for the report.

The purpose of interrogation determines the medium and form to be used. The so-called "depth interview," for example, can produce specific details that a questionnaire distributed to many different persons cannot produce. The questions asked grow out of free discussion and vary with each interview. On the other hand, the questionnaire asks identical questions of many persons and thus permits statistical tabulation.

The best depth interview gets the relevant information as quickly as possible, but under conditions that create good will. This requires planning. Why approach this particular person? What can you learn about him in advance? What kind of information do you hope to get from him? How shall you introduce the interview? What questions should you ask—and in what order? Of course you may alter the plan during the interview; the questions should fit the conditions, and new questions may come to mind. But preliminary planning saves time and confusion.

The interview ought to be informal. If possible, avoid taking notes during an interview except to jot down precise figures, proper names, or unfamiliar technical terms. Immediately *after* the interview, however, write down details you must remember while they are still fresh in your mind.

The formal questionnaire is the best means of collecting most statistical data. It may be mailed to a list of persons who constitute a representative sample of the population you wish to investigate—a "public" consisting of employees, customers, prospects, or colleagues in your field. It may be delivered in person and then picked up at a later time, or it may be administered by telephone or through personal interviews. The significant characteristic of the questionnaire is that everyone answers precisely the same questions.

Each method of administering a questionnaire has advantages and disadvantages.

The telephone is a fast and inexpensive method. If nobody answers the phone at the first call, it is possible to call again. Unless the questionnaire is abnormally long, nearly everybody will answer the questions. It is easy to standardize the questions and to train assistants to do the telephoning. The telephone survey, however, has many disadvantages: Telephone subscribers may not represent the whole population that you want to cover; it is not possible to tell the age of the person answering; and of course the answers may be thoughtless or irresponsible.

The direct interview permits some classification of the person answering the questionnaire (for example, sex, age, and probable economic status); it nearly always procures a larger percentage of answers than one can expect by mail. But it is the most expensive method, and there is also the risk that the interviewer himself may unconsciously influence the answers.

Mail is the least expensive method. It permits one to think before he answers, and it eliminates possible influence by an interviewer. But a considerable percentage of the questionnaires may not be returned, and it is often impossible to know how representative the actual returns will be. Identification questions included in the questionnaire are one means of making classification of replies possible (for example, sex, age, occupation).

Here are a few suggestions for preparing efficient questionnaires:

1. Classify the general areas of information that you intend the questionnaire to produce. Determine the general aims before you start listing specific questions.

2. Within the areas you intend to cover, jot down all the questions that seem potentially useful.

3. Run through the list to reduce the number:

    3.1 If several questions seem repetitious, select the best phrasing and discard the others.

    3.2 Place subordinate questions in subordinate positions.

    3.3 Reject all questions for which information can be obtained more easily or reliably elsewhere.

    3.4 Discard every question that seems unlikely to produce useful evidence.

    The fewer questions included, the more likelihood they will be answered and the easier your work of tabulating will be. You want all the relevant information you can get—but no waste.

4. Test each question for clarity and meaning. Be sure that only one interpretation is possible.

    "Do you read the professional journals in your field?" is ambiguous. One may answer "Yes" whether he reads a dozen journals regularly and thoroughly or whether he reads only one or two journals occasionally.

    "Do you trade in town?" is equally ambiguous. The person who answers "Yes" may make all his purchases in town or only a tenth of them.

5. Rephrase "loaded" questions (those that suggest the answers):

    "Do you find the process inefficient?" is prejudiced phrasing. "Do you think it is more patriotic to buy American-made goods?" "Do you oppose unnecessary appropriations?"

    Impartial phrasing often requires the multiple-choice rather than the yes-no question:

How efficient do you find the process?	Very efficient	_____
	Fairly efficient	_____
	Not very efficient	_____
	Very inefficient	_____
How much has this machine been out of service for repairs during the past year?	Never	_____
	Less than a week	_____
	One week to one month	_____
	More than a month	_____

6. Generally, prefer questions of fact to questions of opinion. Avoid those that call for broad guesses or estimates or place undue emphasis on memory.

"What is your average food bill per year?" is a hard question for most families to answer. Most of them do not have an accurate record at hand.

"Do you like to bowl?" may bring misleading answers. "How often have you bowled in the past year?" would bring more useful replies.

7. Name possibly limiting factors that would influence the answer:

Not: Would you like electric heat in your new home?

Better: Would you prefer electric heat in your new home if the cost is not more than 10 per cent above the cost of oil?

8. Style questions, when possible, so that they can be answered with check marks. The less writing required, the easier to answer and the easier to tabulate replies.

9. Place the most important, the most interesting, and the simplest questions first. A simple *and* interesting question gets a more favorable and immediate response. Since earlier questions may get more attention, those you consider especially important should appear early in the questionnaire.

10. Create a willingness to answer. Some brief introduction is necessary to stimulate curiosity and interest. A telephone call may start with an interesting question. An interview or mail questionnaire needs a brief introduction to explain the purpose and perhaps the possible benefits to those who cooperate. A short cover letter may introduce the mail questionnaire. A standardized, memorized statement may be used to begin each interview so that nothing in the interviewer's comments will create different conditions and so influence possibly different attitudes for different interviews.

11. Try to run a simple pretest of the questionnaire before you put it in final form and set out to administer it. You may test the questions on a dozen or so representative persons. Do they understand each question in the way you mean it? Do they respond well? Do you get useful answers? If not, you can make changes before it is too late.

APPLICATIONS OF LOGIC

Since the data of a report are important only when they lead to some logical conclusion, it follows that logic is as much a consideration in selecting the data as in writing the report itself. Various inferences require the report writer to apply rules of logic.

Evaluations play a frequent role in reports. Logic demands that the writer define his criteria for judgment and apply them rigidly. In *il-logical* evaluations the criteria applied are not really relevant, or the evidence does not justify the judgment. An illogical evaluation may judge safety by standards of beauty, efficiency by some superficial external appearance.

Generalizations based upon sampling should be used with caution. The rule of logic is to make certain the sample is a fair and representative part of the whole it is used to represent. The sample must be large enough to permit a generalization (two or three bad letters in a company's files do not prove a need for "complete reorganization of our methods of communication"), and must be typical of the whole.

Analogies lead to numerous conclusions in reports. Conditions in one plant are compared with conditions in another; experience with a process at one place is used as evidence of its probable results at a similar place. The rule of logic is to ascertain that things so compared *be essentially alike in all significant respects.* An office arrangement that functions well should function equally well in another office *essentially like it*—not necessarily in an office with quite different problems and personnel.

Inferences of *cause and effect* appear in nearly every report. What influences led to the strike? What caused the breakdown? Why did profits decrease in the third quarter? How will this change affect operating costs? One frequent fallacy in such interferences is to confuse mere coincidence with cause. If workers in the state receiving high wages are shown to produce more than workers receiving low pay, what is the cause-and-effect relationship? Do high wages encourage greater production, or do those who produce more get higher wages because of their competence to produce? Cold weather in late November regularly precedes a marked increase in department store sales, but Christmas shopping is a more plausible explanation than the weather. The *controls* demanded in scientific experiment are designed to single out actual causes and to separate them from irrelevant antecedents. The report writer should, when possible, search for a similar protection. He should always ask, "What *other* differences were present that might have had an effect?" or "Have *all* possible factors been considered and given proper weight?"

The report writer should never claim more for his evidence than it logically deserves. Sometimes all available data are insufficient to prove very much; they disclose a problem, but no clear solution. If so, the report may conclude that "the problem seems serious enough to warrant further study." Sometimes the evidence is largely negative: no fatal accidents in a plant for a year, for example. Negative evidence may be highly significant, but it must be used cautiously. Absence of serious accidents is not conclusive proof that no safety hazards exist. The good report writer arrives at his conclusions thoughtfully. He distinguishes certainties from probabilities and probabilities from mere possibilities. He asserts only what he can prove; when proof is uncertain or incomplete, he qualifies his conclusions.

RECORDING THE DATA—NOTE-TAKING

The writer needs a really efficient method of recording data for later use. If he conducts certain tests, he needs to have specific details on paper for future reference. He needs records of inspections, interviews, and committee discussions. From his reading he needs essential notes in usable form.

Not all possible data need be in the form of notes. Letters, memos, contracts, specifications, unpublished reports, and other documents may be at hand for convenient reference if needed. If books and other published sources can be immediately available during the writing process, it is seldom useful to copy many details from them in separate notes. Insertion of index slips at appropriate places in a book will permit ready reference to details the writer wants to use. But for long reports involving considerable data from numerous sources, an orderly system of note-taking is generally necessary.

A quantity of notes seems good, but some writers seem to think the more the better and waste time copying down what they already know or what they cannot hope to use in a report. Too many notes may make the writing process more complex than it needs to be.

Good preliminary analysis of the problem saves time, as we have pointed out before. It suggests the topics to be covered and the questions to be answered. Nothing need be taken down in notes that does not fit somehow into that general plan. Again, it is possible to evaluate sources and evidence during the process of collecting data. If facts or figures seem trivial, unreliable, or of doubtful logical value, it is better to exclude them from the notes.

Finally, it is often possible to appraise, interpret, and understand much of your material well enough to *remember*. You should not strain memory to retain precise figures, proper names, or exact phrasing, but you can learn to remember general principles, arguments, explanations, and ideas without writing everything out in notes. If you learn to *think* as you go, you will learn to reduce the number of notes you have to handle. Notes cannot take the place of constructive thinking.

Some research projects require that original records be preserved for future reference. Notes are then recorded in ink in a bound notebook *as they are taken*. Each page and each entry bears the date and often the signature or initials of the person responsible.

Short reports often contain so little data that almost any kind of note-taking will do. Essential information may be jotted down on a single page of a small notebook—or even on the back of an envelope.

On the other hand, the long report including quantities of varied data introduces more complex problems. It is for such reports that systematic note-taking becomes really necessary. The method adopted must:

> Guard against serious omissions.
>
> Permit rearrangement of data if the ultimate plan is changed.
>
> Permit fitting data easily into the proper place in the final report.
>
> Avoid the necessity of going back to sources at a later time to check and verify details.
>
> Include full documentation (names, dates, titles of sources).

Notes may be taken on 3 x 5 cards or on half-sheets of ordinary typewriter paper. In any case, each note should cover only *one* item of evidence from *one* source under *one* topic in the preliminary outline or analysis. This preliminary outline should always be at hand during the process of taking notes. Appropriate symbols on the outline appear on the notes to indicate where they belong:

OUTLINE
1. Preliminary
    1.1 Reason for study
    1.2 Background
    1.3 Definitions
2. Present system
3. Present and future demand
4. Comparison of possibilities
    4.1 Enlarging present reservoir
    4.2 Building additional reservoir
    4.3 Drilling series of wells
    4.4 Consolidation with nearby systems

Water Consumption

2

Pres. ave.   consump: 1,755,000 g/day
        min.   1,465,000
        max.   2,150,000

Observation: 2/7/64

Water Authority Records

Gap Test

5

"Water from the test wells in
Galbraith Gap tested 75 ppm."

(wells driven 8/64)

Interview: 11/5/64

—R. N. Jones, City Eng.

FUTURE OF IR

3.3

"Information expands fantastically — but how
get at what we want when we want it?
I (nformation) R (etrieval) systems are intended
to analyze, store, and, on demand, accurately
retrieve what has been published."

Experts say devising more difficult than dev. tel
or tel or electron computer. I R problem "involves the way men classify and relate ideas,
the way they express themselves in language,
and ultimately the way men think."

[Major advantage will be in translating quickly —
quick access to foreign scientists. Q: How used
by pvt. companies?]

Francis Bello, "How To Cope with Information,"
Fortune, Sept, 1960, pp. 162-67.

It is always important to distinguish exact quotations from your own paraphrase or summary. The following note makes such distinctions, employing brackets to set off impressions of the note-taker that are not to be confused with anything in the original source:

```
                                              3.2.3

        Price Support for Poorest Farmers

"...first flaw" in system:  "little for the large portion of farm
population that genuinely needs help."  Poorest farmers get
least help.   /Note:  Lamoile Co. farmer complaints/

est.  2.7 million farms selling less that $2500 of prod.
      avg. $109 in benefits from price supports 1956-7

      1.3 million farms selling $5000 plus
      avg. $1993 in benefits....

      Rockefeller Panel Reports    294
```

Here are a few suggestions for taking good notes:
1. Indicate the exact section of your outline to which each note pertains with the appropriate symbol (in these examples the outline symbol appears in the upper right-hand corner).
2. When convenient, give each note a heading to indicate its specific subject.
3. Distinguish exact quotations from your own summaries. Use quotation marks to set off phrases and sentences directly copied. Use brackets to set off reminders entirely your own.
4. Include the exact source of each note. For convenience, you may number your bibliography or list of sources and indicate the source merely by number: *Source 23* or merely *23* at the bottom of the note.
5. Use separate notes for evidence concerning different sections of your preliminary outline.
6. Use abbreviations freely—but be sure every abbreviation is entirely clear to *you,* and be especially careful to preserve the exact phrasing of all quotations. Remember that your notes are your own property; if you understand them yourself, you need not worry about what others think of them.

For tallying statistical data from questionnaires, interviews, or other surveys, a *recap sheet* is the usual device, though various electronic devices may be used for extensive surveys. Eventually, of course, the results may be simplified and summarized on single note cards.

A FINAL CHECKLIST

Ask yourself these questions about the data you collect:

1. Are all these facts relevant? Do they help answer significant questions?
2. Is the evidence up-to-date? Is it recent enough to be applicable? (If not, throw out that which is too old.)
3. Have the sources been investigated thoroughly? Are they reputable, competent, and reliable? Have all important details been noted: names, titles, chapter or pages, dates, and so forth?
4. Can logical conclusions be reached from the data? What conclusions?
5. Is the evidence adequate to justify the conclusions reached. If not, is there any way to get more?

Exercises

1. Make a complete plan for sampling:
    (a) Engineering schools of the United States to determine entrance requirements.
    (b) Members of a labor union to determine attitudes toward union leadership.
    (c) Homeowners who heat with electricity to learn cost and efficiency.
    (d) Clerks in department stores to get data on hours, wages, and working conditions.
    (e) College graduates with degrees in a specific curriculum to determine the kinds of positions they hold.

2. Prepare a questionnaire to be sent:
    (a) To members of college athletic teams for information on the effects of athletic participation on scholarship and other activities.
    (b) To automobile mechanics regarding comparative repair costs of three different cars.
    (c) To contractors in an attempt to estimate comparative demand for "modern" and "traditional" houses.
    (d) To local employers for a record of their relations with unions.
    (e) To undergraduates in one college regarding their vocational aims.

3. Prepare an outline for an interview with:
    (a) An authority in your field, to get suggestions for preparing a report or term paper.
    (b) A well-known professional man on opportunities in his profession or field.
    (c) An unskilled workman on his living conditions.
    (d) A research scientist on the purposes of his research.
    (e) A college or university president on the prospects of his institution for the next decade.

CHAPTER 5

Planning
the
Report

A THOROUGH preliminary analysis of the central problem together with an efficient process of collecting essential data should make the final task of planning the report comparatively easy. The significant elements of the report will be the main points that the investigation covered. For example, an investigation leading to proposed office reorganization included these considerations:

Floor plan	Light, heat, and ventilation
Furniture and machines	Wall, ceiling, and floor coverings

Various subdivisions were also necessary.

The annual report of a corporation had to cover these elements:

Consolidated balance sheet	Transportation
Consolidated statement of income and surplus	Marketing
	Research and development
Production	Personnel relations

With such main factors already determined, the report writer can proceed to his final plan.

CENTRAL THESIS AND SUPPORT

Every good report has a central idea—a main point to present and defend. Before you start even a rough draft of the report, it is well to express that central idea in words: a single sentence that becomes the thesis or epitome of your report. For example, the epitome of a department's monthly report:

> Though payrolls increased and various repairs slowed production, the record for the past month shows a slight rise over the preceding month and a 12% rise over the same month last year.

The epitome of a progress report:

> As a result of good weather conditions and prompt delivery of materials and equipment, we find ourselves about ten days ahead of schedule with good prospects of completing construction by early July.

The epitome of a recommendation report based on a survey:

> A study of potential markets in Rayburn and surrounding areas leads to the recommendation that we increase appropriations for radio, television, and local newspaper advertising as the Miller-Gross Agency has proposed.

The epitome should be the most concise and accurate statement you can make of your final judgment—the general conclusion you are prepared to support in the report.

When considerable data must be presented in a comparatively long report, it is often useful to prepare a *brief* that includes main points and evidence to support the main thesis. Notes recording relevant data may be numbered and keyed into the brief. This is the method of such a brief:

> THESIS: To improve memos and reports we should: (1) employ a report-writing consultant; (2) publish a 20-page "writer's manual"; (3) adopt standard printed forms for interoffice memos and reports, *because*

1. We find waste and inefficiency in interoffice communications.
    1.1 Letters and memos are inefficient, because
        1.1.1 Too many full letters are written (N[*notes*]—16.3).
        1.1.2 Memos often omit vital information (N—16.6).
        1.1.3 Writing is verbose and unclear (N—16.8).
        1.1.4 Important suggestions are often not emphasized (N—16.2).
    1.2 Reports are often inefficient, because
        1.2.1 They waste the reader's time.
            1.2.1.1 Organization is inefficient (N—17.3).
            1.2.1.2 They are often hard to read (N—17.7–8).
            1.2.1.3 Many are too long (N—17.1).
        1.2.2 Reports often duplicate work previously done (N—17.2).
        1.2.3 Too many reports lack essential data (N—17.5).

2. Standard printed forms for memos and short reports will be efficient, because
    2.1 They guarantee certain essential information, such as date, sender, destination.
    2.2 They encourage a clear statement of subject.
    2.3 The necessary subject line will encourage unity.

Of course the brief does not necessarily represent the order of the finished report. Its advantage is in forcing the writer to examine his ideas and test them. It makes him aware of his materials and the uses he will make of them. It makes him equally aware of weaknesses in evidence and supporting arguments.

LENGTH AND FORM

"Too long!" is a common complaint of executives about the reports they read. No report should be any longer than it has to be. Yet of course a report may be too short to include information it ought to have, or too short to back up its conclusions. Each writer makes his own decision. He must ask himself who will read his report and why, what supporting data his reader needs and how much can be left out, and how much data should be included somewhere for future reference. Every report writer who had done his preliminary work thoroughly finds that he has collected much data that he can never use. Even if it hurts, he must learn to discard what he can do without.

Many routine reports are best presented on printed forms. Often these have the appearance of a questionnaire. They are usually easy to fill out and easy to read. When the same kinds of data appear regularly in many different reports, the standardized form is efficient. For example:

WEATHER:
    Temperature range
    Precipitation [daily in inches]

RIVER STAGE AND DISCHARGE:

EMPLOYEES THIS PERIOD:

PAYROLL TOTAL:

ACCIDENTS:
    Number
    Total lost time in man-hours

Usually the aim is to have the answers represented as figures, names, yes-or-no, or mere check marks. A good form is easy to fill out, but preparing such forms is not so easy: every item must be absolutely clear and unambiguous, a place must be provided for all essential information, and the order and phrasing must be right for both writer and reader.

Less routine situations requiring short reports generally call for the letter or memo form. We have already considered these in Chapter 2.

Reports requiring four or five pages and more of text may adopt the "long form" with title page, table of contents, and other elements not found in a letter or memorandum. Reports of this kind naturally require the most planning. Subtitles usually appear throughout the text, and all subtitles will be listed in the table of contents if the report is long enough to need one. The table of contents represents the writer's final plan.

PERIODIC REPORT PLANS

The periodic report covers the activities, condition, and prospects of an organization or a division of an organization. It is due at specified intervals—daily, weekly, monthly, quarterly, or annually. The corporation's annual report to stockholders must be based on many lesser periodic reports of departments, plants, offices, and operations.

Often the plan of a periodic report is fixed by convention. The simplest of them appear on standardized forms; longer ones may follow nearly the same pattern every time:

New men hired   Accidents during month
Men separated or retired   Lost time
Promotions   Compensation
Salaries   Safety equipment
Training programs   Safety education
              Orders filled
              New orders received
              Orders returned for adjustment
              Special problems

Every organization has its own special needs and responsibilities.

The way the president of a company plans his annual report illustrates some of the common problems. First he brings together various materials for possible use:

Financial statements of accountant, accountant's summary, auditor's report
Engineering Department's quarterly reports
Sales manager's monthly reports
Personnel director's annual report
Company annual reports for the past ten years
His own notes, jotted down during the year

He must evaluate, condense, and arrange his facts for his readers. The plan may develop as follows:

General view (brief summary of the year: total production and sales, general financial condition, forecast)
Administration (largely from his own notes)
Profits (from accountant's report)
Sales (from sales manager's reports)
Production (from Engineering Department reports)
Personnel relations (from personnel director's report)
Plant and equipment (from Engineering Department reports)
The Outlook (his own appraisal)
Financial statements (from Accounting Department)

The periodic report should start with a good *summary;* the busy reader wants a view of the whole before he turns to details.

Two representative outlines follow:

ANNUAL REPORT OF A PLANT MANAGER

General summary
Organization
    Administrative personnel
    Labor
Equipment
    Buildings
    Machinery
Operation
    Production
    Plant efficiency
    Cost of production
    Return
Tables and charts: statistical data

ANNUAL REPORT OF A HOUSING ASSOCIATION

The Year's Record (an introductory summary)
Inspection Service
Special Surveys
    Dwelling Construction During the Year
    Demolitions
    House Rents in the City
Legislation
Public Information
Financial Statements (receipts and disbursements)

PROGRESS REPORT PLANS

Like the periodic report, the progress report usually (not always) covers a specified period of time. It reports progress on a special project rather than in a continuing organization. A series of progress reports will provide a running account of work related to the project from start to finish; when the project is concluded, the progress reports stop. They may concern extensive construction, reorganization, surveys, or research. The data for them usually come from daily records.

A common general plan for progress reports is as follows:

1. Summary: Purpose of the project, timetable, work to date, prospects, and needs or recommendations, if any.
2. Earlier work reported: A brief summary of previous progress reports—what happened before the current reporting period.
3. New progress: Work completed, difficulties encountered, men employed, methods used.
4. Forecast: What can be reasonably expected, likely problems, suggestions for facilitating the work.

The following detailed outline is an adaptation of this general plan:

FOURTH PROGRESS REPORT
MIDSTATE PARKWAY

Summary
    Progress since last report
    Suggestions
    Forecast
Introduction
    Description of project
    Summary of progress previously reported
Details of recent progress
    Section I: Haven-Lycoming
        Grading
        Structures
            Bridges
            Culverts
            Retaining walls
        Surfacing
    Section II: Lycoming-Westover
        Structures
            Bridges
            Tunnel
Exterior considerations
    Right-of-way litigation
    Intersected traffic
Personnel
Tabulated data
    Costs
    Construction data

INVESTIGATIVE REPORT PLANS

Reports based on extensive investigations often cause the most difficulties in planning. They differ widely, and each different investigation may introduce problems all its own. Many companies have suggested or required at least general plans for investigative reports by their own personnel. Sometimes these outlines appear in company style manuals intended for technical specialists and others who will be writing reports. Here are some representative outlines:

THE DETROIT EDISON COMPANY

Short-Form Report	*Long-Form Report*
Summary	(Title page)
Detailed results	(Table of contents)
Discussion	Statement of problem
Procedure	Conclusions and summary of results
[Title, date, authorship, and authorization appear at top of first page]	Procedure
	Results
	Discussion of results
	[Graphs, drawings, etc., included in report body]

OWENS-CORNING FIBERGLAS
CORPORATION
(Title page)
(Table of contents)
Abstract
Statement of problem
Summary of results
Procedure
Test results
Discussion
Appendix

THE GOODYEAR TIRE & RUBBER
COMPANY
Summary
    Subject
    Statement of problem
    Abstract
Introduction
    More complete statement of
        problem
    Historical background
Test procedure and data
Compilation of results
Conclusions
Proposed future work

DUPONT DE NEMOURS &
COMPANY
Engineering Department
(Cover)
(Title page)
Abstract
(Table of contents)
Summary
Discussion
    Introduction
    Text
    Basis for conclusions
    Basis for recommendations
Appendix
Bibliography

ARMSTRONG CORK COMPANY
Title
(Table of contents)
Abstract
Conclusions
Recommendations
Body of report
    Introduction

NATIONAL
BUREAU OF STANDARDS
Abstract
(Table of contents)
Introduction:
    Scope, objective
Test equipment
Test procedure
Test results
Methods of computing data
Conclusions
References

THE TENNESSEE VALLEY
AUTHORITY
(Title page)
Letter of transmittal
(Table of contents)
Summary
Detailed report
    Introduction
    Body of report
    Acknowledgments
    Bibliography
Appendixes
Exhibits

BATTELLE MEMORIAL INSTITUTE
(Title page)
Abstract
(Table of contents)
(List of tables)
(List of figures)
Body of report
    Introductory section
    Summary section
    Experimental work section
    Discussion section
    Conclusions section
    Future work section
Bibliography or list of references
Appendixes

WESTERN UNION TELEGRAPH
COMPANY
Instruction Manual
Introduction
    Description of equipment and
        its function
    Over-all system in which it will
        operate

ARMSTRONG CORK COMPANY (*Cont.*)   COMPANY (*Cont.*)
    Experimental work   Equipment   it   replaces   or
    Discussion   works with
    Results   Physical Description
    Future plans   Installation
  Bibliography   Operation and Controls
  Appendix   Theory
        Over-all system
        Individual parts

Title page and table of contents are matters of general make-up rather than actual planning, although including them in an outline does suggest the intended form of the report. If we omit those elements, we may arrive at a representative outline for reports based on investigation:

  Summary or abstract

  Introduction
    Problem—purpose
    Scope of investigation
    General procedures

  Discussion of data [This, of course, includes the whole body of the report; it must be broken down into divisions similar to those in the working outline; each report will have its own factors to discuss.]

  Conclusions

  Appendix
    Details of methods used in investigation
    Tabulations
    Graphs
    Exhibits
    References, bibliography

In fairly short reports, the preliminary summary or abstract may be omitted and the conclusions placed as follows:

  Introduction [Object and scope of the report.]

  Conclusions

  Discussion of supporting data [The body of the report divided into appropriate main sections.]

  Appendix [Methods, data, references, and other supplementary details.]

The function of an *appendix* deserves serious consideration. A good report places everything that the reader must not miss in a position where he cannot miss it. Details of minor importance, including data necessary for the record that the reader may not immediately care to examine, belong in a place where they will not get in the reader's way. The most important statements, the most important evidence, should appear early in the report. The least important elements should appear at the end. Whether the actual word *appendix* is useful or not, an appendix section often is useful. Here is a place for a detailed explanation of methods used in investigation, for complete tables that are only summarized earlier in the text, for full accounts of interviews or tests, and even for some questionable raw data. When in doubt about whether certain information belongs in the report or not, one solution is to place it in the appendix. If your reader wants it, there it is; if he does not want it, at least it cannot get seriously in his way.

PLANS FOR PROPOSALS AND RECOMMENDATION REPORTS

A *proposal* is a preliminary report suggesting or recommending an investigation. A *recommendation report* advises definite action (or no action), and is usually based on supporting evidence from investigation.

A typical *proposal* report may follow this general plan:

The proposal summarized: what it is, why it is made
Conditions suggesting a need
    Existing problems
    Earlier investigations (if any)
Proposed investigation
    Questions to be answered
    Methods to be used
    Personnel
Requirements
    Equipment
    Estimated cost
    Time
Probable results

Sometimes investigation leads clearly to a recommendation; if so, the plan for an investigative report is a good plan for the recommendation report—only a heading "Recommendations" need be added. Other problems resulting in recommendation reports require a different approach. A recommendation report may advocate a clearly defined action (or no action) and devote the whole discussion to defending what it recommends. Another recommendation report may need to define the recommendation in detail, sometimes devoting half or more of the whole report to a definition of what it recommends. The first kind is illustrated with this outline:

THE ADVISABILITY OF INSTALLING MACROFAX INSTRUMENTS IN
THE LORING TESTING LABS

Summary [Including summary of conclusions and recommendation.]
Introduction: Object and scope, including definition of Macrofax
Instruments now in use
    Accuracy
    Adaptability to our needs

Macrofax
    Accuracy
    Adaptability to our needs
Conclusions
Recommendation
Test data

The following outline represents a plan for the second kind of recommendation report:

PROPOSED CITY PLAN

General summary of the proposed plan
Survey of city needs
    Population—present and predicted
    Industrial needs
    Commercial needs
    Residential needs
    Recreational needs
    Traffic problems
The new plan
    Zoning
        Industrial
        Commercial
        Residential
    Transportation
    Traffic control
    Parks and playgrounds

The section covering "The new plan" may require more space than does the "Survey of city needs."

REPRESENTATIVE REPORT OUTLINES

ANNUAL REPORT OF RAYTHEON MANUFACTURING COMPANY

Improved Earnings
Record Sales Volume
Improved Financial Position
Capital Requirements
Dividends
Investments
Strengthened Management
Human Relations
The Outlook
A Year of Progress [Photographs and text.]

ANNUAL REPORT OF PURE OIL COMPANY

Financial and Operating Summary [Table comparing various years.]
General Review
Production
Refining

Transportation
Marketing
Research and Development
Consolidated Balance Sheet
Consolidated Statement of Income and Surplus
Auditor's Certificate

ENGINEER'S ANNUAL REPORT OF POWER PLANT

General Summary
Condition of Plant
    Tabulations
    Diagrams
    Discussion
Tests
Materials
    Materials used
    Cost
Labor
    Men employed
    Wages
Cost Per Unit of Production

THIRD PROGRESS REPORT
CONSTRUCTION OF GIVEN DAM AT PENTWOOD, IDAHO

Summary of Work to Date
General Introduction
    General purposes
    Schedule of construction
Progress Previously Reported [Summary of first two progress reports.]
Diversion of Present Stream
    Excavation
    Construction of cofferdams
    Construction of bridges
Preparation of Site
    Analysis of subgrade
      Depth
      Seepage
      Faults
    Provisions for grouting
      Seam washing
      Materials
      Drilling
Personnel
Materials
    Availability
    Transportation
    Inventory
Costs

EXAMINATION OF A MINE

General Conclusions
Location of Property
History
    Shipments
    Profits
    Problems
Economic Geography
    Topography
    Vegetation
    Climate
    Transportation facilities
    Claim and topographical maps
Study of Mineral
    Sampling methods
    Character and extractable value
    Assured mineral
    Prospects and limitations
Present Equipment
    Mine development
    Underground machinery
    Methods of working
    Methods of treatment
Water and Power
    Supply
    Cost
Fuel
    Supply
    Cost
Labor
    Supply
    Cost
Market Conditions
Governmental Conditions
    Taxes
    Legislation
    Police protection
Financial Condition
Estimated Return on Investment
Appendix
    Maps
    Financial Data
    Test Data

ULTRASONIC PROOF TESTING
OF SPARK-PLUG CERAMIC BODIES
Battelle Memorial Institute

Introduction
Summary
Experimental Work
    Types of ceramics studied
    Measurements of velocity of sound
    Elastic constants
    Ultrasonic proof testing
    Mechanical frequency and resonance-frequency inspection
      Theory
      Experiments
    Pulse-echo experiments

Conclusions
Recommendations

SELECTION OF MATERIALS

Summary of Conclusions and Recommendations
Needs of the Business
Sources of Supply
    Arnett & Company
    Cavendish & Petersen

Evaluation of Sources
    Arnett
      Tests of materials
      Evidence of use
      Service
      Dependability
    Cavendish & Petersen
      Tests of materials
      Evidence of use
      Service
      Dependability

Prices
    Arnett
    Cavendish & Petersen

Transportation
    Comparison of methods
    Comparison of routes

PROPOSALS TO IMPROVE INTEROFFICE COMMUNICATION

Summary of Conclusions and Recommendations
The Problem
    Cost of interoffice communications
    Sources of criticism

Study of Current Practices
    Letters and memos

           Form
           Clarity
           Consistency
           Duplication
           Incomplete information
        Reports
           Form
           Length
           General organization
           Style: readability, clarity
           Duplication
           Incompleteness
           Appearance

Proposals
      Standard printed forms for memos
      Standard printed forms for routine reports
      Company style manual
      Employment of communications consultant

Appendix
      Method of investigation
      Tabulated data on interoffice communications

A PLAN FOR INDUSTRIAL DEVELOPMENT OF THE REGION

Introduction
      The regional problem
      Industrial history

General Conclusions
Recommendations
Possible Expansion of Present Industries
      Possible markets
      Capital requirements
      Labor supply
      Transportation
      Governmental influence
      Available land for expansion

Possibilities of Attracting New Industries
      Accessibility to materials
      Accessibility to markets
      Variety of available labor
      Local living conditions for new personnel
      Utilities
         Light and power
         Water
         Disposal of wastes
      Available sites
      Governmental influences
         Taxes
         Ordinances
         Police protection
         Other services

Possible financial inducements
Kinds of industry most likely to be attracted
Appendix
    Maps of the region
    Statistics:
        Employment and unemployment in the region
        Summary of financial statements of present industries

PROPOSED POLICIES TO MEET AUTOMATION IN THE TRUCKING INDUSTRY

Synopsis
Introduction
Areas Affected by Automation
    Bills of lading, shipping orders, etc.
    Tariffs
    Billing procedures
    Dock handling procedures
Education Necessary to Meet Automation
    Technical education
    Communications
    Social Sciences
    Humanities
Management's Re-Evaluation of Itself
    Employee policies
    Employee indoctrination
    Employer's view toward employees

Assignment

Prepare final outlines for your major report assignments:
    State your thesis or epitome.
    Phrase a tentative title.
    Name your audience—the reader or readers for whom it is intended.
    Include in your outline every section and subsection that seems useful.
        Include the contents of your appendix if one seems desirable.

Exercises

1. Name title, reader, writer, and make a complete outline for the following kinds of reports:

    (a) The annual report of a small corporation.

    (b) A progress report on a specific project.

    (c) A report comparing alternatives—based on investigation.

    (d) An inspection report.

    (e) A report on the advisability of adopting a new procedure.

    (f) A report elaborating a proposed plan.

2. Suppose an annual report is required of all recognized extra-curricular activities on your campus. Each group is to prepare a section covering its own program for the year. Write a complete outline of the entire report.

3. Write a *brief* for a report you expect to submit.

CHAPTER 6

Preparing

the

Manuscript:

Rhetorical

Elements

ALL elements of a report apply some method or methods of exposition: definition, classification, analysis, deductive and inductive reasoning. The purpose of each element, like the purpose of the report itself, is expository: to inform and explain. It seems clear, then, that anybody who can write good exposition should be able to write a good report.

Planning certainly must precede the actual writing. A good plan reminds the writer of the relationship of every part of his report to every other part. To be sure, the actual writing need not follow the exact order of an outline. The writer may postpone writing his introduction till he has finished everything else, and he may think it wise to write his concluding paragraphs first. Nevertheless, his proposed outline shows clearly what the various elements of the report are to be and where they will probably be placed.

In writing each section of your report, concentrate first on expressing your ideas as well as you can without devoting special attention to spelling, punctuation, or even grammar and phrasing. You can proofread later. Write in "blocks of thought" to get your ideas down on paper. Think of a whole section at a time rather than the separate sentences in it. *After* you have the substance clearly in mind and on paper, you may then consider paragraphing. Finally, of course, you must give close attention to revising, editing, and proofreading. Some writers triple-space early drafts to allow for plenty of revisions and insertions.

This chapter discusses the common elements of reports and suggests ways to adapt principles of general rhetoric to the peculiar problems of report writing. Because reports differ so widely in plan, the chapter is not intended to suggest the exact order that these elements take in a report.

PREFACES

In long formal reports the preliminary sections often appear in the order shown on the following page.

Preface, Foreword, Letter of Transmittal, or Cover Letter
Summary, Abstract, or Synopsis
Introduction, Object and Scope, or Statement of Problem

The early summary is especially characteristic of reports in twentieth-century America. Busy readers, especially executives who need guidelines to help them make decisions, expect such a summary. The writer, however, must usually postpone the actual writing of his introductory summary until he has finished the rest of his report. For that reason, and because a good report needs summaries at other points than the beginning, we shall discuss "Summaries" later in this chapter.

Consider first the problems related to prefaces and introductions.

Letter of Transmittal

The traditional preface for long, formal reports is called the letter of transmittal. It still persists in reports of some government agencies but rarely appears in technical and business reports of private industry. It may or may not serve a useful function.

Consider the possibilities of such a letter:

1. It may state the authorization for the report (who assigned it, where, when, and how) or, if the report was not officially assigned, what custom or general policy makes such a report appropriate? The authorization must usually be stated *somewhere*—either here or in the introduction.

2. It may suggest the writer's qualifications, the interest and training behind the report, the "team" that worked on it, the time spent on it. Thus the letter aims to win respect for those responsible for the report. "Acknowledgments" are a means to that end. If the writer had assistance in investigating and preparing for the report, he should give credit to those who helped. Such credit is more than conventional courtesy; it actually tends to increase the reader's confidence in what he reads.

3. The letter may emphasize the uses of the report. What is it good for? Who will derive benefit from it?

4. It may summarize the report. A good epitome may be useful here, or even the equivalent of a full abstract or synopsis.

5. It may direct the reader's attention to specific sections of the report which must not be overlooked.

In many public agencies the letter of transmittal has become little more than a conventional nuisance. It formally states the authorization for the report and nothing more. To eliminate such letters entirely would be a gain.

In some private companies this letter is also a mere tradition. A whole page is wasted to tell the reader what might be said, and said better, in the introduction.

JACKSTOWN STEEL TUBING COMPANY

South Gary, Indiana

May 8, 1965

Mr. Samuel B. LeConte
General Sales Manager
Jackstown Steel Tubing Company
123 Hiclory Street
New York 5, N. Y.

Dear Mr. LeConte:

As your instructions of February 18 requested, I am submitting the following
report on results of tests to which our #435-H seamless steel tubing was
subjected to determine its suitability for use in high-temperature oil-cracking
systems.

The report first considers various types of high-temperature applications in
such a system, then discusses the various tests to which the tubing was subjected to determine how suitable it is for each type of service.

In addition to strength, the tubing must possess surface and structural stability,
must be free from temper embrittlement, must retain its original properties
during service, and must maintain good hot-ductility.

The report discusses the merits of this tubing with regard to all these qualities.
A set of graphs in the appendix provides a clear picture of the results at a glance.

In the tests we placed special emphasis on creep and stress-rupture characteristics. The report omits the short-time tests for indicating load-carrying ability
because the data they yield is not pertinent to the question.

The tests we used are wholly endorsed by the American Society for Metals and
are valid.

Based on the results of these tests, we recommend our #435-H seamless steel
tubing for high-temperature oil-cracking systems.

Respectfully yours

Barton E. Radokovich

Barton E. Radokovich
Research Engineer

FIGURE 8. LETTER OF TRANSMITTAL.

The examples opposite and below illustrate intelligent use of the letter of transmittal. Generally, include one only when it serves a purpose not served elsewhere.

March 5, 1965

Mr. Ramsey Gill, President
Fields, Inc.

Dear Sir:

Proposals for establishing a by-products mill at Pine Hall are incorporated in the following report, which gives attention to all the factors you named in your letter of February 17.

Though I am a native of Pine Hall, I believe you will find the report objective. However, I do want to express the personal opinion that you should give special attention in choosing men for the Industrial Relations Department at the new mill. As I point out in Section IV of the report, competent labor is plentiful in the vicinity—but accustomed to rather exceptional working conditions. No "outside" industry has ever come into the town, and you may find a bit of suspicion about the new management for awhile. Strong-arm methods could prove very embarrassing.

Mr. Petrona from the Omaha office has provided invaluable information for Section X of the report. He was in Pine Hall for over a week, checked all the data in this report, and agrees with the conclusions.

Respectfully yours

Gregory Grimes

Gregory Grimes
Industrial Engineer

Cover Letters

Unlike the letter of transmittal, a cover letter is not bound in with the report. It is a personal note addressed to an individual who receives a copy of a report that may go to numerous readers. Because it is personal, and usually different from notes sent to other readers, it serves a purpose that the letter of transmittal cannot so well serve.

The cover letter emphasizes the particular values of *this* report to *this* particular reader. The letter is usually informal in tone. Often, of course, it is more a note than a letter. For communications within an organization the memorandum form is common. See examples on page 96.

THE INTRODUCTION

The preface (or letter of transmittal) is not the real introduction to the report. Strictly speaking, a preface comes *before* the actual report while the introduction is the first section of the report proper.

TO: John Minns, Sales Department   DATE: Aug. 7, 1964

FROM: Ed Magnus, Engineering

Mr. O'Brien thinks you will be interested in the accompanying report on recent tests we performed to discover a better protective cover for the Z-15.

I am sure you will not want to give much time to all the technical detail in this report, but the conclusions we reach on page 3 may provide some useful ideas for Sales.

I suggest that you also read some of Section 4, pages 9-11, because the data there may prove interesting to prospects who want more evidence.

If I can add anything that might help you further, I'll be glad to drop over for a talk.

TO: Adam Wylie, Shipping Department   DATE: Aug. 7, 1964

FROM: Ed Magnus, Engineering

I am sending you the accompanying report because a number of its recommendations directly affect the shipping of our Z-15.

Note first our recommendation No. 5, page 4, regarding the kind of packing necessary to protect the new cover. Then turn to pages 14-15 for details.

We think we have found something from our recent tests that will reduce numerous complaints, and of course the shipping department will play an important role.

If you find anything that isn't clear, call me.

The function of the introduction is to state the purpose and scope of the report and prepare the way for an understanding of the discussion that follows. The *purpose* is necessarily dependent on the authorization for the report. Somebody assigned it, custom requires it, or the writer has taken advantage of invitations and encouragements to undertake it voluntarily. His statement of object makes it all clear, though often in few words:

> The purpose of this study is to determine which of the four sites under consideration for the new plant will best meet the needs pointed out in your instructions of May 7.
> As the Director requested in his memo of March 3, this report outlines an effective program for training new employees.
> *Object:* to test safety controls or winding machines.

The *scope* of the report is the ground it covers: what questions it intends to answer, and what means were used to find the answers. Usually the significant questions determine the main sections of the report itself, but the introduction may point them out:

> The report considers the factors that influence the potential market:
> Population of the area
> Income levels
> Buying preferences
> Competition

The methods employed to get essential data may be unusual and important enough to require explanation in the introduction also. However, when the methods are technical and involved, most readers are impatient with long explanations; full details can be relegated to the appendix.

Definitions often belong in the introduction, especially of key terms, but a glossary of technical terms is seldom helpful at this point. The best place to define is at the point in the report where the unfamiliar or ambiguous term is actually used.

The introduction frequently needs background information. What conditions led to this investigation? What previous studies suggested this study? What past events help us understand this report? A certain amount of general history may explain a current problem, especially the local history of this plant, this department, or this town. Such background information is not vital new evidence leading to the conclusions of the report, but it provides a basis for understanding such new evidence better when it appears in later sections.

Some background information may include summaries of what other investigators have done. Many reports need some review of the literature on the subject so that the reader will know what this report contributes beyond what has been done before. Sometimes a review of theory is called for, but in the introduction never more than a brief summary. When a thorough theoretical defense of the whole investigation seems necessary, it justifies a full section by itself.

Here are three examples of introductions:

INTRODUCTION

The Engineering Department needs to know the tensile properties of several steels at temperatures above 1500F to assist it in designing a new hot-strip mill. The steels selected for this study were a low carbon steel, a medium carbon steel, a medium strength Yoloy steel, and an experimental Yoloy steel designed with a 90,000 psi minimum yield strength at room temperature. These steels would cover the expected strength range of the steels to be rolled on this mill.

Although the steel will be rolled at temperatures above 1800F, no tests were made above this temperature because of the temperature limitations of the heating furnace used. A stress-strain curve was recorded for each specimen tested. It was expected that the steels at these elevated temperatures will have a very low modulus of elasticity.

INTRODUCTION

Since success in metalworking depends so greatly upon the lubrication system available between the workpiece and the forming dies, it is important to find the most effective lubricant. This report, confined to a review of the literature on lubrication as applied to metalworking, is intended to serve as the first step in an over-all program to initiate an engineering approach to pressing and drawing operations in the Division.

INTRODUCTION

Purpose of Study

The Department of Highways, planning a new bridge to replace the existing Midland Street Bridge on Route 182, Sioux County, directed the Traffic and Planning Division to make the appropriate traffic study. The bridge connects the City of Billington and the Village of West Billington.

This report presents the results of this traffic study to determine the best location and approach facilities for the new bridge.

Scope of Study

Several suggested locations for the proposed bridge were considered. Each possibility was investigated to determine effects on traffic to be served as well as on the communities.

Several plans for the approaches to the bridge were considered. The aim is to find the approach that provides maximum traffic relief and yet involves minimum property damage.

The study considers physical features that affect adequate connections with the integral highway system.

SUMMARIES

A summary is a condensation or abridgment of something longer. To save a reader time it is often desirable to summarize a book, a technical paper, a contract, a series of statistical tables, or the discussions in a meeting. It is especially desirable to summarize your own report; the executive reader, particularly, wants some brief statement of what the report is all about. Summaries are known by various names: *abstract, digest, synopsis, epitome*—or merely *summary*.

For the report writer, no other qualification counts so much as an ability to summarize effectively. He must learn how to find the essentials from interviews or surveys, how to get the gist of what he reads, and how to boil down masses of data. As he writes his report, he needs brief summaries to introduce his sections and subsections; he must also provide a good summary of the whole report.

There is an important distinction between a mere *topical* summary and an *informative* summary. The first is a sort of table of contents; it indicates topics covered, not substance:

> This report discusses tests conducted on aluminum alloys at the Westminster Plant in February to discover possible causes of failure. The tests located apparent causes and suggest possible remedies. Recommendations are included.

This summary tells the reader what questions he can find discussed, and whether or not he can expect answers; it does not tell him what the answers are. The informative summary does more: it tells the reader what the original *says*. It includes the answers:

> This report on tests of aluminum alloys concludes that the chief reason for past failures is careless and inefficient processing. Reorganization of the processing staff should take care of most of our difficulties.

The topical summary does have its uses in technical indexes, but in actual reports it only duplicates the work of the introduction—defining the scope of the report. When a report reaches real conclusions, the reader expects a summary to tell him what they are.

The following pages discuss various kinds of summary that report writers use.

Epitome

The briefest possible informative summary may be called an *epitome*. It is really the thesis—the central point the report makes, or the general conclusions or judgment it supports. It ought to be the first thing you write, because it can serve as your broad directive in deciding what to include or what to leave out. So the first use of a good epitome is in what it can do for *you*.

In the actual report, this epitome may appear in the preface or in the letter of transmittal. It may occasionally appear in the introduction, although it seldom seems appropriate there. It may become the first or the last sentence of a longer introductory summary. In fairly short reports it occasionally appears by itself under the subtitle *epitome*.

Usually this epitome emphasizes only what it is essential for the executive reader to know:

> Within five years, automation in the industry will require a broad new program of training, re-employment, and indoctrination that should start immediately. An appropriation of $100,000 would permit the Personnel Department to get the program adequately under way.

> Investigation shows that the actual flow of saturated sal soda solution through thin-plate orifices is 21% greater than our theoretical calculations indicated, and that no appreciable back-pressure is evident.

Market possibilities are fairly good. With a total population of half a million, numerous efficient outlets, and at least mild interest in our product even before we undertake extensive advertising, we can anticipate moderate sales within six months.

Abstract

The word *abstract* most often appears in technical, scientific, and scholarly circles. It is always a summary, though unfortunately there is little agreement about what it should include. Some so-called abstracts are informative, some only topical. Some are pages long, some short enough to be called epitomes.

As a report writer you may need to become familiar with the abstracts of other writers; you should also learn how to write abstracts for your own reports. *Chemical Abstracts, Ceramic Abstracts, Metallurgical Abstracts,* and other similar periodicals may prove to be indispensable sources of information about work that has been done in your own field. These publications are, first of all, *indexes* of authors, titles, subjects, to which you may need to refer. They are more than indexes, however, because they also tell something of the nature, scope, or even the substance of what others have written.

Whether you prepare an abstract to appear at the beginning of your own report or prepare one for separate publication, the writing problems are similar. You must reduce the number of words, often to only five percent or even two percent of the original; yet in those few words you must acquaint your reader with the underlying problem, the scope of your investigation, and the results you obtained.

The following rules will help:

1. Calculate how many words five percent allows you for an abstract. That suggests your limit.
2. Outline the report (refer to its table of contents) and decide what proportionate space each section deserves. Include important tables, charts, and curves in your over-all plan.
3. Underline phrases—and especially section titles—that deserve most emphasis.
4. Allot a proportionate number of words to each section, depending on the comparative importance of each.
5. Summarize each part or section as briefly as possible—but include *essentials*. Remember that too many words devoted to one section will distort its comparative importance.
6. Cut unnecessary detail and mere supporting data.
7. Cut deadwood—every word or phrase you can do without. It is a rare writer who cannot find waste in his early drafts. An abstract cannot afford any waste.

8. Use numerals for all numbers, and use abbreviations when they are entirely clear, but do not omit the articles *a, an,* and *the.*

With all this condensing, remember that the abstract must still be readable. It is not a mere outline. It is not a telegram or a compilation of newspaper headlines. It must give the essence of the entire report. The following abstracts have appeared in indexes or collections of abstracts:

> 20741. (DEVELOPMENT OF GEIGER-MÜLLER COUNTERS FOR OPERATION AT HIGH TEMPERATURES) M. Drăghicescu (Inst. of Atomic Physics, Bucharest), p. 345-52 of "Nuclear Electronics. Vol. I." Vienna, International Atomic Energy Agency, 1962. (In French)
>
> Counters of this type are necessary for radioactive logging at great depths; they have to operate normally at temperatures up to 180°C. In order to preserve their characteristics under such conditions, the work function of the cathode has been improved by a special treatment. Tests have been made on counters with graphite, copper, and wolfram cathodes in a glass envelope. The method is simple, and can easily be employed in industry. (auth)*

The following abstracts were both written by a university senior, David J. Andre, to illustrate the difference between topical and informative types.

Topical Abstract
CHEMICAL WEED CONTROL IN CHRISTMAS TREE PLANTATIONS

Kirch, J. H., *et al.,* "Weed and Brush Control in Christmas Tree and Forest Plantations," *The Hormology,* 3(2):1215, November 1961.

Figures are given for acreage and percentage of stocking of Christmas trees on privately owned land and commercial forest areas in the U.S. Included are lists of species desirable for planting in Christmas tree plantations. The major problems encountered in managing these plantations and results to be expected from poor management are discussed.

Explained are methods of removing unwanted vegetation with the percentage of control to be expected from each. Reasons are given for the increasing popularity of chemical weeding. Chemical herbicides and their applications in the removal of undesirable woody plants and herbaceous weeds are analyzed. Amitrole-Simazine compounds are discussed separately to include application techniques, quantities to be used, and species toleration. Tables list weeds, grasses, woody shrubs, and their susceptibilities and resistances to Amitrole-Simazine compounds.

Informative Abstract
CHEMICAL WEED CONTROL IN CHRISTMAS TREE PLANTATIONS

Kirch, J. H., *et al.,* "Weed and Brush Control in Christmas Tree and Forest Plantations," *The Hormology,* 3(2):1215, November 1961.

* Nuclear Science Abstracts, Aug. 31, 1962, p. 2697. Vol. 16, No. 16. Abstract written by original author.

In the U.S., 625,000 acres of privately owned land is devoted to Christmas tree growing. The control of competing weeds and brush is the major problem in these plantations. This competition can mean poor survival, stunted growth, and malformed trees. Methods used to remove this competition are mowing, discing, burning, and bulldozing, but none gives 100 percent control at reasonable cost. Recent developments in application techniques and the use of selective chemicals have made chemical weeding more popular.

The use of 2,4-dichlorophenoxy acetic acid (2,4-D) and 2,4,5-trichlorophenoxy acetic acid (2,4,5-T), both selective herbicides, controls woody plants through applications to the foliage, stem, or base of the plant. Simazine (2-chloro-4,6 bis-s-triazine) is effective on annual and grassy weeds as a pre-emergence treatment if used at the rate of 2-4 lb/25-30 gal water. It has little effect on the foliage of weeds and consequently should be applied only to cleanly cultivated soil. Amitrole (3-amino-1,2,4-triazole) applied at 4-8 lb/50 gal water is effective for controlling all common herbaceous weeds. At present, the most effective weed-control combination is a 3:1 ratio of Simazine and Amitrole. This combination can be expected to give good knock-down and long residual control of most species when applied before, during, or just after planting.

ABSTRACT

[Abstract of 30-page report, Research Laboratories, General Motors Corporation]

Analyses of crankcase vent gases by several methods have shown that crankcase and exhaust hydrocarbon emissions from automobiles are of the same order of magnitude. Internal ventilation of the crankcase to the engine intake system eliminates crankcase emission, thus providing a practical control of this important source of air pollution.

SUMMARY

[Introductory Summary of a 25-page Bureau of Mines report.]

Upon review of German World War II mining practices and equipment for planing coal, the Federal Bureau of Mines initiated research leading to the development of a pneumatic planer for anthracite. The results of tests are here reported.

It was demonstrated (1) that hard anthracite can be planed and (2) that the design and operating requirements are within the limits of present-day engineering and technology.

For hard anthracite, the depth of cut indicated is 4 to 6 inches; with a chain pull of 20 to 40 tons and the speed of planer travel of 18 to 20 feet per minute, a 40-hp motor will be required for the planer hoist. Compressed-air requirements for the planer will be 250 to 300 cfm at 60 to 70 psi. It was learned that the length of the 4 individual sections of the planer should not exceed that of the individual troughs of the armored chain conveyor (5 feet in this instance); otherwise, bottom coal will be left in synclines, and the planer will override the conveyor at anticlines. Pneumatic pushers should be operated from a separate compressed-air line fitted with a pressure regulator.

Results indicate that additional development work is warranted.

Conclusions and Recommendations

Conclusions and recommendations do not always properly come under the head of "summaries," but they should always be stated as concisely as possible, and in one sense they include everything the report intends to prove. They do *not* include any of the supporting data and reasoning which take up most of the report.

In most current reports, conclusions and recommendations appear early, summarized in a preliminary abstract or directly following the introduction. The way they are stated is always important.

Conclusions are either important generalizations about past or present conditions, or predictions of what will happen or what might happen under given circumstances. They are the writer's judgments. Conclusions, as such, do not advocate action. They may *imply* a course of action, but they never explicitly state it. For example:

> We might diminish wastes by introducing an XM system.
>
> The Molding Division is not efficiently organized.
>
> The main reason for our success in Chicago is our effective advertising there.

Recommendations, on the other hand, advocate action. They should always be solidly based on conclusions which are in turn solidly based on factual data. But recommendations go beyond facts: they propose something for the future. For example:

> The company should introduce the XM system immediately.
>
> We suggest in this report a reorganization of the Molding Division which we outline in detail.
>
> In Chicago we should continue the present advertising program without major change.

Both conclusions and recommendations may be stated in separate paragraphs; for separate and distinct emphasis, each of them may be numbered.

Remember, however, that in themselves, the statements of conclusions and recommendations are only opinions. The body of the report is expected to support them with adequate evidence. When the reasons and the data within the report fail to support the conclusions, these conclusions are worthless.

Introductory Summary

In actual position, the introductory summary usually precedes the introduction. It nearly always precedes the formal statement of conclusions and recommendations, though it should usually include them— at least the most important ones. But although the introductory summary eventually appears in first position, the writer generally writes it last. To write a good introductory summary it is necessary to have in view the total report—its exact order, the development of each section, the tables and charts, and even the appendix. The time to write it is after everything else is finished. It is not safe to write a summary until you have before you just what you want to summarize.

We have noted that the subtitles indicating an introductory summary may differ. *Abstract* is the appropriate heading for the technical report; *epitome* may be good for a rather brief summary of a short report of any kind; *synopsis* is the title gaining wide approval among writers of business reports; and the simple word *summary* is a perfectly clear and satisfactory heading.

We need no special rules for the introductory summary that we have not already included in our discussion of the *Abstract*. One thing is clear, however—to be useful, this summary should be informative, not merely topical. The table of contents will list the topics, and the introduction should define the scope of the report. Unless the introductory summary summarizes the findings of the writer and tells what he discovered or what he concludes, it can have little value for the busy reader.

Terminal Summary

The concluding section of the report may be a summary of the report or, more often, a somewhat detailed statement of essential reasons leading to the conclusion or recommendation. Not every report needs such a final summary. When conclusions and recommendations are up front, the report frequently adopts an anticlimactic order—an order of diminishing importance. That is an order generally preferred by executives in private companies.

When a final summary is included, the report should build toward it. An abstract or introductory summary may precede the whole report, but from introduction on, the report should follow climactic order. Then the final summary provides a good synthesis of all the evidence and reasoning that leads to it.

This final summary is quite different from an introductory summary. There is no need here to summarize object and scope of the report because at this point they are obvious to the reader. There is seldom need to summarize apparatus, theory, or techniques of investigation, because those too are now sufficiently understood. Neither is there a need to repeat or sum up all the points that the report has clearly made along the way. What the final summary must do is to show clearly how all the data and logic of the report tie together. To do its job well, the final summary must usually be longer than the introductory summary. For example:

CONCLUSIONS

Even though the gradients were of the order of 400,000 volts per cm, the large currents observed could not be explained on the basis of quantum-mechanical field emission. Eyring and Millikan in 1926 found it necessary to use an electrometer to measure the currents produced by 106 volts per cm gradients at thoroughly outgassed surfaces. Anderson in 1935 measured currents of the order of 0.1 microamp from ¼ cm^2 area at gradients and total voltages comparable with those used here. This current density would give 0.2 ma over our area of 500 cm^2. He "conditioned" his surfaces by sparking and a hydrogen discharge. In this experiment the surfaces were treated by sparking and heat.

A possible explanation of these large currents would be the following mechanism: An electron liberated from some sharp point or region of low work function on the cathode would strike the anode and liberate and ionize an absorbed gas atom. This heavy ion, upon striking the cathode, would liberate one or more secondary electrons. The process would continue until an equilibrium value was reached.

A detailed study of sparks or impulsive breakdowns was not made, since the excessive steady current emission made it difficult to go to the highest voltage. It seems clear that it would not be possible to make a satisfactory high-voltage condenser unless different methods of conditioning the surfaces were developed.[1]

Summaries of Evidence

Summaries of evidence within the body of a report are not set apart with a subtitle; they are incorporated right into the discussion. It is often necessary to summarize evidence from reading, from interviews, from tables and charts, or from other sources. Here you are not summarizing your own writing, nor are you summarizing most other things as you might for a "Digest" or collection of Abstracts. You are summarizing only what you need as evidence to support your own conclusions in this report.

A few rules apply in handling such materials:

1. Select only what is relevant for your purpose. A book, paper, article, or document may contain data or ideas that tie in closely with your problem. A table in your appendix may include several items that you want to use as evidence in one section of your report. Pick out only what is pertinent; ignore everything else. Of course this does not mean that you stack the cards in favor of a preconceived opinion. It only means that you disregard all that does not relate to the question at hand.

2. Distinguish direct quotations from paraphrase or restatements of your own. *Use quotation marks* around every phrase or sentence

---

[1] From Westinghouse Research Laboratories Report, *Electrical Breakdown Between Cylinders in Vacuum,* by H. S. Siefert, August 1942.

directly taken from others. But never use quotation marks unless the enclosed passage is accurately quoted.

3. Name your sources. The name of an authority, or even an ordinary workman, often adds weight to the evidence you take from him. When you summarize evidence from others, the reader deserves to know where you got it.

Though these condensations of evidence within the report are not formally labeled *summary,* the reader should never be in doubt of what they are. Here are some examples taken from reports:

A point-by-point comparison of Table 11 and Table 9 indicates that fuels containing commercial and synthetic alkylates of equal octane quality have essentially equal ratings. The behavior of commercial alkylates at concentrations of 40 volume percent and less is as would be predicted from Table 9 and Figure 9, although the range of octane qualities covered is somewhat smaller for the commercial materials. Thus, representation of commercial alkylates by synthetic material appears to be an adequate approximation.

McGrady reports various studies that were conducted to determine whether cigarette smokers and nonsmokers differ, emotionally or in personality. Results indicated that smokers married more often, were hospitalized more often, moved and changed their jobs more often than nonsmokers. Smokers are physically less masculine than nonsmokers—and the more they smoke the less masculine the smoking men appear. Smokers are more likely to be shy, more self-conscious, more inhibited. Smokers tend to rank higher in verbal functions than nonsmokers, and possibly lower in mathematical aptitude.

DEFINITIONS

Some reports make very little use of definitions; others use them a great deal. Because definition is a kind of necessary evil, it is a good rule never to define when you can do as well without it. Unfortunately, the need is often present. When a complex problem is discussed in a report or when the report involves technical investigations, the explanations required must often concern *meanings,* and the explanation of meanings is what we call *definition.*

Two kinds of terms need definition in reports: the special or technical term that the reader possibly never saw before, and the common, everyday term used in a special or restricted way. If you suspect that your reader is not familiar with "depolymerized" substances and you must use the term to explain what follows, then you need definition. Or if you think your reader may have a misconception of the common term "random sampling" and it seems essential to make clear the sense in which you are using it, then you want to define *random* in the way you apply it. Perhaps the most frequent need of definition in reports is to explain the restricted meaning of a very common word.

The real purpose of any definition is to set boundary lines around a subject—to make quite clear what belongs inside and what belongs out. If you really succeed in doing that, you have a perfect definition.

The one-sentence logical definition achieves its purpose by means of three parts. the *term* defined, the *genus* or class to which the term here belongs, and the *differentiae* or characteristics that differentiate the term from everything else in the same genus.

Note these examples:

Term	Genus	Differentiae
Melancholia	a disordered mental condition	characterized by extremely depressing delusions
A machine	any combination of mechanism	for utilizing or applying power
ESP (extrasensory perception)	the recognition of actualities	without use of the normal senses

Occasionally such a brief statement of meaning will be enough. More often it serves as topic sentence for a somewhat more extensive explanation. For example, to understand the meaning of *melancholia,* your reader may need to know something more about the nature of *delusion,* and even what is meant by *disordered* and *depressing.* Perhaps ESP will not be entirely clear until something further is included with the single sentence about the meaning of *normal senses.*

Nevertheless, this formula for definition is a genuine help for the report writer. It can become the summary of a much longer definition, should one be needed, and it encourages clear and economical expression. The more you restrict the genus, the more you limit the meaning in a single step; the less remains to be done with differentiae. For example, one can distinguish a Pulmotor from other kinds of "respiratory apparatus" (limited genus) more easily than from "mechanisms" (a far broader, more inclusive genus). The attention you give to expressing the meaning in one sentence reduces the time you must give to a longer definition.

For more extensive definition, various methods are useful:

1. *Examples.* You may clarify general or abstract definition by illustrations: examples of *automation, cybernetics,* or *clerical workers* (categories or even individual names). Examples *plus* general statement often does the defining job well.

2. *Elements and details.* To define a process or mechanism, it is usually necessary to analyze details. The "job description" so common in modern industry (for example, to specify the precise

duties of a crane operator, a junior engineer, or a medical technologist) illustrates this method of definition.

3. *Contrast or elimination.* Sometimes the best way to define is to eliminate false meanings. You may contrast your meaning of *engineer* with your meaning of *scientist* and thus clarify the meaning of both terms. You may point out the significant differences between *basic* and *applied* research. You may emphasize what is *not* to be included: "*Random* in this sense does not mean haphazard or careless."

The following brief examples of extended definition suggest possibilities:

> A facsimile broadcast station is one that transmits still pictures by means of radio for public use. A special recorder machine must be used in conjunction with the radio receiver in order to print the photograph or other still object so received. Thus, while television is able to transmit moving images, facsimile is limited to reproduction of still pictures, print, writing, symbols, and the like.

> Unfortunately, the word *rate,* as applied to domestic service, has been used ambiguously. Sometimes it refers only to the energy charge. In the following discussion the term refers to the whole amount paid for electric service during a given period divided by the number of kilowatt hours of electricity used during that period. This seems the best measure of the cost of service to the consumer.

> The term *sewage* here refers to human waste matters, together with the polluted water of the household—such as water from bathing, scrubbing, dishwashing, clothes washing, and food cleansing. The *sewerage* system, on the other hand, refers to the system of piping designed to carry off any or all of these wastes.

Some reports neglect to define important terms—especially everyday terms to which a writer applies his own arbitrary meanings. Some reports, on the other hand, define too much; it is never necessary to define the special terms of a shop, trade, or industry to readers who are familiar with the terms. And it is seldom useful to define terms with a mere dictionary definition. The dictionary may be a good starting point for the report writer's definition, but it is usually no more than that. The average reader may be disturbed by formal definitions—dictionary meanings—of terms that he thinks every reader of normal intelligence ought to understand.

When a considerable part of a report on a technical problem must be adapted to nontechnical readers, one good possibility is translation into simple everyday language. Rather than trying to define scores of technical words as you come to them, it is often possible to make a simple paraphrase. Perhaps that is an art in itself—something it will take time to learn—but for one whose superiors or employers are laymen unacquainted with his field of specialization, it is something that must be learned. The ability to translate technical language is especially important for psychologists, economists, sociologists, accountants, industrial engineers, and a good many other specialists who frequently must write their reports for men who never took a course in the subject being discussed. For these specialists, learning how to translate for laymen is often the key to success.

When a definition is necessary, the best place for it is usually right at the point where the term first appears, for that is where the reader is first likely to be puzzled by it. When your reader *needs* to have the meaning, he ought to get it immediately. A list of definitions of unfamiliar words in the introduction seldom helps very much. Occasionally, however, a preliminary glossary is a good thing. If the terms included are not especially technical and are easy to remember, this list may save time and make ensuing discussions clearer. Here is one example:

> In this report the terms related to cars and parking have these meanings:
>
> CENTRAL BUSINESS DISTRICT: This is the district shown in blue on the map. It is bounded on the west by Centre Street from West Avenue to Birch Avenue, on the north by Birch Avenue, on the east by Clinton Street to West Avenue, and on the south by West Avenue to Centre.
>
> COMMERCIAL VEHICLES: Trucks and buses (not taxis, etc.).
>
> DESTINATION: The exact location of the place where a motorist went after parking his or her car.

A few general rules for definitions:

1. Never define terms that your reader can readily understand from the context.
2. Define all common and familiar words that you intend to use in a restricted or special way. If a word has several meanings, be sure *your* meaning is clear.
3. If your reader may have trouble with technical language, translate it whenever possible into everyday nontechnical language.
4. Avoid defining in a circle; that is, avoid using derivatives of the term defined or mere synonyms that are not any better understood than the term itself. (For example, "a monogamist is one who practices monogamy," "the exit here is an egress," "courage is a quality of bravery.")
5. Do not confuse the reader with irrelevant detail. For example, perhaps "most spinners belong to a union," but that is not part of a definition of *spinner* because membership in a union is not an essential characteristic of the occupation.

EXPLANATION OF MECHANISMS, PROCESSES, AND ORGANIZATIONS

In one way or another every report concerns a process, a mechanism, or an organization. To explain such units requires analysis (a division or breaking apart into important elements) and synthesis (a means of showing the essential relationships that produce the whole).

Mechanism, process, and organization are not hard to define in general terms. A *mechanism* is a device for achieving some end. A *process* is a series of steps to get something done. An *organization* is a combination of individuals joined together as a group with some common interest. There is always some reason or purpose to help us define each example we find.

The first rule for writing such exposition is to view the subject as a *unit,* not as a mere collection of parts, steps, or divisions. To list all the parts of a machine shows nothing of its capacity to function as a machine. To list the steps in a process or the branches of an organization does not show the interrelationships that really make a process or organization from the parts. Analysis is necessary, of course, but the parts must fit together in exposition as the parts fit together in life.

A clear introductory summary is the most important requirement in exposition of this kind. This introductory summary should state the *purpose* of the mechanism, process, or organization; its *physical nature* or *scope,* and its general *principle.* The reader needs this full view of the whole before he can understand details. Once he understands the general aim, scope, and principle, details fit into place.

The following introductory statements are illustrations:

> The apparatus (shown in the accompanying diagram) consists essentially of a revolving specimen rack with a capacity of 96 specimens so mounted that they travel through three compartments. The largest of these is a high-humidity thermostat, the temperature of which is regulated by the temperature of a layer of water beneath the specimens. Humidity, air circulation, and water circulation are maintained by pumping the thermostat water through a nozzle positioned in the free space in the center of the specimen rack and directed downward in such a way that the water does not strike the samples. The compartment is also provided with baffled sprays to supplement the dew formation that occurs on the samples and to provide means of securing intermittent run-off.

> The Computer Control Company Space Data Automation System (3C/SDAS) is a solid-state electronic system designed to make possible the receipt of technical data from unmanned-spacecraft scientific experiments and to act upon command sequences sent to the spacecraft. The 3C/SDAS allows unmanned spacecraft to vary their command sequences by internally preprogrammed sequences of events, by

external signals sensed by the scientific experiments themselves, or by radio commands to the spacecraft from earth. This system was developed for use in connection with the Mariner Spacecraft and the planetary exploration program. A feature of the 3C/SDAS is that it not only samples all incoming scientific data, but decides exactly what data it will sample again, and at what time. This is accomplished by a stored program in the system which permits sampling rates, timing of experiments, and readout word lengths to be variable at the discretion of the 3C/SDAS. The control exercised by 3C/SDAS in this manner assures optimal efficiency in the type of data sent back to earth.*

Not all explanation need be in words and sentences. Diagrams, photographs, maps, and other visual aids are often indispensable to supplement the written exposition. If the chief interest lies in physical, external appearance, the photograph is most useful; if principles and relationships are of first importance, a diagram is best. An organization chart can show vividly the chain of command in a corporation. A flow sheet can effectively show the steps in an extensive process. Some of these devices do a better job than words, but they nearly always require textual explanations. Written exposition and illustrations can supplement each other.

INTERPRETATION OF DATA

Responsible conclusions rely on sound data—the facts disclosed through observation and experiment, survey, or the records and reports supplied by others. The way you present and explain such data obviously affects the success of your report.

Much of the supporting data in a report may appear in tables, graphs, and other nonverbal devices. We shall discuss these devices in Chapter 7. But in whatever form you display data, these data must be interpreted with clear exposition. You must evaluate sources and evidence, separate the relevant from the irrelevant, simplify, and of course show what conclusions the evidence can reasonably be used to support.

Interpretations of numerical data generally involve these steps:
1. A summary simplification of data deserving attention.
2. A critical evaluation of the data.
3. A logical exposition of what these data signify: the probable causes of a known condition, the indicated trends, or the most reasonable expectations.

Summary and Simplification

The first need is usually to present the really usable evidence in a way the reader will understand. Often you begin developing your report

* From *Digital Systems,* Computer Control Company, Inc., January 1963.

with masses of raw data at hand. Such raw data must be sifted, organized, and translated for the reader. Suppose you have conducted a telephone survey of 450 customers who have been carefully selected to represent about 20,000 customers of the Mizener Company. Your reader has no interest in learning that "227 customers dislike our metal containers" or that "305 customers consider our service least adequate." His interest is in the 20,000—or in percentages or fractions of the 20,000. You must translate or project your raw data to make the meaning clear: "Our survey shows that about 10,000 of our customers dislike our metal containers," or "The survey shows that two-thirds of our customers are moderately satisfied with the service we give." Do not force a reader to do the arithmetic; that is the report writer's job. Once a reader understands what the data really say, he can give attention to their possible significance.

Sometimes the task of simplifying involves whole batteries of tables or complicated charts. The elements of possible significance must be extracted for special attention. For example, out of the figures for the last forty-eight months, it may be sufficient to call attention to just four representative months—the four that emphasize the general trend. A statistical table gives equal emphasis to every item in it; the writer's job is to provide the comparative emphasis that different items deserve.

A summary of data frequently requires definitions. The average reader often gets false impressions from statistical statements that he does not fully understand. The *statistical unit*—the thing counted or weighed—may be misinterpreted. "Profits," for example, may refer to gross profits or to net profits, to dollar profits or to percentage of invested capital or even to percentage of the sale-price dollar (wholesale or retail). Perhaps a short phrase will serve as definition, but if longer explanation is needed, it must be included. A report critical of "inefficient policies" must define what is considered inefficient and what is not. A report citing figures on "unnecessary accidents" must obviously point out the distinction between those counted as "unnecessary" and those counted as "unavoidable."

To simplify essential evidence as much as possible, the writer often translates totals into rates or percentages. The number of industrial accidents in Chicago cannot usefully be compared with the number in Altoona; but the accident *rates* in the two cities (accidents per hundred thousand man-hours, for example) can be compared. The layman's preference for a simple "three out of seven" or "three in a hundred" is sometimes accurate enough for the writer's purpose. When a simple expression can be both colorful *and* accurate, that is exactly the one to use.

Evaluating the Data

The report writer is of course responsible to his reader for the reliability and validity of what he reports. When he rejects evidence as unreliable, he must know why; often he should explain why to his reader. When he accepts evidence and uses it to support his conclusions, he is responsible for its truth and accuracy; usually he should justify his evaluations.

Most reports for laymen or executive readers do not include detailed explanations of method in the body of the report. Extensive explanations of an investigation, if necessary at all, usually belong in the appendix (often that is also the best place for a full evaluation of evidence). Sometimes, however, the evidence you get from other sources is so important a basis for your conclusions that it must be clearly defended in the report.

Evaluation of evidence and sources of evidence, wherever it appears, is an important responsibility of the report writer.

For *sources,* we suggest a few tests:

1. How well qualified is the source (the agency, the man, the publication, or the group supplying the data)? If technical qualifications are specified, what are they? What is the reputation of this man or agency for accurate, careful, reliable reporting?
2. Is the source sufficiently unprejudiced? A labor union's statistics on the relation of wages to corporation profits must be received as cautiously as similar statistics from the National Association of Manufacturers. Neither source is unprejudiced; each has its own axe to grind. Of course you should not *reject* every prejudiced source without a hearing. You simply view the evidence with more critical attention than might otherwise be necessary.

For *internal evidence,* we suggest this test:

1. How consistent is the evidence (a) within itself, (b) with other evidence, and (c) with established physical laws and laws of human nature? Sometimes one statement appears to contradict another. For example, a report may say "workers dislike the system intensely" yet also show that fewer workers are leaving their jobs. If tables show an increased number of hours lost for repairs but a decrease in the cost of repairs, the apparent discrepancy calls for explanation.

Logical Inferences

The conclusions stated in a report should, of course, be logical inferences from that data. Interpretation of data obviously includes explanations of these inferences. It must meet the tests of logic.

Interpretations of statistics are sometimes illogical because key terms are ambiguous. The word *average* is a frequent source of confusion. In common speech it has three different meanings: the arithmetic mean, the median or mid-point on a scale, and the "mode" or typical number. The report about "average drivers," for example, should make the meaning clear as it applies to this report. If it says that "the average driver travels about 12,000 miles in his car each year," does that represent the arithmetical mean, the median, or simply the miles driven by a typical driver? Sometimes the three differ widely.

In using percentages, some writers fail to answer clearly the question: "Percentage of what?" Note possible differences:

Percentage of riveters killed in accidents	*or*	Percentage of men killed in accidents who are riveters
Percentage of women under the pension plan	*or*	Percentage of those under the pension plan who are women

Some conclusions are generalizations from evidence about existing conditions; some are broader generalizations covering future conditions. In either, the *sample* that the evidence includes should be an adequate one:

1. Is it large enough for the purpose?
2. Is it truly representative of the conditions covered by the conclusion?

Some conclusions are based on controlled experiments or on reasoning that involves the same general principle of control. The important test is whether *all* conditions except the one being investigated are essentially the same. If two gasolines are to be tested or two alloys to be compared for use in construction, the rule of logic is the same: all conditions must be identical for both gasolines and for both alloys.

Interpretations concerned with *causes* (influences, factors, necessary antecedents) should consider these questions:

1. How many separate elements are involved?
2. Is it possible, in any way, to isolate some of the elements and test them alone?
3. If we cannot completely isolate any element, how close can we come to it? How much can we reduce the differences?
4. From what we know from past experience, can we estimate the comparative weight or influence of the various elements?

We expect the report writer to have something of the scientific spirit in his nature. We expect him to raise pertinent questions, to use intelligent methods, and to check carefully. We expect him to avoid unqualified assertions until he is positive, but nevertheless to arrive at reasonable conclusions that he can defend.

Assignments

For major report assignments—reports to be submitted at a later date:

1. Define the object and scope. (Write in a form suitable for the introduction of a finished report.)

2. Define briefly but clearly certain key terms—terms either unfamiliar to prospective readers or requiring restricted meanings in your own reports.

3. Write one section of a report to interpret significant data: simplify, summarize, and draw logical inferences from the data.

4. Write two "cover letters" addressed to different readers who are to receive copies of one of your reports.

5. Write an introductory summary (abstract or synopsis or "summary") of one of your reports *after* you have prepared a final outline and written enough of the whole report to know its length, order, and content.

Exercises

1. Abstract a chapter from a textbook in your major field.

2. Abstract an article from *Fortune* magazine.

3. Study the introductory section of three recently published annual reports of large corporations. Write a comparative analysis pointing out (a) what they all include, (b) what they all emphasize, (c) where they differ in content and emphasis, and (d) how they agree or differ in tone and style.

4. Define one of the following terms in a short paragraph, adapting the dictionary definition for requirements of a specific report:

Technical personnel	Permanent employees
Insurance	Cost
Profits	Income
Easement	Profession
Research	Report

5. Write formal conclusions and recommendations for a report on your curriculum to be submitted to your dean.

6. Write an interpretation of one of the following sets of data:

   (a) The population of the city decreased in the past decade from 69,205 to 63,518.
   The total population within a 25-mile radius increased from 102,860 to 113,716.
   Assessed valuation of property within city limits increased 22%.
   The city's budget increased 58%.
   The city's total indebtedness increased 76%.
   Average per capita income of city residents increased 6%, of suburban residents 23%.
   Total employment within the city limits increased 12%.

Total employment in the whole area (25-mile radius) increased 11%.

Of city taxes, 88% is derived from real estate; the city levies no wage or income tax.

(b)

U.S. POPULATION DISTRIBUTION BY AGE

	UNDER 5	5-19	20-44	45-64	65 AND OVER
1870	14.3	35.4	35.4	11.9	3.0
1900	12.1	32.3	37.8	13.7	4.1
1930	9.3	29.5	38.3	17.5	5.4
1960	11.3	27.2	32.2	20.1	9.2

—U.S. Bureau of the Census

(c)

WORKING POPULATION OF THE U.S.

	NUMBER EMPLOYED (THOUSANDS)	PER CENT OF POP-ULATION EMPLOYED	PER CENT OF EMPLOYED IN:	
			FARM OCCUPATION	NONFARM OCCUPATION
1870	12,925	44.4	53.0	47.0
1900	29,073	50.2	37.5	62.5
1930	48,830	49.5	21.4	78.6
1960	70,636	55.9	8.9	91.1

—U.S. Bureau of the Census

(d)

LIFE EXPECTANCY, 1959

AGE	WHITE MALE	WHITE FEMALE
0	67.3	73.9
10	59.6	65.8
20	50.1	56.0
30	40.8	46.4
50	23.0	27.8
60	15.8	19.4
70	9.8	11.8

—Metropolitan Life Insurance Company

(e)

HIGH SCHOOL AND COLLEGE GRADUATES
(PUBLIC AND PRIVATE SCHOOLS)

	HIGH SCHOOL	COLLEGE
1900	94,883	27,410
1920	311,266	48,622
1940	1,221,475	186,500
1960	1,639,000	381,923

(f)

RELATION OF INTELLIGENCE TO EDUCATIONAL OPPORTUNITY

EDUCATIONAL ADVANCE	FAMILY INCOME ABOVE AVERAGE		FAMILY INCOME BELOW AVERAGE		TOTAL GROUP	
	No.	Per Cent	No.	Per Cent	No.	Per Cent
Dropped school at eighth grade or below	4	0.07	27	7.9	31	3.4
Completed eleventh grade but did not graduate from high school	36	6.2	69	20.2	105	11.6
Graduated from high school but did not attend college	206	36.3	202	59.0	408	44.8
Attended college	322	56.8	44	12.9	366	40.2
Total	568	100.0	342	100.0	910	100.0

7. Write an interpretation (400-600 words) explaining the trends indicated by these data and what they mean to technology, economics, and government in the United States:

DECLINE IN DEATH RATE (U.S.), 1920-1960

FROM	PERCENTAGE
All childhood diseases	87
All causes (children 5-14)	60
Scarlet fever	92
Whooping cough	92
Diphtheria	93
Tuberculosis & pneumonia (children 9-14)	75

YEAR	U.S. POPULATION (IN MILLIONS)	LIFE EXPECTANCY (IN YEARS)	PERCENTAGE OF MALE POPULATION GAINFULLY EMPLOYED (BY AGE GROUPS)		
			10-15	16-64	OVER 64
1900	76	49	26	92	68
1920	106	54	17	93	60
1940	132	65	1	95	42
1960	180	70	(insignificant)	97	40

DISTRIBUTION OF AGE GROUPS IN U.S. POPULATION
(PERCENTAGES ROUNDED OFF)

	0-4	5-19	20-29	30-44	45-64	OVER 64
1900	12	32	18	20	14	4
1920	11	30	17	21	16	5
1940	8	26	17	21	21	7
1960	6	22	15	23	23	11

8. Comment on the following interpretation of the data below:

An argument that has been raging for years has finally been settled. Figures on scholastic averages at Great Western University, released by the Office of the Registrar for the Fall Semester 1964, show that fraternity membership is a definite aid to scholarship.

Table 1

SCHOLASTIC AVERAGES

Fraternity men	74.6%
All-University men	73.7
Nonfraternity men	72.9

Table 2

PERCENTAGE OF STUDENTS DROPPED AT END OF SPRING SEMESTER 1965

Freshmen	18.3
Sophomores	14.8
Juniors	8.9
Seniors	2.6

Table 3

ENROLLMENT BY CLASSES
FALL SEMESTER 1964

	NO.	PER CENT
Freshmen	2247	32.3
Sophomores	1555	22.4
Juniors	1452	20.9
Seniors	1697	24.4
Total	6951	100.0

Table 4

CLASS DISTRIBUTION OF FRATERNITY AND NONFRATERNITY MEN, FALL 1964

	FRA-TERNITY	NONFRA-TERNITY
Seniors	33.0%	19.4%
Juniors	27.7	17.7
Sophomores	39.3	20.4
Freshmen	0.9	42.5
Total	100.0%	100.0%

9. Write an interpretation of the following table:

TRENDS IN EMPLOYMENT
(FIGURES ROUNDED OFF TO NEAREST INTEGER)

	1860	1880	1900	1920	1940	1960
Total man-hours (in billions)	36	56	82	116	110	122
Hours per week	68	64	60	50	40	38
Net output per man-hour (in cents)	20	24	36	43	70	105
Employment (in millions)	10	17	27	40	50	60
National income (in billions of dollars, 1940 prices)	7	13	30	49	78	130

10. Consider the following proposal: "Every state should enact legislation prohibiting the employment of engineers who are not registered." What problems might arise if this proposal were adopted? What is your own recommendation with respect to the proposal?

CHAPTER 7

Preparing the Manuscript: Format

THIS chapter considers the final stages of preparing the long-form report. Most problems in planning and writing have been discussed in earlier chapters; the emphasis here is on the format and arrangement of the various report elements. We shall examine them in the physical order in which they usually appear in the modern report. The order, of course, is arbitrary—one of convenience. Few reports would contain every element we consider, but all good reports contain many of them. A particular report can and should be shaped to the requirements of its particular reader. The reader's requirements *always* come first—in content, expression, and format.

IMPORTANCE OF APPEARANCE

The tremendous growth of the packaging industry indicates the importance of appearance in any product. Certainly attractive appearance never *hurts* a report, and whether all readers realize it or not, they are unconsciously impressed by it. Thoughtful arrangement of display pages (cover, title page, and table of contents); judicious use of white space; a discernible system of headings; neat curves, tables, and diagrams; clean typing—all contribute dynamically to the effectiveness of your report. Never slight them.

As a report writer you have one advantage over most other writers: you can design and generally control the physical make-up in which your writing appears. You ought to exploit that advantage. For example, use additional space or a cover or title page to separate and emphasize the elements; emphasize an itemized list by the use of wide margins and additional space above and below; line your tables and diagrams to give them unity and clarity; give thought to your table of contents and make your heads and subheads distinctive and physically easy for a reader to locate and understand.

THE REPORT BINDER

If the report is to be printed, the writer is seldom concerned with the manner in which it will be bound. If is to be typed, however, either the company or the writer must select a prepared binder on which the variables can be lettered or typed.

The binder should be:

1. Attractive in appearance. (Every reader will see it—and see *it* first.)
2. Rugged in construction. (Most long reports contain enough information of permanent value to merit inclusion in permanent files. Most of them represent considerable investment in time and materials.)
3. Complete in identification. (The front cover must include at least an informative title, the full names of the writer and his intended reader, and the date of submittal.)

If the writer has a cover already prepared for him or an art department to prepare one, he has little concern with the matter. If he is expected to take that responsibility himself, he may well decide that he can make a more attractive lettering on the cover with pen than with typewriter. Suitable binders, containing semipermanent fasteners, are available at modest cost.

THE TITLE PAGE

The title page, especially in typewritten reports, often includes exactly the same information that appears on the outside cover. It must provide:

1. The complete title.
2. The name of the person or organization to which the report is being submitted.
3. The full name of the writer and his capacity or title.
4. The date when the report is submitted.

All this information is of real importance, particularly for any later reference that may be made to the report. Other information—for example, the department of origin, a serial number, a distribution list (where copies are to be sent), an approval list (signatures or superiors who perhaps authorized the investigation and now accept the report as satisfactory)—is often included as well; *what* information depends on company requirements.

Every title page needs a complete and informative title. The title of a technical or business report is not usually a catchy phrase. It should be as descriptive as possible; it should indicate not only what the report

PROPOSED SYSTEM FOR TREATING

SPENT SULPHITE LIQUOR

AT THE ERIE MILL

EBAUGH PAPER COMPANY

Submitted to

Dr. Robert T. Wright, Head
Process Development Department

_____

12 May 1965

_____

By

George L. Fischer
Development Engineer

_____

Copy No. _____   Approved:
Of 50 Copies
                          _____
                          Director of Research
                          _____
                          Patent Manager

FIGURE 9. SPECIMEN TITLE PAGE.

is about but also what it is for and what it does. Conciseness is also desirable, but a title may sometimes run to forty or more words if that many are required to convey complete understanding. Compare these titles:

> Argon and Liquid Oxygen
>
> The Economic Feasibility of Manufacturing Argon from Excess Liquid Oxygen

The short title provides hardly a suggestion of the real subject; the long one defines the subject specifically *and* points out the function of the report.

In research reports the complete title is especially characteristic because it must be definitive enough to satisfy both the immediate readers and those who may later discover it in a library file or bibliography.

The periodic-report title must always include the period covered by the report, since that is the only item that will inevitably distinguish it from all other reports in the same series:

> Annual Report of the Sales Manager for 1963
>
> Monthly Report of the Shipping Department, March 1963

The title of a progress report is also one of a series, all alike except for the difference in date:

> Report on Progress of the Blanchard Project for May 1964
>
> Progress Report: Raystown Bypass, July 1 to October 1, 1963

In an investigative report the title does not usually include a date, but for exact identification it sometimes does include the word *preliminary* or *final:*

> Preliminary Survey of Absenteeism at the Wabash Plant
>
> Study of Profit-Sharing Systems in the Textile Industry
>
> Final Report on Proposed Relocation

Recommendation reports should be distinguishable from other investigative reports by their titles:

> Advisability of Installing Magnetic Separators in No. 2 Plant
>
> Proposed Plan for Relocating Coral Harbor Storage Silos

Note that key words denote the *function* of the report: *progress; survey, study, investigation, examination;* or *advisability, feasibility, proposals, recommended.*

A specimen title page (typed) appears on page 121.

TABLE OF CONTENTS

Any report of more than a few pages needs a table of contents. A good table of contents serves two purposes: (1) it provides the reader,

CONTENTS

Summary   i

Introduction   1

Land Site and Ocean Site Compared   2
    Continental Site   3
    Oceanio-Island Site   4
    Deep-Ocean Site   4

Latitudinal and Longitudinal Location   6
    Proximity of Operation Bases   7
    Degree of Exploration   7

Submarine Relief   8
    Topographic Features   8
       Canyons   9
       Basins   9
       Trenches   10
    North Atlantic Floor   11
    North Pacific Floor   12
    Sediments in Trenches   14
       Sands   14
       Clays   15

Earthquakes   16
    Relation to Trenches   16
       Heat Flow   16
       Sea Avalanches   17
    History of Earthquakes in Areas Considered   18
       Guadalupe   18
       Clipperton   19
       Bermuda   20
       Puerto Rico   20

Ocean Currents   21
    Surface   21
    Subsurface   22
    Abyssal   23
       Pacific Deeps   23
       Atlantic Deeps   24

FIGURE 10. SPECIMEN TABLE OF CONTENTS.

CONTENTS (cont.)

Weather Conditions 25
    Preferred Latitudes 26
    Temperatures 29
    Mean Annual Precipitation 31
    Hurricanes 33

Major Conclusions 34

Appendix 36
    Divisions of the Earth 36
        Crust 36
        Mantle 37
        Outer Core 38
        Inner Core 38
    Definition of the Moho 39
    Isostatic Adjustment 40

Bibliography 41

FIGURES

Fig. 1 Schematic Cross Section of the Earth's Crust 2
Fig. 2 Feasible Areas for Drilling 3
Fig. 3 Profile of a Typical Submarine Canyon 9
Fig. 4 Profile of a Typical Basin 10

TABLES

Table 1 Average Number of Tropical Cyclones of Hurricane or Near-
        Hurricane Strength 33
Table 2 Comparative Summation of Sites 35

NOTE:

    1. The summary is included in the table of contents, the title page is not.
    2. Spacing and dotted leads increase efficiency.
    3. Absence of letter and number symbols. If ASA numbering had been employed, the third major section would have looked like this:

3. Submarine Relief . . . .

    3.1 Topographic Features . . .   /Some writers might begin to
        3.1.1 Canyons . . . . . .   number with the summary. If
        3.1.2 Basins . . . .   that were done here, the section
        3.1.3 Trenches . . . . . .   would be 5 and the subsections
    3.2 North Atlantic Floor . . . .   5.1, etc./
    3.3 North Pacific Floor . . . .
    3.4 Sediments in Trenches . . .
        3.4.1 Sands . . . .
        3.4.2 Clays . . . .

FIGURE 10 (*cont.*). SECOND PAGE OF SPECIMEN TABLE OF CONTENTS.

present or future, with a guide to sections and subsections, and (2) it reveals the skeletal structure of the report. Thus a reader can not only find what he is looking for, but he can also see its relationship to other elements in the report.

In preparing a table of contents, observe these rules:

1. List every title, every heading, and every subheading that appears in the report itself, including preliminary and appendix sections which follow the table of contents. Use *exactly* the same wording that you use in the text.
2. Indicate decreasing importance of headings by increasing indention.
3. Unless there is real need for an elaborate outline, do not use numbers or letters to label the section titles. If distinction *is* needed, use the same symbols in both table of contents and text.

When an exceptionally long and complex report requires more than four orders of heads, it is common to list only the first four in the table of contents. Obviously any system of indenting would prove inadequate for such subdividing; hence subdivisions are indicated by a numbering system like that recommended by the American Standards Association and used throughout the Handbook Section of this text, pp. 211-63.

THE SUMMARY

A good introductory summary is a compact unit that poses no appreciable problem in format. Many companies restrict introductory summaries to one page—and hope for less. Subdivisions and subheadings of such summaries are usually unnecessary.

In long formal reports, the summary belongs on a page by itself. Place it either before or immediately after the table of contents. If it is before the table of contents, give it a lower-case roman numeral (*i*); if it follows the table of contents, it must be numbered as the first page of the report.

INTRODUCTION

As a rule, introductions should be so short that subdivisions will be unnecessary. Subtitles like *Purpose, Scope, Background, Problems to be Solved* may occasionally seem desirable, but usually they only invite overlap and repetition. Before you think of subdividing, make sure in your own mind that it will serve a useful purpose.

CONCLUSIONS AND RECOMMENDATIONS

Some reports, especially very short ones, omit an introductory summary and place conclusions and recommendations immediately after the introduction. A separate subtitle must appear to guide the reader to this most important section: *Conclusions* or *Conclusions and Recommendations.*

Wherever conclusions and recommendations appear, each conclusion and each recommendation usually deserves a separate paragraph. Usually, too, conclusions and recommendations should appear on a page by themselves where the reader can give them undivided attention.

THE MAIN TEXT

Divide the main text of the report into sections and subsections according to the outline prepared when the material was organized. The trend in the modern report is to use smaller and smaller subsections. The advantages are clear:

1. You do not compel the reader to concentrate on complex discussions over long periods of time.
2. You enable a reader who wishes to refer to only one part of the report to locate that part quickly.
3. The heads and subheads in the table of contents give the reader a quick but comprehensive view of the report contents and arrangement.

To make these things possible, a system of heads is necessary:

1. Each heading should clearly indicate the relative importance of the section it heads.
2. Conversely, headings of the same relative importance should be identical in form.
3. Headings should be readily distinguishable from other orders of headings.
4. Headings should be clearly distinguishable from text.
5. No major heading should be placed more than two-thirds of the way down the page (some companies insist they be placed only at the top) and no heading of any order should be placed at the bottom.

To satisfy these requirements on a typewriter involves careful planning. Distinction on the typed page is obtainable in only two ways, spatially and typographically. Consequently, heads can be differentiated from each other and from the text only by the position they occupy or by reason of some typographical distinction such as capitalization, underlining, or the use of identifying symbols (roman numerals, single capital letters, and so forth).

If the title of the report appears at the beginning of the text, or above the introduction, give it the most prominent treatment:

THEORIES FOR THE PREVENTION OF TOOTH DECAY

or, for a longer title:

THE ADVISABILITY
OF ESTABLISHING A PILOT PLANT FOR THE MANUFACTURE
OF BLOATED SLATE AGGREGATE AND CONCRETE BLOCKS

or, when you wish to distinguish it from the head of a major section (such as INTRODUCTION) appearing just below it:

MARKET SURVEY: TROY, OHIO

A MARKET SURVEY
TROY, OHIO

A suggested method for handling other heads and subheads is illustrated in Figure 11, page 128.

Three levels of heads are sufficient for most reports. Distinguish main divisions by centered titles, capital letters, surrounding space, and sometimes by identifying numbers as well. Distinguish lesser divisions by titles set against the left margin and above the section they are to control, still smaller sections by inserting the heading in the first line of the paragraph. Underscore all typewritten heads and subheads to differentiate them, especially those of the second or third level, from the text.

It is always better to show the relationship of sections in the report by the position and style of heading than by such symbols as I, A, l, a. Symbols detract from the appearance and are often more difficult for the reader to follow.

More than any other factor, the length of a report determines the number and complexity of the subdivisions. There are, however, other determining conditions. When a very thorough and comprehensive explanation of the subject is demanded, or when the material is logically subdivided, the writer must employ a more complicated system than is necessary under ordinary circumstances.

Unless titles are systematic, reading is made exceedingly difficult. Of particular importance is the arrangement of the parts of the report. Every title found in the table of contents must appear in the text of the report. There must be the same order and the same distinction between the sections, the subdivisions, and the sub-subdivisions. All headings of the same class should introduce subjects of equal rank; and, further, they should agree in their relationship to the whole work. Divisions that are given the same prominence in title should not overlap; nor should one title ever be subordinated to another of equal standing.

TERMINAL SUMMARY

The final summary, if one seems necessary at all, usually poses no special problems in format. If it itemizes and classifies numerous con-

A FIRST-ORDER HEAD

The first-order head is centered horizontally at the top of the page. It should never appear near the bottom of a page. It is completely capitalized and underscored.

If two orders of heads are needed, the second order appears against the left margin, also underscored, but in small letters except for initial capitals.

A Second-Order Head

A third-order head. The third-order head is indented into the paragraph, underscored, and typed in small letters (except for proper names and the first letter of the first word). It is followed by a period or a colon, two or three spaces, and then the first sentence of the paragraph. It is not good practice to use any head as part of the sentence which follows it.

Another Second-Order Head

If only two orders of heads are required, the third-order head illustrated here is discarded. When more than three orders are required, either appearance or distinction must be sacrificed. For example, an additional order can be squeezed between the first two orders here. It would be centered horizontally, underscored, and typed in small letters except for initial capitals. The present second-order head would then become the third, and the third, of course, the fourth. Five or more levels would require the complementary use of number symbols.

Still Another Second-Order Head

Appearance is improved and the head tied more closely to the section it controls by skipping more space above than below it. Whatever the ratio used, it should be maintained consistently.

Another third-order head. Every head should be underscored. Without the underlining this head would be indistinguishable from the paragraph text.

FIGURE 11. SPECIMEN HEADINGS.

clusions, however, each conclusion should be numbered; subheads are a useful means of emphasizing different divisions of conclusions.

APPENDIXES

Appendixes, when they are needed, represent the section into which all material not directly contributory to the reader's understanding of the subject is placed. The writer must decide whether or not tables, charts, maps, curves, photographs, and the like are sufficiently helpful to reader comprehension to be included in the report text. Sometimes the decision is an easy one. Calculations, for example, are rarely useful in the body of the report—yet they must be available for reference. Tables which are summarized in the text are seldom of use there and should be placed in an appendix. But if the text refers to a table or curve in such a way that the reader must look at it to understand what is being said, then the table should be placed where it will be most convenient to him. Often the reader must refer to a diagram (flow sheet, and so forth) at several places in the report. When this is true, it is probably desirable to put the diagram in the appendix at the end of the report, or, better, to put it on a "pull-out" where it can be referred to continually without search.

Occasionally, by-product or "tangential" information uncovered during an investigation is too valuable to be discarded, yet it is not directly relevant to the purpose of the report. Such material is also included in an appendix.

BIBLIOGRAPHY AND REFERENCES

Any report that has used information obtained from other investigators or authorities must include a bibliography or a list of references. A *bibliography* lists the written material consulted—but not necessarily used—in constructing the report. It does not list interviews or unpublished correspondence. *References* is a broader term in one sense, a narrower one in another: it lists *every* source, written or otherwise, but only those that influenced the report at hand. To future investigators of the same or related problems these lists may prove more valuable than the report itself. For this reason, bibliographies may include sources not cited in your report.

Standard practice places the bibliography or a list of references at the end of the report. In other respects bibliographical practice varies widely, often in the same publication. But any *good* bibliography must:

Identify the authority from whom the writer took material.
Make it easy for readers to locate that material.

Capitalize, punctuate, and arrange the bibliographical entries logically and consistently.

The relatively standard method outlined below satisfies all three requirements. (Numbers on "shelves" (_/) refer to the entries in the specimen list of references, page 132.)

1. Index and number each article, book, bulletin, or report alphabetically by the author's surname followed by his given name or initials.

   1.1 If no personal author is given, index by the corporate author—the organization or agency responsible for the work (see 7/ and 10/). And if neither personal nor corporate author is given, index by the first significant word of the title (see 9/).

   1.2 If two or three authors are given, list all, but invert only the first (see 1/ and 6/).

   1.3 If more than three authors are given, use the name appearing first on the title page of a book or by-line of an article and add "and others" (see 8/).

   1.4 If two or more entries by the same author are to be listed, repeat the author's name with each entry and arrange the entries alphabetically by the first significant word of the title (see 4/ and 5/). The substitution of a short line for the author's name in the second and subsequent entries is confusing: the same device sometimes indicates "no known author."

2. In *all* titles, capitalize the first letter of all principal words, including the first and last words.

3. Italicize (by underlining) the title of a book or periodical.

4. Place quotations around the title of an article within a periodical or a chapter within a book (see 8/).

5. Separate all elements by commas.

   EXCEPTIONS: a. Use a colon after city of publication.
   b. Use brackets around an editorial insertion of your own making.
   c. Do not separate month from year unless the date is also given: March 1964; *but* March 2, 1964.

6. For books, list in order: author, title, edition (if any), city of publication, publisher, date of publication (see 1/, 3/).

7. For articles, list in order: author, title, name of periodical, volume number (Vol. 88), page number or numbers (p. 36; pp. 97-106), date (see 2/, 4/, 5/, 6/, 8/).

8. For a chapter or section within a book, insert the chapter number

or inclusive page numbers and the chapter title in quotation marks.

9. For a report, list in order: author, title, department or division of origin, the name of the company or governmental agency, the report number (if any), and the date.

10. For a special bulletin, particularly a government publication, include exact and complete names of the subdivision (bureau, agency, administration, commission) responsible and any identifying details used by that agency (see 7/).

11. For newspaper articles, list in order: author (if any), title or heading (in quotes), name of newspaper, page number, column number, and date (see 9/). If no meaningful heading exists, supply one in brackets.

12. For interviews, which are preferably listed separately, give in order: the name of the person interviewed, his title or capacity, the subject of the interview (not italicized or in quotes unless the interview is formal and the subject preannounced), and the date (see 11/).

13. For correspondence (also listed separately), follow the same procedure as for the interview (see 12/).

14. Spacing: Single-space each entry; double-space between entries. Readability is improved by indenting the second and third lines of entries and by skipping extra spaces between the elements within entries.

15. Paging: Give inclusive page numbers in complete numbers (927-933, not 927-33). Some bibliographers indicate that articles are carried over to back pages by adding a plus sign after the last page number, 927-933+.

16. Abbreviating: Do not abbreviate the name of a month. However, *Vol.* (for volume), *No.* (for number—seldom needed), and *p.* (for page) are standard; these three abbreviations are unusual in having plural forms (*Vols., Nos.,* and *pp.*). Note, too, that since they are not technical abbreviations, they require periods.

DOCUMENTATION—ACKNOWLEDGING CONTRIBUTIONS OF OTHERS

The report writer is often indebted for much of his material to other investigators. Unless he is summarizing information about an organization or division for which he is personally responsible, he must be careful to give credit for every fact or statement he borrows. Even the executive finds it good practice to credit subordinates who have helped him.

The introduction or the letter of transmittal sometimes mentions indebtedness to individuals, but general acknowledgment is seldom

REFERENCES

Bibliography

1. Fairchild, Johnson E. and David Laudman, editors, America Faces the Nuclear Age, New York: Sheridan House, 1961.

2. Graver, C. T., "Power Supply for Nuclear Research Laboratory," Electrical Engineering, Vol. 72, pp. 212-218, March 1953.

3. Harris, Saul J., Nuclear Power Safety Economics, Second edition, New York: Pilot Books, 1961.

4. Hill, D. L., "Distribution-Energy for Alpha-Particles and Protons from U235 Fission," Physical Review, Vol. 87. pp. 1049-1051, September 15, 1951.

5. Hill, D. L., "Neutron Energy Spectrum from U235 Thermal Fission," Physical Review, Vol. 88, pp. 724-727, February 15, 1952.

6. Hughes, W. F. and R. A. Elco, "Magnetohydrodynamic Lubrication Flow Between Parallel Rotating Disks," Journal of Fluid Mechanics, Vol. 13, pp. 21-32, May 1962.

7. "Inter-American Symposium on the Peaceful Application of Atomic Energy, Rio de Janeiro, 1960," Industrial Application of Nuclear Energy, Washington: Pan-American Union, 1961.

8. Miller, D. W. and others, "Total Cross Sections of Heavy Nuclei for Fast Neutrons," Physical Review, Vol. 88, pp. 83-90, October 1, 1952.

9. "TVA and Oak Ridge Study Experimental Gas-Cooled Reactor," The New York Times, p. 15, col. 3, July 18, 1962.

10. U.S. Bureau of the Census, Statistical Abstract of the United States: 1962, Eighty-third edition, Washington, D. C., 1962.

Interview

11. Doe, John, Director of Research, Ossining Laboratories, May 24, 1963, Subject: Tracers in biochemistry.

Correspondence

12. Smith, John, Head, Atomic Physics Section, National Bureau of Standards, May 21, 1963, Subject: Tests with tracers.

FIGURE 12. SPECIMEN REFERENCES.

enough. The writer must give specific credit at the point of citation. The primary reason for doing this is common honesty. An *un*-acknowledged quotation becomes a theft. Any verbatim sentence or larger unit belongs in quotation marks. A lesser group of words should be quoted if the *phrasing* itself possesses value or evidences artistry of expression. Quotation is required even though the source is identified, whether by footnote or by direct reference in the text. A quotation of more than a few lines should be distinctively set off: separated from the text by extra space, indented from both left and right margins, and single-spaced. A word of introduction (followed by a colon) should identify the source. Omissions in a directly quoted passage must be indicated by ellipses (. . .) and additions by brackets (see page 251).

The second reason for acknowledging either fact or judgment supplied by others is to add weight to your statements by revealing the authority behind them. Data and opinions impress a thoughtful reader only when he knows who is responsible for them. The careful writer, then, will add significant strength to his conclusions by making certain his sources are identified.

Footnotes

When the reader is interested in sources, he wants answers to two specific questions: Who said so? When? Whatever system of identifying sources you use, it must answer these questions, preferably at the point of citation.

In citing an authority important enough to lend weight to a statement, incorporate his name in the text:

> Vannevar Bush [3] pleaded for government support of pure research as far back as 1945.

Or, if his capacity is meaningful:

> Vannevar Bush,[3] Head of the Office of Scientific Research and Development (OSRD), pleaded. . . .

Any reader who wishes further bibliographical detail can follow the index figure to a footnote, or, in endnoting, to the numbered bibliography. When, however, the identity of the source is *not* meaningful to the reader, use the traditional footnote for complete documentation.

Footnotes supply the exact source of quotations from books, periodicals, bulletins, or other reports. They acknowledge contributions of data, point to further substantiation of a statement in the text, or give supplementary information. Use them only when the information they contain would interrupt the reader's thought if inserted in the text.

With the reader's convenience in mind, the most satisfactory method of footnoting is as follows:

1. Place the footnote at the bottom of the page on which the

reference occurs. (EXCEPTION: In referring to a table or an item in a table, place the footnote directly below the table.)

2. Number the footnotes consecutively from the beginning of the report to the end, or page by page if there are more than 99 footnotes in the report.

3. For indexes to the footnotes, use arabic numerals in the text, lower-case letters or asterisks in tables.

4. Place the index number at the point in the text where the reader naturally questions the source—and outside all marks of punctuation but the dash:

. . . according to Hipple's theory,[6] traces of. . . .

5. When typewritten reports are double-spaced, there is sufficient space for full-size numerals as superior figures. In single-spaced copy, the index number can be placed on a shelf (see page 130) on the same line as the typing—inside all marks of punctuation.

6. Separate footnotes from the bottom of the text by a solid line with extra space above and below. The line should begin at the left margin and extend part or all the way to the right one.

7. Single-space each footnote and treat each as a separate paragraph.

8. Identify sources (author, title, publication, volume, date, and so forth) as completely as in the bibliography itself (see page 139), but identify the specific page from which the information was taken instead of inclusive pages. EXCEPTION: when some of the elements—author and date, for example—are mentioned in the text, there is no need to repeat them in the footnote.

9. Use *ibid.* ("in the same place") only when the reference cited is identical to the one *immediately* before it except for the change in page number. Use *op. cit.* ("in the work cited") followed by a new page number after the name of an author whose work was cited earlier in the report.

If this were the last paragraph on a report page requiring five footnote references (Nos. 18-22 in the report), the bottom of the page would look like this:

---

[18]Emery, K. O., The Sea Off Southern California (New York: John Wiley & Sons, Inc., 1960), p. 171.
[19]Ibid., p. 308.
[20]Some authorities estimate it will take three years longer.
[21]Bascom, Willard, "Mohole," Scientific American, Vol. 31, pp. B24–B27, August 1959.
[22]Emery, op cit., p. 332.

In the example on the previous page, footnote 19 can use *ibid.* only in referring to footnote 18, but footnote 22 could use *op. cit.* for Emery's book so long as it had been cited anywhere from footnote 1 to 20 inclusive. Footnote 20, of course, is informational, not bibliographical.

So elaborate a system is obviously demanding in time, space, and patience. To conserve all these, short-cut substitutes are often desirable.

Endnotes

One time-saving method of annotation is to number citations consecutively throughout the report and to present them in a reference section at the end, usually just before the bibliography. The method saves time and space, yet supplies complete bibliographical data, page numbers included. Its disadvantage is that it forces the reader to leave his reading for either bibliographical or informational footnotes.

The simplest method involves direct index reference to a numbered bibliography. Assume that the eighth entry in your bibliography is an article by Lawrence Berra. Each time you cite his article you simply insert the index figure 8 in the text at the point of citation. Your reader then need only look for the eighth item in your bibliography. For periodical literature or for reports containing only a handful of references, this system is sensible. The few bibliographical items can be arranged, not alphabetically, but in the order of citation.

When the bibliography is long and references to it are many, endnoting does not do the whole job. It continually forces the reader who wishes to evaluate what he is reading to interrupt his train of thought, shuttle back to the bibliography, return to the point of citation, and retrack his thoughts. Yet this method, too, is economical in time and space—so much so that it is outstripping other methods in popularity.

Compromise Method

The following compromise between the complexity of traditional footnoting and the oversimplification of endnoting is simple and economical. It answers the reader's Who? and When?—and it answers them at the point of citation with a minimum of interruption.

The method requires a numbered bibliography arranged alphabetically by author. Then, if an article by Berra is cited, the report writer inserts in the text: (Berra, 1962), or if paging is desired: (Berra, 1962, p. 159). An anonymous reference is cited by using its number: (Ref. 8, 1962, p. 233). Informational footnotes (such as footnote 20 in the example on page 134) must, of course, be placed at the bottom of the page to which they apply. The professional reader will like this method, for he can hurdle those small parentheses in stride.

PAPER

In general, use 8½ by 11 opaque paper; government agencies supply their own paper, which is a slightly smaller size. The report will then fit standard manila folders and can be filed in standard files.

Reports should always be written on paper of good quality. Twenty-pound bond is recommended. Thin, translucent paper is undesirable except for carbon copies. Since a real report probably has lasting value, the paper must last as long as the report is useful. In some organizations, various colors of paper and covers serve to distinguish communications from different departments or on different subjects. Nevertheless, white paper is generally preferred.

STANDARDS FOR MARGINS AND SPACING

Good make-up for the text of a report approaches the appearance of the printed page. There should be uniform margins and spacing, and a generous amount of space on every page.

The left-hand margin is, of course, even. Since the margins after binding should appear to be about equal, it is usually necessary to allow half an inch more margin at the left than at the right. Margins at the top and bottom of the page must be at least 1 inch in depth. An attractive page can be achieved with a top margin of 1¼ inches, a left of 1½ inches, a right of ¾ inch, and a bottom of 1 inch. The wider left margin allows for binding.

If the report is consistent and neat in make-up, the choice between single and double spacing is not of great importance; there are, however, conditions that have weight in determining which to use. When corrections, changes, or minor additions are required in the finished copy, the report must be double-spaced to allow sufficient room for these changes. Furthermore, if numerous quotations are to be included, they are more readily distinguishable when spaced differently from the text proper—as, for example, when they are single-spaced in the body of double-spaced text. The advantage of single-spacing under normal conditions is, nevertheless, considerable. Much more can be put on a single page. The report is less bulky. Tables and figures may be referred to more readily, since the explanations regarding them need not cover so much space. All references, in fact, are likely to be made with greater speed and ease.

An indented quotation and (unless it is very short) the letter of transmittal should always be single-spaced to allow for rapid reading and to give an impression of brevity and conciseness.

It is not good judgment to save space by sacrificing either appearance or reader convenience. Very few typed reports use more than one side of the paper. Headings for major sections are customarily placed at the top of the page, regardless of where on the previous page the last section ended. No heading or subheading should be placed at the bottom of the page without text below it. Similarly, a paragraph should not be begun on the last line of the page. Liberal space should be allowed for all headings, more for the major heading than for the minor. Figures, tables, and graphic devices of other kinds should not be crowded. Quotations over a few lines in length should be indented from both margins from six to eight spaces. A few companies include flyleaves at the beginning and end and between major sections of the report; for the most part, however, flyleaves add unnecessary bulk.

PAGE NUMBERING

Beginning with the first page of the report itself, every page must be numbered. Since the place first seen by most readers is the upper right-hand corner, most writers place the number there. When the title appears at the top of the first page, it is standard practice to omit the number. It is also standard practice to number the pages preceding the table of contents with lower-case Roman numerals (*ii, vii,* and so forth). The numbering in the appendix should be a continuation of that in the text.

SUBMITTING THE MANUSCRIPT TO THE PRINTER

A manuscript submitted to the printer must be legible beyond possibility of error. The chief requisite is, of course, to give full directions for all matters that are to be decided by the writer, and leave other matters to the good judgment of the printer.

However, it must be remembered that the average printer will follow copy rather literally in such matters as indentions of quoted material, paragraphing, italicizing, capitalization of headings, use of boldface type, and so forth. For instance, if the author of the report wishes a certain heading to be set in boldface, that is, heavy type, he should underscore it with a wavy line. If he wishes it italicized, he should use a straight underscore. Before composition is started, it is always wise to have a personal conference with the printer for the purpose of deciding all details of style.

All illustrations, charts, photographs, and other cuts should be submitted separately, because they are not handled by typesetters. To insure that these will be all properly placed in the printed report, the author should mark the position of each in the text with a number corresponding to that found on the illustration.

TYPES OF MECHANICAL AIDS

Most long-form reports use tables, maps, graphs, diagrams, photographs, or other such mechanical aids to present material more exactly, quickly, and vividly than they could do with words alone. But these devices should never become mere embellishments. It is helpful, of course, to make a report attractive, but such devices ought to do more than that. They ought to contribute something to understanding.

Here we can discuss only general principles that apply to tables and figures. For special needs you may require experts to design exactly what you want.

Tables

Because statistics are often essential to reports, the writer must determine the most effective ways to present them. Too many figures in the text itself are often confusing; they also require annoying repetitions. Good tables, however, may show relations and comparisons in a way that a reader can quickly see.

A good table simplifies and emphasizes what a writer wants to show, yet it does more than make comparisons easy for the reader. It emphasizes tendencies, eliminates much that is irrelevant, and organizes data in some logical way.

The effectiveness of a table depends to a great extent on its make-up. To obtain good make-up, observe the following rules:
1. Give every table an arabic number and number tables consecutively throughout the report.
2. Give every table a clear, informative title. The reader should understand the data without referring to the text.

> *Not:* SCIENTIFIC RESEARCH AND DEVELOPMENT
> *But:* Table 12. FEDERAL EXPENDITURES FOR SCIENTIFIC RESEARCH AND DEVELOPMENT, 1951-1960

3. Center the table number and title directly *above* the tables. Titles of figures are centered *below* the figures.
4. Be sure that the units in which the data are given are specified at the top of each column or at the beginning of each line.
5. Use the same unit throughout a column or line; do not, for example, use feet in some cells of the column and inches or centimeters in others.
6. Similarly, be sure that comparisons are made on the same basis. For example, if in testing two pumps a two-inch intake is used for one and a four-inch for the other, the data must not be directly compared.

7. Mention any factors that have important bearing on the data. For example, in tabulating the volume of flow through a pipe, indicate the diameter of the pipe.

8. Box or frame all but the simplest tables, and even in simple tables separate major sections with interior lines. A relatively simple table is illustrated below, a more elaborate one on page 140.

Table 12
INTEREST PER $100

TIME (IN MONTHS)	INTEREST RATE (IN DOLLARS, TO NEAREST CENT)				
	4%	5%	6%	7%	8%
1	0.33	0.42	0.50	0.58	0.67
2	0.67	0.83	1.00	1.17	1.33
3	1.00	1.25	1.50	1.75	2.00
6	2.00	2.50	3.00	3.50	4.00
12	4.00	5.00	6.00	7.00	8.00

9. Use a heading for each column, a line heading for each line. If, to make them clear, you must make them too long to fit the column, set them vertically to read up (left to right when the report is turned a quarter turn clockwise).

10. Use only standard abbreviations and symbols.

11. Use decimals for column data unless the units are more commonly given in fractions (pipe and lumber sizes, for example).

12. Omit unnecessary zeros. If, for example, all the numbers in a column are in even thousands, put "in thousands" in the column head and drop three zeros from each number.

13. Align vertical columns on the right-hand digit for whole numbers, on the decimal point for decimals, and on the right-hand integer for mixed numbers.

14. Indicate missing or omitted data by using a blank cell, a dash, a short series of dots or asterisks, or, if necessary, the word *none*. Do *not* use a zero.

15. Indicate repetition of the same number by a vertical arrow or by actual repetition. Do *not* use quotation (ditto) marks or any of the devices mentioned in Rule 14.

16. Use lower-case letters (*a, b, c,* and so forth) for footnote indexes within a table. Place the footnotes and source credit immediately below the table.

17. Use the column heading above the stub (the left-hand column) to refer *only* to the line heads and subheads below it, not to other column heads.

18. Try to arrange the table to be read without turning the report, but if a table is too wide for its page, place it so that it can be read normally when the report is turned a quarter turn clockwise (that is, when the right side of the report becomes the bottom).

No. 525. WHITE-COLLAR EMPLOYEES IN THE FEDERAL GOVERNMENT, BY MAJOR
OCCUPATIONAL GROUP: 1959

/As of October 31. Covers full-time employees; includes Alaska, Hawaii, outlying areas of the United
States, and foreign countries, but excludes foreign nationals overseas. Average grade is median based
on employees reported by General Schedule grades; average salary is arithmetic mean based on mean
salary for each grade for General Schedule positions and actual salary for those not reported by grades.
Employees for whom neither grades nor salaries were reported are included in employment totals but
excluded from computation of averages. The General Schedule is a compensation scale for Federal employees set up by the Classification Act of 1949, as amended, which established a system of grades 1 to
18 for grouping of positions, based on relative difficulty of duties and responsibilities/

OCCUPATIONAL GROUPS	ALL POSITIONS			PROFESSIONAL			NONPROFESSIONAL		
	Number	Aver-age grade	Aver-age salary	Number	Aver-age grade	Aver-age salary	Number	Aver-age grade	Aver-age salary
All groups	1,459,226	6	$5,557	219,821	11	$8,085	1,239,405	5	$5,107
General administrative, cler-									
ical, and office services	757,584	4	4,817	-------	-----	-----	757,584	4	4,817
Accounting and budget	99,274	6	5,792	27,791	11	7,949	71,483	5	4,953
Medical, hospital, dental,									
and public health	83,243	4	5,230	38,352	7	6,626	44,891	3	4,037
Engineering	94,164	11	7,821	57,808	12	9,204	36,356	7	5,621
Supply	70,865	5	5,089	-------	-----	-----	70,865	5	5,089
Business and industry	37,321	9	7,232	-------	-----	-----	37,321	9	7,232
Biological Sciences	33,366	7	6,199	21,446	9	7,163	11,920	5	4,465
Legal and kindred	33,229	9	7,208	11,416	12	9,725	21,813	7	5,601
Physical sciences	27,958	9	7,563	18,978	11	8,693	8,980	6	5,174
Investigation	29,583	9	7,397	-------	-----	-----	29,583	9	7,397
Personnel administration									
and industrial relations	26,361	7	6,278	20	12	8,308	26,341	7	6,277
Transportation	26,164	8	6,367	-------	-----	-----	26,164	8	6,367
Mechanic	14,803	9	7,041	-------	-----	-----	14,803	9	7,041
Social Science, psychology,									
and welfare	17,968	11	8,295	14,647	12	8,902	3,321	7	5,620
Mathematics and statistics	14,004	5	5,817	4,542	11	8,460	9,462	4	4,548
Education	16,960	7	6,370	15,778	7	,6,400	1,182	8	5,962
Inspection and grading	11,776	9	6,479	-------	-----	-----	11,776	9	6,479
Fine and applied arts	6,266	8	6,417	1,244	11	8,897	5,022	7	5,802
Library and archives	5,671	7	5,658	3,430	9	6,585	2,241	4	4,240
Veterinary science	2,016	11	7,603	2,016	11	7,603	-------	-----	-----
Copyright, patent, and									
trademark	1,498	11	9,062	1,498	11	9,062	-------	-----	-----
Trades, crafts, and labor	18	3	3,732	-------	-----	-----	18	3	3,732
Miscellaneous occupations	49,134	5	5,279	855	11	9,363	48,279	5	5,207

FIGURE 13. TYPICAL TABLE. (Source: Civil Service Commission. Reproduced
in *Statistical Abstract of the United States, 1961.*)

140

N/C Control Compared to Other Systems

Control element	Appropriate production runs	Machine flexibility	Design freedom	Management control of technique	Lead Time to production	Tooling costs	Chip-making hours per shift	Quality reliability	Maintenance costs
N/C	1 to low hundreds	High	High	High	Short	Low	High	High	(High)
Human operator	1 to 50	High	High	(None)	(Long)	(High)	(Low)	(Low)	Low
Tracer	10 to low hundreds	Medium	Medium	(Low)	(Long)	(High)	Medium	Medium	Medium
Fixed program (Detroit)	Low thousands to millions	(Low)	(Low)	High	(Long)	See* below	High	High	Medium

Of the four kinds of machine-tool controls listed above, N/C shows up best for all jobs but those involving mass production. Except for maintenance costs, always high on novel equipment, N/C is free of negative values (shown in parentheses). For long runs, fixed-program control is still best, although N/C might eventually be a contender even for such jobs. This table is necessarily oversimplified for convenience of presentation, but it reflects the consensus of makers, users, and other informed parties.

*Evaluation of "Detroit automation" tooling costs depends on how one regards an automobile production line: as one huge special machine tool needing no supplementary tooling; or as a series of machines, each requiring costly special tooling.

FIGURE 14. TEXTUAL TABLE. (Courtesy of *Fortune* [March, 1962].)

19. Avoid breaking tables. However, if a table is so large it must be continued from one page to the next:

   (a) Mark the first part of the table "continued on the next page" and mark the second part "continued from the preceding page." Use exactly the same form and dimensions for both parts, and repeat every column head whether or not any data appear below it.

   (b) If possible, use a summary table to recapitulate the major points and place the large table in the appendix.

   (c) If the table is long and narrow, it can be split and the two halves placed side by side—with repeated headings, of course.

Tabular treatment can be effective in comparing nonnumerical data or even mixed data. In evaluating two or more sites, processes, or pieces of equipment, for example, a summary table might show how each compared to others in every respect considered important. Figure 14 shows a "Textual Table" that includes no actual figures whatever.

Figures

The term *figure* customarily refers to any visual aid except a table. One basic rule applies to all such devices: Keep them simple. Help the reader, do not puzzle him.

Surround every illustration, of whatever kind, with a frame or border and with plenty of space. Provide each with an explanatory title placed directly below the figure. Identify units, symbols, and scale. Keep simple and avoid crowding; remember that these figures, together with any lettering on them, are often reduced in size.

PHOTOGRAPHS. Photographs often contribute vividness to a report. They usually provide a more exact impression of actual appearance than any other device can do. When they help substantiate statements in the text they become valuable as evidence as well as illustration and explanation.

In reports that are severely technical, photographs are ordinarily not useful. They provide only a knowledge of the appearance of a mechanism or development. A photograph covers only externals, and to the reader primarily interested in technical relationships and principles it may seem mere window dressing.

DIAGRAMS AND MAPS. In routine and technical reports, diagrams and maps are usually more useful than photographs. For example, the map of a property gives a more nearly exact impression of dimensions and relative positions than a photograph can. Similarly, a diagram of a machine shows the relationship of parts and makes it possible for the

FIGURE 15. SPECIMEN PHOTO. (Wilson Dam. Unit 19 penstock erection by contractor. Rock in immediate foreground at elevation 372±.)

reader to understand the working principle. Better than either photograph or diagram alone, however, is the possible combination of the two. What the camera misses or misrepresents may be caught by the sketch, and what might be misleading in the sketch is rectified by the photograph.

GRAPHS. Though statistics in tabular form are exceedingly useful in presenting information accurately and concisely, the tabular treatment lacks the impressiveness and interest of graphic methods. A curve (or battery of curves) is more effective, too, in revealing trends and relationships. And graphical charts in all forms have the important advantage of dramatizing comparisons between adjacent sets of statistics.

Effective graphic presentation is not achieved without planning. As the American Standards Association points out in its *Engineering and Scientific Graphs for Publication:* *

> The preparation of a graph deserves and usually requires at least as much time as the preparation of its equivalent in text. To obtain effective design and layout, it is good practice to make a preliminary freehand sketch roughly to scale. It is often helpful to submit such a sketch to others, preferably typical of the intended readers, for their reaction.

* American Standard Z15.3–1943. This informative manual, too long for reproduction here, can be obtained at a nominal charge by writing the Association at 70 East 45th Street, New York, N. Y. 10017.

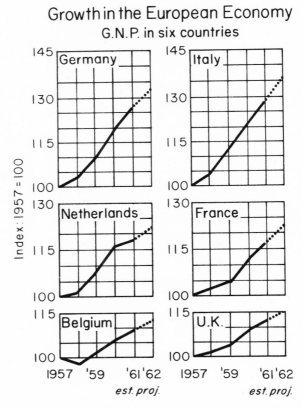

Figure 16. Specimen Set of Curves. (Courtesy of *Fortune* [March, 1962]. Why did the editors of *Fortune* use six different graphs, all on the same scale, instead of six curves on one graph? Why is each curve segmented at the right? Is *G.N.P.* meaningful to the readers of *Fortune?*)

The effectiveness of the graph, like that of the table, depends on the care with which it is made up. The following rules should be observed in its construction:

1. Give every graph a clear title.
2. Clearly identify every unit, every scale, every curve. (This important rule is often overlooked—to the frustration of the reader, who may be forced to grope about in the text for his information.)
3. In identifying the scale, indicate both the variable measured and the unit of measurement:

   Production (in tons)   Viscosity (in centistokes)

4. Use abbreviations only to conserve space; use standard symbols or abbreviations; unusual abbreviations should be defined in the legend or in a footnote.
5. Indicate with crosshatching or color when an area rather than a line is significant.
6. Select the most efficient scale for your purpose. For example, when you wish to show "whether the rate of change of the dependent variable is increasing, constant, or decreasing, a logarithmic vertical scale should be used in conjunction with an arithmetic horizontal scale." *
7. Present no more than three curves on the same graph unless they are similar in shape and clearly separated.
8. If you present two or more curves on the same graph, distinguish them by using lines of different types, different widths, or different colors.
9. When you wish you indicate only trend or shape, omit the grid, using only "ticks." (See Figure 17, page 146.) Since most curves are intended to reveal relationships, not absolute quantities, use only enough grid to guide the eye.
10. Observed points are shown by dots, circles, squares, triangles, and the like; lines are coded by using combinations of dots and dashes of varying lengths. If these points are only approximate (as in physical measurement), the curve is generally "rounded" and need not pass exactly through each point. A smooth curve may actually be more useful, perhaps even more accurate, than the data used in plotting—and the distance by which the curve misses certain points may indicate the degree of error involved in determining those points. Straight-line graphs (lines drawn directly from point to point) should be used to indicate that there is no available data to indicate what occurred, if anything, between points, and thus a rounded curve has not been inferred.
11. Represent extrapolated sections of curves by dotted lines.

* *Ibid,* p. 11.

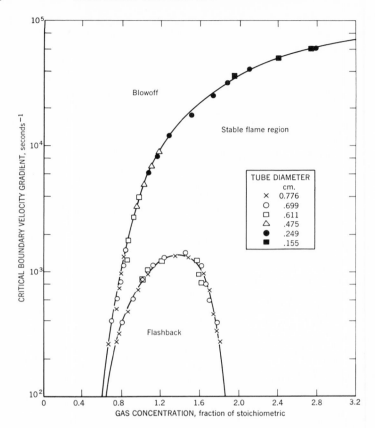

FIGURE 17. SPECIMEN PLOTTED GRAPH. (From U.S. Bureau of Mines *Illustration Guide.*)

SPECIAL CHARTS. The resourceful report writer will often devise special graphic aids for his readers. Bar charts, pie charts, organization charts, and flow sheets are among the devices that will make statistical concepts easy for the reader to grasp. Some idea of their effectiveness can be obtained by glancing through the pages of *Fortune*. This publication, it is true, makes excellent use of color (too expensive for most industrial reports), but most of the figures could be converted to black and white without serious loss in interest or effectiveness.

Pictographs are especially striking in depicting a relationship such as growth. Thus, the Bell Telephone Company printed a series of progressively larger telephones showing the increase in telephone connections. A row of successively taller men will show the increase in a company's personnel, an insurance company's policyholders, or the number of students attending a college.

It should be noted that we may run into constructive falsehoods if we use a figure which may be misinterpreted. Thus, if we present two phones for comparison, the second twice the height of the first, the visual impression is that the value of the second is four times that of the first; the *area,* therefore, produces a false picture of the facts. The right to use figures in this way becomes, of course, an ethical question. In any case, the numerical data should be available somewhere near the graph, so that the careful and intelligent reader need not go astray.

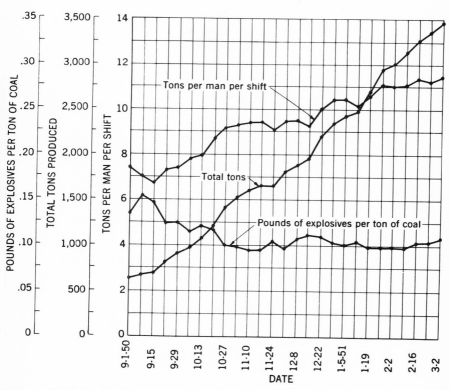

FIGURE 18. SPECIMEN BATTERY OF CURVES. (From U.S. Bureau of Mines *Illustration Guide.*)

NOTE: 1. Clarity of three separated curves on one graph.
2. Broken grid to admit labels.
3. Three different ordinate (vertical) scales.
4. Complete identification on units.
5. Omission of cipher before decimal point.
6. Use of comma in four-digit number.

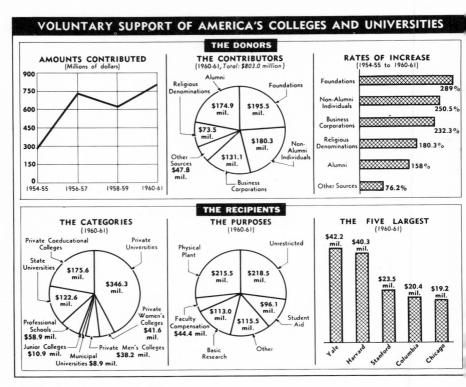

FIGURE 19. VARIED GRAPHIC TREATMENT OF THE SAME GENERAL SUBJECT. (© 1962 by The New York Times Company. Reprinted by permission.)

A popular form of graph, which, nevertheless, is not the most accurate presentation of the facts, is the "pie" diagram. A circle is divided into segments representing the quantities to be studied. This form is widely used for showing proportional expenditures from income, the sources of government taxes, and similar data. (See Figures 19 and 21.)

Most persons are familiar with the shaded map. It is used to show the density of population, the comparative output or consumption of a commodity, the various "zones" in a modern city, or similar information. To give varying degrees of density or concentration, it is possible to use different shades of the same color or to employ several styles of cross-hatching. Geographical distribution of data is also frequently shown by the use of "dot" maps in which each dot represents a given number of units.

The report writer should remember that the tabular treatment of statistics is more accurate than any graphic method he can devise. The graph or chart (which is always based on data in a table) merely sim-

FIGURE 20. SPECIMEN PIE CHART SHOWING SOURCES OF MUNICIPAL INCOME. (Courtesy of HRB-Singer, Inc.)

plifies the facts and makes their interpretation easier. To a reader making a thorough study of all aspects of a report, charts must be less significant than tables. The intelligent writer will determine the needs of his reader and then accordingly select tables, graphs, charts, or a combination of them.

Organization charts. A special type of chart not based upon statistics is the "organization" chart, on which circles or rectangles (properly labeled) are drawn in such a relation to each other as to indicate the plan of organization of a business or corporation staff. It shows where each man stands in the organization, to whom he is responsible, over whom he has control, and what his relations are to others in the same or different branches of the organization.

FIGURE 21. SPECIMEN PIE CHART SHOWING PERCENTAGE DISTRIBUTION OF EXPENDITURES. (Courtesy of HRB-Singer, Inc.)

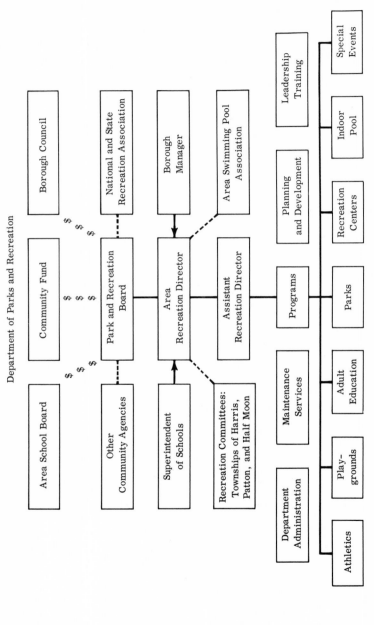

PIEDMONT AREA

Department of Parks and Recreation

FIGURE 22. SPECIMEN ORGANIZATION CHART [Note: This chart was set up on a typewriter, then ruled. It shows lines of authority (solid), lines of cooperation (dotted), and sources of revenue ($$$).]

The organization chart may be so complete that it traces the entire range of authority and responsibility from the president of the company down through various departments to the lowest subforeman. Such a chart is illustrated in Figure 22.

Similar charts may be used in a report to show the organization of a field force conducting some engineering work, research, or other project.

Flow sheets. Of the same general appearance, though used for a different purpose, is a chart showing the flow of product from its beginning as raw material to its completed form. Machines and processes are shown conventionally as rectangles or circles; these are joined by arrowheaded lines indicating the direction in which the product moves.

Size of Mechanical Aids

All mechanical aids should be as simple and compact as possible—but they must not be crowded. Accuracy and completeness must not be endangered for minor savings in space. In both tables and graphics, the titles and legends must be clear and the units and symbols easily identified.

Remember that many original drawings, photographs, and tables will have to be reduced to fit report or book pages. Heavy lines will thin; small numbers or letters will blur.

Allow extra left margin to permit binding.

Placement of Mechanical Aids

Some companies eliminate the placement problem by putting all non-textual elements in an appendix as "exhibits." The method has obvious advantages. If a graph, however, speeds or increases reader comprehension it belongs in the text, as close as possible to the section of the report referring to it. Put another way, *complementary* figures (or tables) belong in the text but *supplementary* ones do not. To a reader interested in site selection, for example, a map showing transportation facilities, market area, labor potential, and so forth is essential, but no reader wants to be slowed down by tables which are nothing more than storehouses for raw data. Such data would interest only the person who wished to check the work or to repeat the experiment.

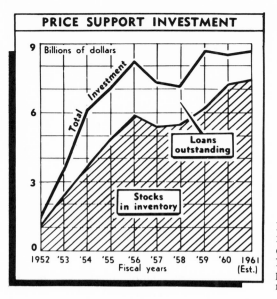

FIGURE 23. CURVES EM-
PLOYING THE AREA CON-
CEPT (© 1962 by The
New York Times Com-
pany. Reprinted by per-
mission.)

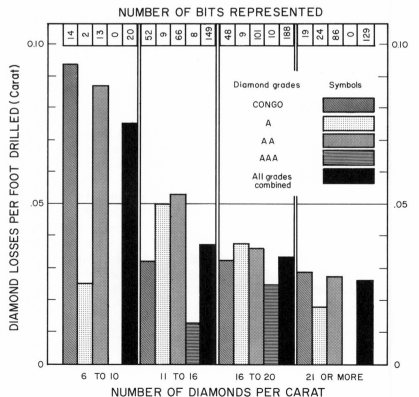

FIGURE 24. SPECIMEN BAR CHART. (From U.S. Bureau of Mines *Illustration
Guide*.)

SPECIMEN REPORTS

The reports and excerpts from reports presented on the following pages are intended for critical study. Although they concern specialized fields, they illustrate general report-writing problems. It is important to keep in mind that they are not necessarily models. Examine each report to see if you can improve it—in presentation, in arrangement, by addition, or by deletion. How consistently does it conform or fail to conform to the rules laid down in the Handbook Section? Is there unnecessary repetition? How attractive is the physical make-up? Can you improve the graphic or tabular presentation? Some of the graphic work was originally in color. Can you see where color would be particularly effective, either in the figures included or in others you would have added had you written the report? Finally, how clearly and how effectively does the report convey its message to the intended reader?

The student should also study the specimen outlines in Chapter 6 for a better understanding of the basic organization of reports.

SPECIMEN NO. 1

This is a typewritten report by a better-than-average under-graduate enrolled in the Petroleum and Natural Gas cur-riculum. It is complete except for the binder, but the follow-ing changes have been made in the interest of economy:

1. It is printed on both sides of the paper.

2. Black and white has been substituted for color.

THE FEASIBILITY OF

USING RADIOISOTOPES TO MEASURE

CATALYST CIRCULATION RATES IN THE CATALYTIC CRACKING UNIT

OF THE SUNGEI GERONG REFINERIES

Submitted to

Mr. E. C. Salmon
Superintendent
Sungei Gerong Refineries

By

Raden B. Sumantri
Process-Engineer

20 December 1958

TABLE OF CONTENTS

Summary 1
Introduction 2
Conclusions 2
Recommendations 2
The Airlift Thermofor Catalytic Cracking Process 3
　Applications 3
　Description of Process 3
　Variables Controlling the Process 3
　Effect of Catalyst-to-Oil Ratio on the Yield Structure 4
The Correlation Method of Measuring Catalyst Circulation Rates . . 4
The Radioisotope Tracer Method of Measuring Catalyst Circulation
　Rates 5
　Method of Measurement 5
　Tracer Bead Requirements 5
　Radioisotope Requirements 5
　Safety Considerations 6
　　Shipping and Storage of Radioactive Material 6
　　　Permit for import 6
　　　Crating for shipping 6
　　　Storage 7
　　Mixing of Tracers and Catalyst Mass 7
　　Inhalation of Catalyst Fines Through Stack Losses 7
　　Disposal 7
　Instrumentation 8
　Personnel Requirements 8
　Personnel Training 9
　　Training in Indonesia 9
　　Training in the United States 9
　　Comparison 10
　Cost Estimate 10
　　Total Fixed Charges 10
　　Process-Charges 10
Comparison Between the Correlation Method and the Tracer Method . 11
Bibliography 12
Interview 12

APPENDIX

Table
　1　The Change of Yield Structure with Variation of the Catalyst
　　　to-Oil Ratio 13
　2　Half-Lifes and Energy Values of Selected Isotopes 13
　3　Tolerance Levels of Radioisotopes for Concentrations in Air　14
　4　Price of Complete Package of Instruments for the
　　　Radioisotope Tracer Method 14
　5　Estimates of Total Fixed Charges for the Radioisotope
　　　Tracer Method 15
　6　Estimate of Process Costs for the Radioisotope Tracer
　　　Method 15

157

APPENDIX
(continued)

Figure
1   The Airlift Thermofor Catalytic Cracking Unit 16
2   The Radioisotope Tracer Method of Measuring Catalyst
     Circulation Rates 17
3   A Recording of the Passage of a Radioactive Tracer 18

SUMMARY

There is a general dissatisfaction with the reliability of the correlation method to measure catalyst circulation rates. This study on the merits of the radioisotope tracer method reveals that this new method is simpler, faster, and more accurate than the correlation method.

There is little ground for excessive fear of radiation hazards, since at any phase of the operation the radiation level never exceeds 12 per cent of the permissible tolerance.

Since no extra shielding material is required, the cost is on the level of ordinary laboratory requirements.

INTRODUCTION

Catalyst circulation rates in the Airlift Thermofor Catalytic Cracking Unit of the Sungei Gerong Refineries are now being determined by correlation with the lift-air rate. This method is found to be unreliable, too involved technically, and useful only during short test periods.

In the last five years much research has been done to develop a radioisotope tracer method to solve the problem of determining the catalyst circulation rate. The purpose of this report is to study the feasibility of the use of the tracer method for the Airlift TCC Unit of the Sungei Gerong Refineries.

This report, based on literature study only, is not intended to give detailed analytical results.

CONCLUSIONS

1. The radioisotope tracer method is a simple, fast, and reliable method of determining catalyst circulation rate, and is feasible for use on the Airlift Thermofor Catalytic Cracking Unit of the Sungei Gerong Refineries.

2. The radiation level at any phase of the operation can be contained far below accepted tolerance doses, the highest level being only 12 per cent of the tolerance dose.

3. The cost of installation and application of the tracer method ($8400) is a small fraction of any shut-down costs resulting from unreliable operating conditions.

RECOMMENDATIONS

1. The Company should adopt the radioisotope tracer method to obtain reliable measurements of the catalyst circulation rates of the Airlift Thermofor Catalytic Cracking Unit.

2. The Company should send a junior process-engineer to the United States for a short training course in radioisotope tracer techniques.

3. The Company should start on education of the process-control personnel for work with radioactive material.

4. The Company should revise its safety program to include radiation safety practices.

THE AIRLIFT THERMOFOR
CATALYTIC CRACKING PROCESS

Application

The Airlift Thermofor Catalytic Cracking Process as developed by So-
cony Vacuum Oil Company is mainly used with the following objectives:[1]
   a. To produce high-quality gasoline.
   b. To increase the yield of distillate fuel fractions.
   c. To reduce the yield of residual fuels.

Description of Process

A simplified schematic diagram of the Airlift TCC unit is presented in
Figure 1. The feed is charged to the reactor as a mixture of liquid and
vapor. Regenerated catalyst flows by gravity down the seal leg from the
surge-separator into the reactor. In the reactor the catalyst flows
through the reaction-bed, is then purged with steam, and flows out of the
reactor. Purged spent catalyst gravitates into the thermofor kiln, is regenerated by combustion with air, and is cooled by a water spray. The
regenerated catalyst flows from the cooler into the airlift-pot, is picked
up by low-pressure air, and is lifted to the surge-separator at the top of
the unit.[2]

Variables Controlling the Process

In commercial operation the variables most commonly controlled to obtain the desired-yield structure are the following:[3]
   a. The average reactor temperature, which is a function of oil-and-
      catalyst inlet temperatures, and the catalyst-to-oil ratio.
   b. The space velocity in the reactor, which is a function of the reac-
      tion-bed depth.
   c. The catalyst-to-oil ratio, being a function of the catalyst circulation
      rate.

---

1. "Process-Handbook," Petroleum Refiner, Vol. 35, No. 9, p. 228,
   September 1956.
2. Ibid.
3. Hamilton, W. W., Eastwood, S. C., et al, "Wide Range of Feed Stocks
   Possible with Airlift TCC." Petroleum Refiner, Vol. 31, No. 8, p. 72,
   August 1952.

Effect of Catalyst-to-Oil Ratio on the Yield Structure

The extent of the change of yield structure with variation of the catalyst-to-oil ratio is reported by T. P. Simpson, S. C. Eastwood, et al.[4] High-lights of their findings are presented in Table 1. Keeping other variables constant, the catalyst-to-oil ratio was varied from 1.09 to 6.0. Motor-gasoline yield thereby varied from 40.9 to 51.4 per cent, and the gas-oil yield varied from 56.5 to 19.2 per cent.

THE CORRELATION METHOD OF MEASURING
CATALYST CIRCULATION RATES

This method uses the rate of lift-air to estimate the catalyst circulation rate employing Rausch correlation.

Rausch used the ratio between catalyst particle diameter and the pipe diameter to relate it to a hypothetical quantity Q_A, which is the catalyst flow-rate in air under standard conditions. He obtained a straight-line relationship on a log-log plot between

$$\frac{D_o}{D_p} \quad \text{and} \quad \frac{Q_A \sqrt{\tan \beta_A}}{C \, C_o \sqrt{g} \; \rho_B \, D_p^{2.5}} \qquad 5/$$

where: Q_A = solids' flow-rate in standard air, lb/sec.
  β_A = angle of repose of solids in standard air.
  g = acceleration of gravity, 32.2 ft/sec^2
  C = bulk density of wall-effect correction.
  C_o = correction factor for cone angle at bottom of surge-separator
  ρ_B = normal-bulk density of solids, lb/cu ft.
  D_o = orifice or pipe diameter, ft.
  D_p = particle diameter, ft.

The flow-rate of the catalyst in the actual medium of oil and vapor under actual conditions is then calculated, using the relationship:

$$Q_M = Q_A \sqrt{\frac{\tan \beta_A \, (1- \rho_M/ \rho_P)}{\tan \beta_M}} \qquad 5/$$

where: Q_M = solids flow rate in the surrounding medium, lb/sec.
  ρ_M = density of surrounding fluid medium, lb/cu ft.
  ρ_P = true density of particle, lb/cu ft.
This method is fairly reliable for use during testing periods of short duration. It has been proved that this method is almost useless in actual process because of the change in particle diameter.

---

4. "Liquid Charge Technique in TCC Processing," Petroleum Refiner, Vol. 24, No. 11, p. 115, 1945.
5. Zenz, Frederick A., Petroleum Refiner, Vol. 36, p. 163, 1957.

THE RADIOISOTOPE TRACER METHOD
OF MEASURING CATALYST CIRCULATION RATES

Method of Measurement

In the radioisotope tracer method a small number of radioactive catalyst
beads is added to the catalyst mass. The radioactive tracer beads will
flow at the same rate as the ordinary catalyst mass. The circulation
rate of the catalyst mass is then determined by timing the passage of the
individual tracer beads from one detector to another one located further
down the seal leg of the cracking unit (see Fig. 2.)[6]

Figure 3 shows the recording of the passage of a tracer bead. The elapsed
time of passage, which is the time-span between the peaks, can be cali-
brated directly as catalyst circulation rate since the catalyst density, the
cross section of the pipe, and the distance between the points of detection
are known. It was found that one or two radioactive beads mixed into
10 million ordinary catalyst beads are sufficient to give circulation-rate
readings with satisfactory frequency.[7]

Tracer Bead Requirements

The tracer beads should match the used ordinary beads closely qua weight,
size, and form.[8] Only then can it be ensured that the tracer beads will
have the same circulation rate as the ordinary catalyst beads. The logical way to obtain identical beads is to impregnate used ordinary beads
with the radioactive substance.

Radioisotope Requirements

The radioisotope to be used should fullfill the following requirements:[9]
   a. It should have a penetrating gamma ray strong enough for satisfac-
      tory detection through the walls of the seal leg.
   b. It should have a half-life comparable to the average lifetime of the
      catalyst mass. If the half-life is too short, more frequent replen-
      ishment of the tracer beads is necessary. This entails higher pro-
      cess-cost. If the half-life is much too long, there will be danger
      created by accumulation of radioactivity in the discarded catalyst
      mass.

6. Weber, G., "How Isotopes Work for Refiners," Oil and Gas Journal,
   Vol. 55, p. 93, September 23, 1957.
7. Ibid., p. 94.
8. Singer, E., et al., "Catalyst Mixing Patterns in Commercial Catalytic
   Cracking Units," Industrial and Engineering Chemistry, Vol. 49, p. 11,
   1957.
9. Ibid.

6

    c. The isotope should be chemically stable and it should adhere to the tracer bead under the high oxidizing temperature of 1100° F in the regenerator, and the high reducing temperature of 900° F in the reactor.

A study of above requirements and the commercially available radio-isotopes narrowed down the choice to the isotopes tabulated in Table 2. Since the average life of the catalyst mass is about two months, a good choice will be Zr-95, which has a half-life of 65 days. It is reported that Salt Lake Refining Company, California, has used Zr-95 with satisfactory results on their Houdry-flow catalytic cracking unit. [10]

Safety Considerations

Radioisotopes are more and more being used by industry for an ever wider variety of purposes, ranging from small-vessel reaction studies to waterflooding studies on extensive petroleum deposits. However, there are still many more industries that could employ radiotracer techniques to good advantage, but are reluctant to do so mainly for two reasons:

    a. Excessive caution over the radiation hazards involved.
    b. An exaggerated estimate of cost and difficulty of providing the necessary working facilities, equipment, and material.

Several factors pertaining to the case under study will be discussed here.

Shipping and Storage of Radioactive Material

    Permit for import: Since the radioactive material has to be imported from the United States of America, an import permit from the Indonesian Government has to be secured. The Indonesian Government at present is also buying radioactive material from the United States for use in radiological research. [11] A request for an import permit by the Company probably will find little objection from safety considerations.

    Crating for shipping: The crating of radioactive material has to conform to international shipping regulations. The maximum surface radiation level permitted is 200 milliroentgen per hour. A typical shipment of 10 lb of catalyst material will contain 1 millicurie of 1 mev gamma emitter. If this material is packed in a cubical wooden box 2 ft on a side without any shielding, the box will have a surface radiation level of only

10. Hull, D. E., and R. R. Bowles, "Measuring Catalyst Flow Rate in Catalytic Crackers," Oil and Gas Journal, Vol. 51, p. 299, 1953.
11. Ahimsa, D. D., (interview,) Nuclear Engineering, Walker Laboratory, Pennsylvania State University.

6 milliroentgen per hour, which is about 3 per cent of the maximum permissible level. [12]

Storage: The material should be left inside the box until use. It will be sufficient to place the box in a separate room where no people are working nearby. The accepted weekly tolerance dose is 300 milliroentgen. Actually even a person working next to the crate 40 hours per week will receive only 40 x 6 = 240 milliroentgen per week. [13]

Mixing of Tracers and Catalyst Mass

Mixing of the tracer beads should be done by a radiochemist or someone who has adequate knowledge of handling radioactive material. The tracer beads will have a radiation level in the order of 200 milliroentgen per hour. The time required for mixing is less than 10 minutes; therefore, the exposure will amount to 10/60 x 200 mr/hr = 34 milliroentgen, roughly 12 per cent of the maximum permissible dose.

Once the tracer beads are mixed into the catalyst mass (in the ratio of 2 beads per 10 million ordinary ones) the dilution is so enormous that the radiation level will drop to 0.01 milliroentgen per hour. This level is lower by a factor of 100 than the radiation level of a typical luminous-dial watch. The catalyst mass therefore can be handled as if there were no radioactive material present. [14]

Inhalation of Catalyst Fines Through Stack Losses

Stack loss of catalyst fines ordinarily amounts to 1 per cent per day. With this rate, the specific activity of the stack fines will be about 2×10^{-6} gamma microcurie per gram. Permissible tolerances for concentration of radioactive material in air are given in Table 3. The permissible tolerance for Zr-95 is 8×10^{-6} microcurie/cubic centimeter. Using this value, it is calculated that one would literally have to inhale 17 tons of stack fines to reach the tolerance level. This certainly discounts any appreciable hazard from inhalation of stack fines. [15]

Disposal

It has already been proved that the radiation level of the catalyst mass will be about one hundredth of that of a luminous-dial watch. Therefore no problem will be encountered in the disposal of spent catalyst.

---

12. Singer, E., et al., Industrial and Engineering Chemistry, Vol. 49, p. 13, 1957.
13. Guinn, V. P., Nucleonics, Vol. 14, No. 5, p. 70, May 1956.
14. Ibid., p. 71.
15. Ibid., p. 71.

Instrumentation

The choice of instruments in a radioactive-tracer application is usually dictated by the following factors:[16]

    a. Isotope used
    b. Desired accuracy
    c. Level of radioactivity handled
    d. Amount of work done

Using above-mentioned criteria, it was found that the instruments needed for the purpose under study are:[17]

    a. Two sets of Geiger counters
    b. One preamplifier
    c. One ratemeter
    d. One flowrate computer
    e. One recorder

Tracerlab, Inc. offers a package set of the instruments for the price of $4500. A survey of other suppliers, as shown on Table 4, confirms the price asked by Tracerlab to be reasonable.

Additional tools needed are:[18]

    a. Handling tools
    b. Storage containers
    c. Survey Geiger counter
    d. Filmbadges
    e. Dosimeter

These tools will cost $300.

Personnel Requirements

Mixing the radioactive tracer beads into the catalyst mass should be done by someone who has adequate knowledge of handling radioactive material. Since the mixing can be done once a month, there is no justification to employ a special radiochemist. A junior process-engineer, if given a short course training him in radiochemical practices, will be able to do the mixing, supervise the process, and make periodical inspection on

---

16. Low, Frank H., Oil and Gas Journal, Vol. 55, p. 122, February 4, 1957.
17. Weber, G., Oil and Gas Journal, Vol. 55, p. 98, September 23, 1957.
18. Ibid., p. 99.

radiation levels in the immediate surroundings of the catalytic cracking unit.

No additional work is required from the process-control crew other than making observations on the chart-recorder of the detection-system; therefore no extra personnel need be hired.

Personnel Training

Training of the supervising engineer should include:[19]

a. Actual experience with radioactive material of the type and with the quantities to be used.
b. Standard methods of measuring radioactivity, monitoring, and operation of instruments.
c. Mathematics and calculations basic to the use and measurement of radioactivity.
d. Radiological-health-safety principles and practice.
e. Instruction in biological effects of radiation.

Training can be acquired either in Indonesia or in the United States.

Training in Indonesia

The Radiological Research Center of Indonesia at Djakarta offers a short training course of six months in radiochemical practices. Although the course is intended for agricultural research, the offered experimental practices can be easily adapted to industrial purposes. The Center charges a tuition of 1800 rupiahs, which is equivalent to $60.[20]

Training in the United States[21]

Training facilities in the United States are plentiful.

a. The Oak Ridge Institute for Nuclear Studies offers a four-week course in radioisotope techniques; this course is given several times a year.
b. Many universities have regular academic courses in radiochemistry and radiological and health physics.
c. Commercial laboratories, like the Tracerlab, Inc., have arranged

---

19. Gallaghar, R. G., Petroleum Processing, Vol. 12, p. 69, March 1957.
20. Ahimsa, D. D. (interview), Nuclear Engineering, Walker Laboratory, Pennsylvania State University.
21. Low, Frank H., Oil and Gas Journal, Vol. 55, p. 123, February 4, 1957.

one- or two-week courses specially adapted to the need and convenience of the participants.

The cost of training in the United States is about $300.

Comparison

Training in Indonesia is the least adapted to industrial use. Training in the United States, however, should include cost of travel, which is about $3000.

In deciding on the choice of training facility, it should be borne in mind that if the instruments are to be bought from Tracerlab, Inc., training of the supervising engineer at that laboratory will automatically include direct use of the projected instruments. This arrangement will reduce the trial period of the instruments on the process.

Cost Estimate

Total Fixed Charges

Estimates on total fixed charges are presented on Table 5. With training in Indonesia the total fixed charges are $5226; if training is done in the United States the total fixed charges will be $8400.

Process Charges

Process charges per year will amount to $1020, as presented on Table 6.

COMPARISON BETWEEN THE CORRELATION METHOD
AND THE TRACER METHOD

There is no question that the tracer method is far more reliable than the correlation method. To document this statement is the case of the Houdry Cracking Unit of Standard Oil of California.[22] This unit formerly used the conventional correlation method. The normal catalyst rate was 300 tons per day, with a catalyst loss of 2 1/2 tons per day.

Early in 1953 an emergency developed at the Houdry unit: the operating efficiency and the capacity of the unit declined sharply, while the catalyst loss increased to 10 tons per day. Catalyst price was $300 per ton; the cost of catalyst replacement therefore increased from $750 to $3000 per day. A shut-down was scheduled for internal inspection of vessels and lines. Then, an offer from California Research Corporation to use the radioactive tracer method was accepted. The inspection, which was performed without shut-down, proved within 3 days that the actual catalyst circulation rate was 350 tons per day instead of the normal 300 tons per day.

Evidently the abnormally high catalyst circulation rate prevented proper regeneration of the catalyst, resulting in decrease of conversion rates and gasoline yields. When the rate was brought back to its initial value of 300 tons per day, the process immediately returned to normal condition. A shutdown would have cost the company $100,000.

It has been proved that the radiation hazards can be contained within the permissible values during every phase of the operation. However, the main problem of using the radioactive tracer method will still be to educate the personnel and to increase their knowledge of routine radiation work and safety practices.

22. Hull, D. E., and R. R. Bowles, Oil and Gas Journal, Vol. 51, p. 298, 1953.

12

BIBLIOGRAPHY

1. Brunton, D. C., "Cobalt-60 Readied for Industry," Canadian Chemistry and Process Industries, Vol. 41, p. 50, April 1957.

2. Catch, J. R., "Radioisotopes as Tracers," Canadian Chemistry and Process Industries, Vol. 41, p. 92, February 1957.

3. Friedlander, Gerhart, and Joseph W. Kennedy, Nuclear and Radiochemistry, New York: John Wiley & Sons, Inc., 1956.

4. Gallaghar, R. G., "Going into Radioactivity?" Petroleum Processing, Vol. 12, pp. 68-74, March 1957.

5. Guinn, V. P., "Tracing Catalysts in Refinery Crackers," Nucleonics, Vol. 14, pp. 68-72, May 1956.

6. Hamilton, W. W., S. C. Eastwood, et al., "Wide Range of Feed Stocks Possible with Airlift TCC," Petroleum Refiner, Vol. 31, p. 72, August 1952.

7. Hull, D. E., and R. R. Bowles, "Measuring Catalyst Flow Rate in Catalytic Crackers," Oil and Gas Journal, Vol. 51, pp. 295-299, 1953.

8. King, W. A., "Isotopes in the Refinery," Chemical and Engineering News, Vol. 35, pp. 76-77, April 15, 1957.

9. Kirk, R. E., and D. F. Othmer, Encyclopedia of Chemical Technology, New York: The Interscience Encyclopedia, Inc., 1947-1956.

10. Low, Frank H., "Are You Overlooking Nuclear Radiation?" Oil and Gas Journal, Vol. 55, pp. 121-124, February 4, 1957.

11. Singer, E., et al., "Catalyst Mixing Patterns in Commercial Catalytic Cracking Units," Industrial and Engineering Chemistry, Vol. 49, pp. 11-19, 1957.

12. Weber, G., "How Isotopes Work for Refiners," Oil and Gas Journal, Vol. 55, pp. 91-100, September 25, 1957.

13. Zenz, Frederick A., "How to Predict Gravity Flow," Petroleum Refiner, Vol. 36, pp. 162-170, October 1957.

INTERVIEW

1. Ahimsa, D. D., Nuclear Engineering, Walker Laboratory, Pennsylvania State University. November 1958.

170

Table 1
The Change of Yield Structure with
Variation of the Catalyst-to-Oil Ratio

Stock	Wide-cut	East Texas	Flash	Distillate
Catalyst-to-oil ratio, volume	1.09	2.9	4.6	6.0
Yields:				
Motor-gasoline (10 lb Reid-pressure; 90 per cent point at 365° F,) per cent volume.	40.9	45.2	51.4	43.9
Excess C-4 cut above motor-gasoline, per cent volume.	3.2	6.0	11.3	14.5
Catalytic gas-oil, per cent volume.	56.5	47.7	33.1	19.2

From: Simpson, T. P., et al, Petroleum Refiner, Vol. 24, No. 11,
p. 115, 1945.

Table 2
Half-Lifes and Energy Values
of Selected Isotopes

Isotope	Half-Life	Gamma-Rays in Mev		Beta-Ray in Mev
Zr-95	65 days	0.754	0.722	0.45
Sc-46	85 days	0.885	1.119	0.357
Ce-144	282 days	0.034	0.134	0.304

From: Friedlander, Gerhart, and Joseph W. Kennedy, Nuclear and
Radiochemistry, New York: John Wiley & Sons, Inc., 1956.

Table 3
Tolerance Levels of Radioisotopes
for Concentrations in Air

Isotope	Tolerance Level in Air in $\mu c/cm^3$
Ce-144	7×10^{-9}
Cr-51	8×10^{-6}
Sc-46	7×10^{-8}
Zr-95	8×10^{-6}

From: Guinn, V. P., Nucleonics, Vol. 14, p. 70, May 1956.

Table 4
Price of Complete Package of Instruments
for the Radioisotope Tracer Method

Manufacturer	Price Asked
Tracerlab, Inc.	$4500
Radiation Counter Laboratories, Inc.	$4970
British Nuclear, Inc.	$4650

Table 5
Estimates of Total Fixed Charges
for the Radioisotope Tracer Method

Item	(1)	(2)
Instrumentation	$4500	$4500
Installation	300	300
Additional tools	300	300
Training in Indonesia	60	---
Travel expenses for training in Indonesia	66	---
Training in the United States	---	300
Travel expenses for training in the United States	---	3000
Total fixed charges	$5226	$8400

Column (1): with training in Indonesia.
Column (2): with training in the United States.

Table 6
Estimate of Process Costs
for the Radioisotope Tracer Method

Item	Amount
Radioactive tracer beads 6 mc of Zr-95 @ $150	$ 900
Handling costs	$ 120
Total process costs per year	$1020

Figure 1
The Airlift Thermofor Catalytic Cracking Unit

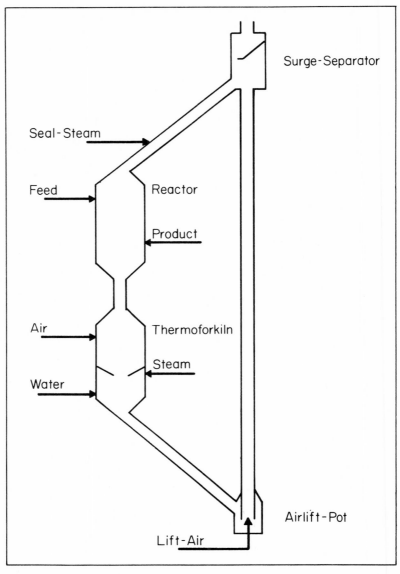

Surge-Separator

Seal-Steam

Feed

Reactor

Product

Air

Thermoforkiln

Steam

Water

Airlift-Pot

Lift-Air

Adapted from: "Process Handbook," Hydrocarbon Processing and
Petroleum Refiner, Vol. 35, No. 9, p. 229, September 1956. c
1956 by Gulf Publishing Company, Houston, Texas.

Figure 2
The Radioisotope Tracer Method of Measuring
Catalyst Circulation Rates

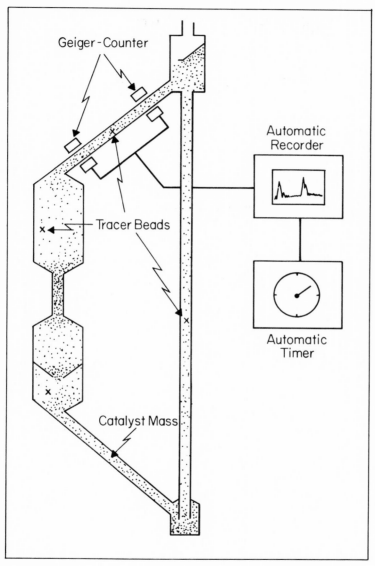

Adapted from E. Singer, et al, Industrial and Engineering
Chemistry, Vol. 49, No. 1, p. 12, January 1957.

Figure 3
A Recording of the Passage of a Radioactive Tracer

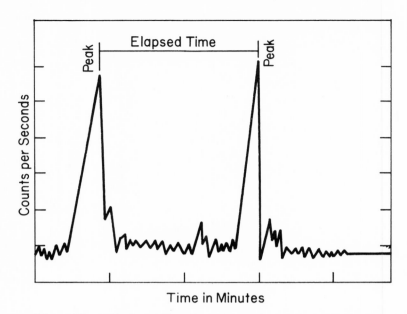

Adapted from D. E. Hull and R. R. Bowles, Oil and Gas Journal,
Vol. 51, p. 298, 1953.

SPECIMEN NO. 2

WILSON LOCK
TENNESSEE VALLEY AUTHORITY
CONSTRUCTION PROGRESS

Only the cover, full-page plates, and fold-out drawings have been omitted.

WILSON PROJECT

PERIOD __January 25, 1960__ TO __February 24, 1960__ INCLUSIVE

WEATHER	TEMP: °F	DATE	PRECIPITATION:											
	MAX 73	2/11	INCHES 1.09 .07 .05 .82 .02 .13 .60 .30 .30 .05 .88 .50 .3											
	MIN 15	2/15	DATES 1/26 27 28 29 30 2/3 4 5 14 16 18 21 2											

RIVER STAGE & DISCHARGE			
MAX DISCHARGE 122,700 CFS DATE 2/22/60	MAX EL UPSTREAM 506.18 DATE 1/25/60
MIN DISCHARGE 31,400 CFS DATE 2/3/60	MAX EL DOWNSTREAM 419.58 DATE 2/21/60
MEAN DISCHARGE 77,050 CFS	MIN EL UPSTREAM 504.94 DATE 2/22/60
	MIN EL DOWNSTREAM 413.26 DATE 2/3/60

EMPLOYEES THIS PERIOD	MEN HIRED 74	MEN RELEASED 10	MEN ON PAYROLL 582

PAYROLL TOTALS	THIS PERIOD $313,683	TO DATE $14,038,089

ACCIDENTS (LOST TIME ONLY)		PERIOD	TO DATE	REMARKS: * Reeder Allen, Ironworker, strained back 12/7/59, when constructing timber ramp for unloading shovel from railroad car. Not previously charged. ** Adjusted.
	NUMBER	0	40*	
	TIME LOST THIS PERIOD	96	HRS	
	TIME LOST TO DATE	236,371**	HRS	

ITEM	UNIT	TOTAL THIS PERIOD	TOTAL TO DATE	TOTAL ESTIMATED	PERC(COMPL
Canal					
Excavation, rock – stage 3	CY	16,862	20,390	70,000	29
Excavation, rock – under cofferdam F	CY	0	0	20,000	(
Auxiliary Lock					
Concrete – old culverts	CY	1,464	1,564	1,600	98
Concrete – mass and new culverts	CY	0	0	8,600	(
Excavation, rock	CY	0	0	18,000	(
Remove Concrete	CY	0	0	5,000	(
Units 19-21					
Intake – remove concrete	CY	0	5,040	14,000	3(
Intake – set penstock	T	107	153	930	1(
Intake – place concrete	CY	791	4,407	12,000	3(
Powerhouse – remove apron	CY	0	6,795	6,795	100
Powerhouse – excavate rock	CY	6,875	39,235	42,000	9:
Powerhouse – place concrete	CY	0	223	50,000	

(left margin vertical label: QUANTITIES)

SPECIAL REMARKS: Wilson Dam released water through the spillways during period 8:30 a.m., February 19 through 9:20 a.m., February 24. Maximum spillage for the period was 50,500 cfs.

Rainfall: 5.12" total.

SUMMARY OF PROGRESS

Main and Auxiliary Locks

For the main lock, completion of miscellaneous items continued and installation of the 101-pair telephone cable was advanced to 92 per cent completion.

Concreting of the filling culverts, discharge outlets, and the emptying valve-shafts in the lower chamber of the auxiliary lock advanced with 1,464 cubic yards placed this month.

The emptying valves were removed and dismantling of the lower gate was begun. At the end of the period, operating machinery had been disconnected from the gates, the quoin contact-blocks for the south leaf removed, and removal of rivets along arch rib No. 4 was begun.

Line-drilling and broaching along the north and south walls and around upstream radius for rock excavation in the lower chamber were begun February 4.

Rock excavation in stage 3 area advanced with 16,862 cubic yards excavated for a total to date of 20,390 cubic yards.

Wilson Units 19-21

Concrete placed in blocks 64, 65, and 67 totaled 791 cubic yards, bringing the total to date to 4,407 cubic yards.

Installation of unit-19 trashrack guides was begun February 1. Shop fabrication of unit-20 trashrack guides, draft-tube pier nosings for unit 19, and draft-tube gate guides for units 19-21 made good progress this month.

In the station sump and powerhouse area, rock excavation was advanced with 146 blasts made during the period. Rock excavated was 6,875 cubic yards.

Drilling for lines, blast-holes, and broaching totaled 21,727 feet for a total to date of 237,756 feet.

Chicago Bridge & Iron Company continued erection of unit-19 penstock with twelve ring sections and the upper expansion-joint set in place. Assembly of all remaining sections for unit 19 on the yard is now practically complete; some bent plates for unit 20 have been received.

MONTHLY PROGRESS REPORT

Wilson Lock

Installation of the 101-pair telephone cable from the powerhouse was brought to approximately 92 per cent completion this month. Painting of the basement floors in the operation building was completed.

Placement of permanent distance-markers for the upstream and downstream approaches to the locks was completed except for two markers on Patton Island which must await final grading.

Auxiliary Lock

Concrete was placed this period for six pours in the south-filling culvert, eight pours in the north-filling culvert, one in the discharge outlet of the south culvert, and one each in the north and south emptying valve-shafts. Total concrete placed was 1,464 cubic yards, bringing the total to date to 1,564 cubic yards.

The emptying valves in the north and south culverts were disassembled and removed early in the month.

Preparations for dismantling the miter gate in the lower chamber were begun February 8. At the end of the month, concrete for the jacking pads for the north leaf had been placed; machinery connections, walkways, timber fenders and miscellaneous structural items had been removed. Removal of the quoin contact-blocks for the south leaf was completed and work was begun on the miter contact-blocks.

Line-drilling and broaching along the north and south walls and along radius at upstream end of the lower chamber were begun February 4, when the two quarry-bars and one air-trac drill were moved in. Good progress on the drilling was made during the remainer of the month.

In stage-3 area, rock excavation was advanced with 16,862 cubic yards removed to bring the total excavated to date to 20,390 cubic yards. Excavation equipment consisted of one 2½ cubic yard Northwest shovel, supplemented by a 2 cubic yard Bucyrus-Erie shovel during breakdowns, and from four to seven Euclid rear dump trucks. A sudden increase in leakage under cofferdam F on February 18 was checked by application of cinders on February 20 and 21.

Line and blasthole drilling and broaching in the lower chamber and stage-3 area totaled 39,635 feet for the month, bringing the total to date to 44,891 feet.

Installation of the 2300-volt power feeders A and B from the main to the auxiliary lock was completed February 18.

Wilson Units 19-21

Concrete was placed this month for twenty-one pours in block 67, six in block 65, and nine in block 64, totaling 791 cubic yards. Total concrete placed to date is 4,407 cubic yards.

The permanent pump was installed in the north sump of the inspection gallery. Alterations to CO_2, water and air piping in area of conduit tunnel through the north powerhouse wall was completed February 3.

Installation of unit-19 trashrack guides on upstream face of block 67 was begun on February 1 and is continuing.

Shop fabrication of unit 20-trashrack guides advanced to 90 per cent completion, the draft-tube pier nosings for unit 19 were completed, and the draft-tube gate guides for units 19-21 brought to 20 per cent completion.

Seismograph recordings of all blasts for rock excavation continued until the instrument failed on February 18. Representatives of the Bureau of Mines of the U.S. Department of the Interior completed their experiments and recordings of blasts and left the project February 3.

Blasting progressed throughout the period with 15 blasts set off in the station sump and 131 in rock in the powerhouse area.

Drilling continued for rock excavation at the station sump and in the powerhouse area, with some broaching done as required. Total drilling and broaching for the month was 21,727 feet for a total to date of 237,756 feet.

Excavation in the station sump was advanced to elevation 354± and to a maximum depth of elevation 363± in the unit-19 area. Rock excavated this month was 6,875 cubic yards, bringing the total excavated to date to 39,235 cubic yards.

Chicago Bridge & Iron Company advanced the installation of unit-19 penstock at the powerhouse. Twelve ring sections were set in place this month, along with the upper expansion-joint; welding and X-raying of seams continued. Welding of the bell-mouth section in the lower yard was completed. Some material for unit-20 penstock arrived and was unloaded at the assembly yard.

SPECIMEN NO. 3

Though the following periodic report is entirely concerned with chemical engineering, it illustrates the variety of routine writing problems encountered by any engineer. Consider the report from the viewpoint of its intended readers—the plant manager, the director of research, the sales manager, the chief engineer, and so on. Could it have been better presented to save them more time in reading without jeopardizing its value as a record? Would an initial summary be helpful, and, if so, possible? Could the writing be more concise? (The original was twenty-five pages long.) Are sufficient details included to give the readers a satisfactory understanding of the work done? Can you think of any graphical devices that would have conserved time or space? Is the physical make-up entirely satisfactory?

INTEROFFICE CORRESPONDENCE *
Trona, California
March 9, 1965

To: Copy to:
    Manager's Office   Executive Committee
Attention: Messrs. Mumford
    Mr. A. A. Hoffman   Eason
Subject: Bridgeford
    Monthly Report
    Research and Development
    February 1965

I. PLANT PROBLEMS SECTIONS
(Problems directly connected with present
operations, minor changes, etc.)

1. Concentration Process

    (a) Study of Heater Corrosion

        [Signature]
        T. G. Bernhardi

        During the month, the specific rate of condensation (steam con-
sumed per operating day per degree working-temperature drop)
showed some improvement over the values of recent months and
approached the peak values obtained last fall.

    (b) Salting of Heater Tubes

        There have been no new developments in connection with this
problem during February.

    (c) Liquor Losses from the Heater-Washout Routine

        No time for further sampling of the evaporator heaters was avail-
able during the month because of work on the salt-trap classifier.

    (d) Salt-Trap Filter Behavior and Losses

        There are no new developments in connection with this problem.

    (e) Clarification and Dilution of Concentrated Liquor

        The vapors from the third-effect pan of the No. 3 evaporator unit
were noted to undergo a large pressure-drop between the entrance
and exit of the entrainment separator. A measurement showed this
loss to be equivalent to about one inch of mercury when the absolute
pressure on the third-effect pan is three inches of mercury. A further
study is being made of this.

2. Potash Plant

        Considerable work was done this month in the preparation of a
report on plant KCl production-efficiency for the year 1964.

        The study of potash dryer operation is discussed in connection
with the development of coarse granular potash in a subsequent
section of this report. (See item II-7.)

3. Borax Plant

    (a) Crude Borax Process

        A memorandum covering the proposed mother liquor No. 3 leach
system was distributed during the month to interested parties. (See
last Monthly Research & Development Report.) The Engineering
Department has issued shop orders (Nos. 2066-7-8) to have tempo-

---

* Courtesy of the American Potash & Chemical Corporation.

rary pipe and equipment changes made so that the system can be given a plant trial.

4. Boric Acid Plant

   (a) Plant Operation

      The production of coarse granular boric acid is discussed in a subsequent section of this report. (See item II-3-b.)

   (b) Caking of Boric Acid

      [Signature]

      Hunter Nicholson

      A quantity of air-classified boric acid which had stood in a small bin for several months under conditions of moderate humidity for caking tests (see report for August 1964, et seq.) was returned to the main storage pile during the month. This material was slightly caked, but the lumps were soft enough to be broken easily between the fingers. This is additional confirmation for the theory that boric acid may be kept from caking if the atmospheric humidity is kept sufficiently high to prevent surface dehydration to metaboric acid.

5. Pyrobor Plant

      No problems connected with the Pyrobor plant required. . . .

6. Soda Products Plant

   (a) Plant Operation

      The routine compilation of data and. . . .

7. General Plant Problems

   (a) Paints, Concrete Preservation, etc.

      [Signature]

      Edward P. Pearson

      The routine testing of paints was continued. A few. . . .

   (b) Solubility Work on Plant Liquors

      No opportunity for continuing this work was found because. . . .

   (c) Outside Storages

      No further problems regarding the use of outside. . . .

   (d) Miscellaneous

      As usual, several miscellaneous plant problems and routine subjects of a minor nature were worked upon during the month.

II. PROCESS DEVELOPMENT SECTION
(Problems including possible new developments, major improvements in present processes, etc.)

1. Soda Products Process Modifications

      [Signature]

      L. G. Black

   (a) Process Study

      Additional data on the present process and proposed modifications were collected during the month. These developments are discussed in the following paragraphs under headings similar to those used in previous reports.

   (1) *Sal Soda Cooler Capacity*. The difficulties experienced with entrainment and salting below the liquor level in the high-vacuum crystallizer continued, but no further changes were made in operation pending installation of the axial-flow discharge pump.

184

(2) *Glauber Salt Filtrate Production.* Experiments on the counter-current dissolution. . . .

(3) *Sal Soda Filter and Evaporator.* No time was found available by this. . . .

(4) *Foam Removal.* This subject is discussed under Lithium Recovery. . . .

(5) *Primary NaCl Crystallizer.* [(6), (7), (8), (9), (10) similarly]

2. Light Soda Ash

(a) Dehydration of Sodium Carbonate Hydrates

In line with suggestions from the Los Angeles Sales Office, no further work was done on this method of producing light soda ash pending completion of preliminary cost estimates by the Engineering Department.

(b) Light Ash by Calcination of Trona

[Signature]	[Signature]
C. F. Ritchie	F. H. May

At the end of the month, the experimental equipment for pilot-plant-scale production of light soda ash by this method was ready to run. This equipment consists of a carbonating tank of our own design, fed with boiler flue-gas by a Roots blower which draws the flue-gas from the old boilers through a modification of the Blaw-Knox scrubber. It was found that the Roots blower has to be serviced with a small stream of water which is subsequently removed in a standard centrifugal separator. Thus, with this hook-up the flue-gas is given two scrubbings prior to being delivered in the carbonating tank. The object of the process, as previously reported, is to convert sodium carbonate or sodium carbonate monhydrate into trona, which is then filtered off and calcined to produce light soda ash.

3. Classification Problems

(a) Salt-Trap Salt

[Signature]

T. G. Bernhardi

The salt-trap classified was operated intermittently. . . .

(b) Coarse Granular Boric Acid   [similarly]

(c) Separation of Potash and Borax by. . . .   [similarly]

4. Evaporator Problems   [similarly]

5. Water-Treating Problems   [similarly]

6. Lithium Recovery

(a) Production

[Signature]

J. Phillips

The quantity of lithium concentrate in process of drying was increased during the month when prolonged winds caused delays in sacking material from the exposed solar drying-trays. Only 6.0 tons (dry basis) were sacked.

A shipment of 45.7 tons (dry basis) was made to the Maywood Chemical Works on February 14, leaving 5.6 tons in storage at the end of the month. This shipment contained 6.55 per cent moisture, owing to the fact that this material was sacked while still fairly wet. This was done in order to speed up production and to reduce contamination and loss of lithium concentrate by wind.

Contamination of the product on the solar drying-trays has become a serious problem since the start of the windy season. A batch of 82 sacks, recently produced, contained 7.96 per cent of acid-insoluble material (mostly sand), whereas representative production dried under shelter contained 0.32 per cent of acid-insoluble material.

(b) Process Development

_____[*Signature*]_____
J. Phillips

_____[*Signature*]_____
L. G. Black

Work on the lithium material-balance has been confined to tests and calculations to determine flow-rates at relevant points pending completion of the analyses of samples of the various plant liquors and salts involved (see item IV-3).

As noted in previous reports, flotation of lithium-bearing insolubles from various plant liquors and from the sewer effluent has met with partial success. However, in these tests the recovery and concentration both left much to be desired. In the type of equipment used, it was noted that a good froth could be generated, but that the coarse bubbles did not float the lithium-bearing solids selectively. Past experience in removing suspended matter from burkeite liquor indicated that finely divided particles could be trapped on air bubbles by evacuating dissolved air from the solution. It is planned to investigate this general procedure for the flotation of lithium phosphate by first dissolving air in the solution under pressure, then releasing the pressure and collecting the froth.

(c) Lithium Drying Tests   [similarly]

7. Development of New Potash Products

(a) Coarse Granular Muriate

(1) Agglomeration Process

_____[*Signature*]_____
B. Fitch

SPECIMEN NO. 4
ONE-PAGE STATUS REPORT

RESEARCH TASK REPORT REPORTS CONTROL SYMBOL CSCRD ℓ—(RI)	1. DATE 30 June 1961	
2. SCIENTIFIC FIELD Chemistry	3. SUBFIELD Organic Chemistry	
	RC BR CBA 5010CMR&D 010	

4. DA PROJECT NUMBER AND PROJECT TITLE 599-01-004 Ordnance Basic Research	5. TASK TITLE Studies of Sulfur Containing Organic Compounds
6. SOURCE FOR ADDITIONAL INFORMATION U.S. Army Research Office (Durham) Box CM, Duke Station Durham, N. C.	7. PRINCIPAL INVESTIGATORS Dr. W. E. Parham Dr. M. D. Bhavsar

8. LABORATORIES AND INSTALLATIONS University of Minnesota Minneapolis, Minn.	9. ESTIMATED SUPPORT LEVEL INT. EXT.

CONTRACT OR GRANT NOS. DA-ORD-31-124-61-613

10. BRIEF OF TASK AND STATEMENT OF WORK ASSIGNED

Purpose: To explore the chemistry of organic sulfur containing compounds.

Scope: Work is to cover the following: (1) Carbenes with sulfides, (2) photocatalyzed polymerization of 1,4-dithiodiene, (3) reactions of vinyl sulfones with diazocompounds, (4) miscellaneous studies.

Approach: Work has progressed on the photocatalyzed polymerization of 1,4-dithiodiene. A solid tetramer was obtained which is being examined structurally. The greatest effort has been placed on reactions of vinyl sulfones with diazocompounds. Various additional compounds are prepared and attempts made to identify the products.

Statement of Work Assigned: Program started - 15 Sept. 1960
                               Completion date - 15 Sept. 1961

State of Progress: As detailed in semi-annual report covering the period 15 September 1960 to 31 March 1961. Work is being written up for publication.

SHEET_____OF_____.

11. NAME & TITLE OF REPORTING OFFICER A. C. HANSON Laboratory Director	12. SIGNATURE *G. C. Hanson*

SPECIMEN NO. 5

NEW YORK CENTRAL SYSTEM

BUFFALO YARD
ANALYSIS
RECOMMENDATIONS

DECEMBER 1, 1955

OBJECTIVES

1. To improve service to customers.

2. To develop means of reducing time required for freight car handling in classification yards, now averaging 25 hours 40 minutes in East Buffalo and 21 hours 10 minutes in Gardenville.

3. To design a new yard permitting final classification of cars in one switching operation in order to achieve economy and terminal operating efficiency.

4. To develop necessary track and signal changes to expedite movement of trains over main tracks and through yards in Buffalo area.

5. To accomplish maximum retirement of unnecessary and outmoded facilities.

SUMMARY

Objectives can be attained by:

1. Construction of an electronically controlled classification yard in the East Buffalo territory.

2. Construction of certain additional main tracks and provisions for improved signaling of existing and additional tracks.

3. Elimination of Gardenville Yard, seven scattered East Buffalo Yards, and conversion of the Gardenville Branch into an industrial lead.

Economic results are shown below:

Estimated Net Cost, all improvements	$6,105,000
Estimated Annual Savings	$4,425,000
Estimated Rate of Return	72%
Track retired	208 miles
New track constructed	82 miles
Net reduction in track	126 miles
Present labor force	1,165
Estimated force required for new terminal	731
Estimated reduction in force	434
Present average time for car movement through:	
Gardenville Yard	21 hours 10 minutes
East Buffalo Yards	25 hours 40 minutes
Estimated average time for car movement through proposed new yard	7 hours 55 minutes

PRESENT OPERATION

The Buffalo district of the New York Central Railroad is the western terminus of the Syracuse Division and is the eastern terminus of the Erie and of the Canada Divisions. It consists primarily of a group of yard and terminal facilities for the switching and servicing of local, through freight, and passenger trains, and the switching of cars to and from industries and connecting railroads.

This report is concerned with operations in the East Buffalo and Gardenville areas of the Buffalo district. The East Buffalo yards are presently located on both sides of the main-line tracks running between Bay View and Depew. The Passenger Terminal is located in the East Buffalo area. Gardenville Yard is located on the two-track Gardenville Branch, an alternate route between Bay View and Depew.

Seventeen scheduled eastbound freight trains arrive and depart from East Buffalo and Gardenville yards daily, of which 11 are through schedules; the westbound movement comprises 17 scheduled arrivals and 16 departures, in which are included 9 through trains.

The same main tracks over which freight movements are made to and from the East Buffalo yards are also used by 36 eastbound passenger trains arriving at Central Terminal and the same number westbound. Of these, 19 eastbound and 18 westbound are through schedules.

Two-hundred forty principal industries and 9 interchange connections with 8 railroads are served from 8 classification and 7 industrial yards in the East Buffalo–Gardenville area. The connecting railroads are:

South Buffalo	D.L.&W.
Buffalo Creek	PRR
Lehigh Valley	NKP
Erie	B&O

On an average day about 2,750 cars are switched to industries, delivered in interchange, and classified for road movement at East Buffalo and Gardenville, with a peak of about 3,190 cars.

The yards in the Gardenville and East Buffalo territories of the Buffalo district are shown below:

Territory	Yard	Tracks	Capacity
E. Buffalo	HC (SY & Grain)	51	2,253
E. Buffalo	VI	37	1,664
E. Buffalo	West Shore	20	1,438
E. Buffalo	EA	12	446
E. Buffalo	Train (MI)	23	849
E. Buffalo	FS	6	96
E. Buffalo	Stock Yard	25	1,054
E. Buffalo	Chicago Street	10	267
E. Buffalo	Carroll Street	13	365
E. Buffalo	Louisiana Street	6	132
E. Buffalo	Ohio Street	8	147
E. Buffalo	Howard Street	4	66
E. Buffalo	W. Shore Ore Dock	11	252
E. Buffalo	Depew	3	126
Gardenville	Gardenville	116	9,130

193

A portion of Gardenville Yard, with a 300-car capacity, is used for cleaning and conditioning cars and for loading of various commodities. Car-repair facilities, with combined capacity of 230 cars, are located at Gardenville and East Buffalo. Engine-servicing facilities are located at Gardenville, East Buffalo, the Passenger Terminal, and Black Rock. Required inspection of and necessary work on East Buffalo engines is accomplished at the Passenger Terminal.

Gardenville Yard performs virtually all of the switching of westbound trains originating in the Buffalo district, and in addition also handles through eastbound and westbound freight trains requiring no switching.

Each of the 7 switching yards in the East Buffalo territory performs switching of cars received from road trains, intraterminal movements, and industries. Cars are normally transferred to one of the 7 yards for consolidation before they depart to primary interchange points, large industries, and industrial-base yards.

The present East Buffalo stockyard facility, occupying an area of 25 acres, has a capacity of 400 carloads of livestock.

An average maximum of 50 carloads of stock are run through daily requiring no service.

There are fed and rested at the stockyard, as required by law, an average maximum of 160 carloads daily. Of these 160 carloads, 50 are received at Buffalo from other railroads under existing undesirable-stock tariff regulations.

About 6 carloads of stock originate at Buffalo for rail movement.

There is also a livestock market operation carried on, involving an equivalent of 40 carloads of stock daily. This business is transported in and out of the stockyards by truck.

Present car-distribution practices result in concentration at Gardenville of empty-box and open-top equipment from points east of Buffalo and the Buffalo area for commodity inspection, switching, and distribution to meet car requirements in the Buffalo district and points west of Buffalo. Of the boxcars received, Gardenville prepares about 250 cars per day for Buffalo district feed flour and grain loading requirements.

The average time of cars from arrival in one of the 7 East Buffalo yards until departure to interchange, industry, or road movement is about 25 hours 40 minutes. The average time from arrival in Gardenville Yard until departure is about 21 hours 10 minutes.

Next following is a diagram showing yards, capacity, and interchange points in the Buffalo district. [This diagram has been omitted for economy.]

PROPOSED YARD

Electronically Controlled Yard

The new yard, occupying approximately 170 owned acres, is situated north of the main tracks and extends eastward from a point one mile east of the Passenger Terminal. It comprises groups of tracks for receiving trains, tracks for classification of cars, tracks upon which outbound trains are made up, and long tracks paralleling the main track for the handling of through freight trains.

Receiving and Departure Yards

Three groups of receiving and departure tracks are located as follows: one group is located east of and in line with the classification yard; one group is located on the north side of the classification yard; and the third group is located on the south side of the classification yard. Capacity data of these groups are as shown:

Location	Tracks	Length	Capacity
North	8	70 to 150 cars	1,000 cars
South	12	50 to 150 cars	1,080 cars
East	7	70 to 150 cars	680 cars

Fifteen of the above receiving and departure tracks, with a capacity of 1,380 cars, are normally used to receive trains for switching. The yard is designed to receive and switch 2,000 to 3,000 cars daily.

Classification Yard

Drafts of cars for switching are moved to the crest of a hump either by straight shoves from the east receiving tracks, or by pullbacks from the north and south receiving tracks. Seventy-eight per cent of the trains and drafts presently arriving in the East Buffalo territory have less than 50 cars, so that considerable benefit results from the pullback operation by ability to double two or more drafts in movements to the hump lead track.

The car-retarding (car speed-control) and switching systems are electronically controlled. Cars move from the crest into classification tracks by gravity.

Sixty-three classification tracks are provided in seven 9-track groups with length varying from 30 to 70 cars, except that each of the 3 north tracks has 120-car capacity for the make-up of eastbound and westbound trains. Total capacity of classification-yard tracks is 3,110 cars.

Ingress and Egress

Power-operated switches are provided to permit uninterrupted movement of trains to and from receiving and departure tracks. These switches are controlled from the hump tower and existing interlocking towers.

Buildings

A two-story building with tower, located at the hump, houses control panel and machines for power-operated receiving and departure yard switches in the hump area. Control panel and equipment for automatic switching machine are also contained in this building. Room for hump crews, hump clerks, and car inspectors is also included.

A two-story retarder building with tower contains office for assistant general yardmaster and clerk, automatic retarding system controls and equipment, and communication and signal shop space. Room is also provided in this building for trainmaster, general yardmaster, east-end clerks, and car inspectors.

A two-story building with tower at the west end of the yard accommodates west-end yardmaster and clerks, car inspectors, and yard, train, and engine crew facilities. Included in this building are a 59-room Y.M.C.A. and a cafeteria for away-from-home crews.

Pneumatic tubes connect the east yard office, west yard office, and general yard office—billing bureau.

Adequate communication is furnished throughout the new yard by talkback speakers, yard radios, communicating signals, and telephones.

Teletype transmission of yard hump lists is provided. Yard lighting is furnished according to existing standards.

Yard Design

Next following is a reduced plan of the electronically controlled new yard. Appended to this report is a large-scale plan of the new yard. [These have here been omitted.]

Car Repair Facilities

An 85-car capacity car-repair facility is equipped with adequate lighting for 24-hour operation. Continuous operation of the repair tracks will save one or more days in car detention in servicing both loaded and empty cars, resulting in improved service to customers.

Engine Service Facilities

Facilities are provided to service engines assigned in the immediate vicinity and for inspection of all engines assigned in the Buffalo district.

Stock Yards

A 60-pen stock yard, served by required chutes, is provided in the old West Shore yard area to handle in-transit feed and rest requirements for New York Central livestock. In addition, there is furnished an 18-car servicing platform for in-transit carload hogs.

Car Cleaning Yard

West Shore yard tracks are rearranged to provide a 250-car capacity car cleaning yard for preparation of cars for feed, flour, and grain loading requirements in the Buffalo territory.

General Yard Operation

The assistant general yardmaster has charge of all operations in this new yard.

The yardmaster at the west end of the yard supervises the work in his area. Soundscribers are provided for yard clerks' use to transmit information to the general yard office.

General yard office clerks remain located in the present East Buffalo general yard office building. Billing bureau clerks are transferred from the Passenger Terminal to the general yard office building so that the closely related work of these clerical groups is properly coordinated and integrated.

Clerks in the yard forward waybills, consists, and other data to the general yard office by pneumatic tube. Hump lists for cars arriving without advance train lists are prepared by general yard office clerks and teletyped to yardmaster, assistant general yardmaster, car-retarder operator and the hump office.

General yard office clerks assemble bills for outbound trains and forward them to the yard via pneumatic tube.

The estimated average time for car movement through the proposed new yard is 7 hours 55 minutes, as compared with 21 hours 10 minutes through Gardenville Yard and 25 hours 40 minutes through the East Buffalo yards.

Next following is a graphical representation of the number of cars in proposed receiving yards based on train arrivals and humping rates, and also the number of cars in the proposed classification yard based on humping rates and train departures. [This graph has been omitted.]

MAIN TRACK CHANGES

The redispatching study made of passenger, freight, and yard movements between Bay View, Buffalo, and Depew, using actual movements on a maximum normal day with trains now operating via Gardenville superimposed, produced a favorable movement pattern. Next following is a colored chart showing the highest track density proportion of the redispatching study. [Omitted for economy.]

Certain additional main-track and signaling facilities, described immediately following, are provided to expedite movement of trains through the East Buffalo territory.

A third main track is provided in present two-track territory between Seneca and the Buffalo Creek Railroad crossing, and also between the Buffalo Creek bridge and the PRR crossing just west of the passenger station. These are the areas of heaviest traffic density. Thirty miles per hour crossovers replace 10 miles per hour slip switches west of the passenger station to increase permissible train speeds through the Buffalo territory.

Similarly, two new through main tracks are furnished, from the west end of the passenger depot and south of the depot tracks, to connect with the interlocking which serves the west end of the new yard to permit through movement without interference from passenger-station operations.

Revised signaling permits movement in either direction by signal indication on all main tracks from Bay View to Depew, with control from existing towers. The revision makes possible elimination of three interlocking towers on this route.

One of the Gardenville Branch main tracks is retired and the remaining track converted to an industrial lead. One interlocking tower is eliminated on this route.

Following the redispatching chart is a straight-line diagram showing the existing main tracks and secondary main tracks remaining, existing main track routes retired, and the added main tracks, as described. [Omitted for economy.]

ESTIMATED COST

	GROSS	SALVAGE	NET
Yard	$7,478,000	$1,765,000 Land 1,626,000 Track 919,000 Engines	$3,168,000
Engine and car facilities	842,000	20,000	822,000
Stockyard	688,000		688,000
Car cleaning yard	66,000		66,000
Main tracks	1,485,000	124,000	1.361,000
Total	$10,559,000	$4,454,000	$6,105,000

197

ESTIMATED SAVINGS

FORCE	PRESENT	PRO-POSED	REDUC-TION	SAVINGS
Transportation (crews, clerks, and supervision)	584	335	249	$1,973,359*
Elimination of 4 signal towers	17			77,965
Car inspection	177	130	47	217,693
Car repairs	146	98	48	219,805
Engine servicing	171	148	23	101,572
Stockyard	70	20	50	112,291†
Totals	1,165	731	434	$2,702,685

* Includes $67,000 overtime eliminated from Gardenville payroll and $31,000 from East Buffalo payroll.
† Includes stockyard receipts and expenditures.

PER DIEM	$1,317,039
MAINTENANCE (126 miles of track eliminated)	405,947
TOTAL SAVINGS	$4,425,671
SALVAGE	
Release of 11 locomotives	$ 919,000
Salvage material and equipment	1,770,000
Released land, 311 acres	1,765,000
TOTAL SALVAGE	$4,454,000

OTHER BENEFITS

1. Eight yards are consolidated into one modern yard.

2. Modern consolidated switching facilities reduce switching requirements at other yards.

3. Concentration of operations produces peak utilization of yard engines and road power.

4. Operation of long through road trains is facilitated.

5. Faster train operation between Depew and Bay View results from improved signal and track facilities.

6. Potential equipment and lading damage greatly reduced by installation of automatic switching and retarding equipment and elimination of rehandling of cars.

7. Valuable real estate becomes available for industrial development.

8. Car detention is reduced and service to customers improved by 24-hour daily operation of car-servicing facilities.

SPECIMEN NO. 6

Only the title page, table of contents, and first eight pages of a 57-page report have been reprinted here.

PERFORMANCE OF SMALL INDUSTRIAL-TYPE ANTHRACITE-BURNING STOKERS: ASME CODE TESTS

By R. F. Tenney and J. W. Eckerd

* * * * * * * * * * *   report of investigations 5607

UNITED STATES DEPARTMENT OF THE INTERIOR
Fred A. Seaton, Secretary

BUREAU OF MINES
Marling J. Ankeny, Director

CONTENTS

                                                                    Page

Summary and conclusions 1
Introduction 1
Acknowledgments 4
Experimental procedures and results 4
   Description of boilers and accessory operating equipment 4
     Steam boilers 4
       Furnace settings 5
       Anthracite fuel handling 6
       Ash handling 6
       Feed-water supply 6
       Boiler steam header 6
       Stack, breeching, and damper 6
   Description of plant instrumentation 6
   Description of special test apparatus and connections 9
     Feed-water weighing 9
     Combustion-air temperature recorder 9
     Flue-gas analyzer 9
   Description of stokers tested 11
     Hazleton stoker 11
     Skelly stoker 13
     Other stokers tested 16
       Losch stoker 16
       E.F.M. stoker 19
   Anthracite fuels for tests 21
     Sources 21
     Analyses 21
     Water content 21
   Operating conditions during tests on each stoker 23
     Hazleton stoker runs 23
       Preparations for tests 23
       Test-run schedule 23
       Steam-load characteristics 23
       Stoker air-and-fuel regulation 24
       Fuel-feed weighing and sampling 24
       Boiler feed-water measurement 24
       Flue-gas analyses and regulation 24
       Boiler-room atmosphere 24
       Prerun periods 25
       Test-run routine 25
     Skelly stoker runs 25
       Preparations for test 25
       Test-run schedule 26
       Steam loading 26
       Stoker air-and-fuel regulation 26
       Test-run routine 26
     Losch stoker runs 27
       Preparations for test 27
       Test-run schedule 27
       Stoker air-and-fuel regulation 27
       Test-run routine 27

	Page
E.F.M. stoker runs	28
Preparations for test	28
Test-run schedule	28
Stoker air-and-fuel regulation	28
Test-run routine	28
Summary of run results	28
Complete record of run results	32
Discussion of results	32
Heat efficiencies	32
Anthracite-burning capacities	33
Heat losses	34
Sensible heat in dry flue-gas	34
Unburned carbon monoxide	36
Combustible in dry refuse	37
Moisture in coal fired	38
Moisture from hydrogen in the dry coal	38
Moisture in total air into furnace and boiler	39
Radiation and miscellaneous	39
Evaluation of heat-efficiency results	40
Hazleton tests	42
Skelly tests	42
Losch tests	42
E.F.M. tests	43
Appendix I	44
Appendix II	55
Bibliography	57

ILLUSTRATIONS

Fig.   *Page*

1. Boiler-room firing aisle: Nos. 1 and 2 boiler fronts and charging ends of Skelly and Hazleton stokers, fuel-larry scales and chute, and instrument panel-board 5

2. Diagram of No. 1 boiler and instrument connections 7

3. End view of feed-water weighing apparatus; observer analyzing flue-gas at No. 2 boiler 10

4. Feed end of Hazleton stoker, No. 2 boiler: Fuel hopper, air fan, drive motor and linkage to grate sprockets, and grate surface sections on turn-around sprockets 11

5. Side elevation of Hazleton stoker and furnace setting 12

6. Outside view of Skelly stoker, No. 1 boiler: Fuel hopper, air-intake damper, fan housing and air duct, drive motor, and speed-reducer housing 14

7. Vertical sections of Skelly stoker 15

8. Outside view of Losch stoker, No. 1 boiler: Fuel hopper, fans and drive motor, front-fan air damper, grate-cooling water connections, and furnace observation doors 17

9. Diagram and section of Losch grate and feed hopper 18

10. Outside view of E.F.M. stoker, No. 1 boiler: Fuel hopper, drive motor and fans, fan dampers, grate-cooling water connections, and furnace observation doors 20

Fig.		Page
11.	Relation of boiler output to operating conditions and results in test of barley anthracite on Hazleton stoker	30
12.	Relation of boiler output to operating conditions and results in test of rice anthracite on Skelly stoker	30
13.	Relation of boiler output to operating conditions and results in test of rice anthracite on Losch stoker	31
14.	Relation of boiler output to operating conditions and results in test of rice anthracite on E.F.M. stoker	31

TABLES

1.	Analyses of samples of anthracite from truck deliveries for ASME Boiler-Stoker Code Tests 1957	22
2.	Summary of operating data and results of ASME code test runs on anthracite stokers	29
3.	Data and results of ASME code tests with barley anthracite on Hazleton stoker	44
4.	Data and results of ASME code tests with rice anthracite on Skelly stoker	46
5.	Data and results of ASME code tests with rice anthracite on Losch stoker	49
6.	Data and results of ASME code tests with rice anthracite on E.F.M. stoker	52
7.	Heat losses from dry flue-gases at various excess air rates	55
8.	Heat losses as a result of CO in flue-gas	56
9.	Heat losses as a result of combustible contents of stoker ashes	56

PERFORMANCE OF SMALL INDUSTRIAL-TYPE ANTHRACITE-BURNING STOKERS: ASME CODE TESTS [1]

by

R. F. Tenney [2] and J. W. Eckerd [3, 4]

SUMMARY AND CONCLUSIONS

The performances of four anthracite-burning stokers have been observed under identical 74-hp steam boilers. Fifty runs of 12- and 24-hours' duration have been made in accordance with the test code of the American Society of Mechanical Engineers (ASME). The capacity of each stoker for burning anthracite has been determined, the heat efficiency at each fuel rate has been computed, and the various significant items of heat loss have been estimated. The operating data and results from each run are tabulated in this report in the form used in the test code. The heat efficiencies and most significant operating data for each run are also presented graphically for each stoker to establish the trends with increasing boiler outputs.

The tests show that rice anthracite can be burned on stokers adapted to its use at heat-conversion efficiencies of 82 per cent or more under continuous firing. These high efficiencies are maintained with fuel inputs 30 per cent higher or lower than the peak efficiency rate. Moreover, a heat efficiency of 70 per cent or more is obtained at 50 per cent of the optimum fuel rate, even though the excess air into the furnace cannot be held below 150 per cent.

INTRODUCTION

The Anthracite Institute has estimated that over 98 per cent of the anthracite now being produced is burned in space heaters and boiler plants. This has been true for the past 60 to 70 years since anthracite ceased being an important metallurgical fuel. Thus, the loss in the market for anthracite has been in its use for heating. This loss has occurred in the face of increasing heating and total energy requirements; hence, the loss has been to competitive fuels. Both oil and gas, the chief competitors, are automatic fuels in that they require little attention and virtually no manual labor for their utilization. The anthracite stoker is their counterpart.

Anthracite stokers are divided into three size classifications, according to their burning rates. The most numerous [5] are the domestic units, which

---

[1] Work on manuscript completed October 1959.

[2] Supervisory chemical engineer, Anthracite Experiment Station, Bureau of Mines, Schuylkill Haven, Pa.

[3] Chief, Branch of Utilization and Preparation, Anthracite Experiment Station, Bureau of Mines, Schuylkill Haven, Pa.

[4] In preparing this report, the authors were assisted by A. F. Baker, fuel technologist, and J. D. Sieck, foreman-operating engineer, Anthracite Experiment Station, Bureau of Mines, Schuylkill Haven, Pa.

[5] In a 1957 newspaper advertisement, a Pottsville (Pa.) heating contractor listed 48 trade names of anthracite stokers for which service and small parts were available.

usually burn 15 to 50 pounds per hour. Rice and buckwheat No. 1 anthracites are the usual fuel, but barley may be used in a few units. Attendance by the householder is required not more than once a day for filling the feed magazine and withdrawing the ash container or, with automatic feed and ash removal, at intervals determined by the size of the fuel and ash receptacles. Extensive development and testing of units of this class were undertaken by the Anthracite Institute, who established industry standards and a system of approval and certification. The characteristics and efficiencies of these small units have been well investigated and developed.

The large combustion units for utility and industrial plants have also undergone extensive development under the cost incentives of large initial investment required and fuel quantities consumed. Anthracite sizes used are barley (buckwheat No. 3) and buckwheats Nos. 4 and 5. Operating attendance on such units is usually continuous, skilled, and well supervised. Efficient controls and instruments are maintained.

The small industrial stokers cover the sizes between domestic and power-plant units. Anthracite-burning capacities run from 100 to 1,000 pounds per hour, and installations are made for commercially built boilers with nominal ratings of 15 to 300 hp. These boilers are usually built to the standard specifications of the Steel Boiler Institute (4, 5)[6] with ratings in steps from 525 to 10,200 kBtu per hour (2,200 to 42,500 sq ft of steam radiation). The large field for units in this range includes apartment houses, schools, municipal buildings, small offices, commercial structures, and small industries requiring process steam. Complete automatic controls are provided to limit the attendance necessary. Fuel- and ash-handling equipment may be obtained for further labor saving. Buckwheat No. 1, rice, and barley are the usual anthracite sizes fired.

Little technical information has been published on the operating characteristics and performance of these small industrial anthracite burners. However, several reports on their development were presented at the Annual Anthracite Conferences, formerly held at Lehigh University.

In 1938 Stein (12) described the design characteristics of the Skelly stoker "made available in the past year in sizes to suit the apartment house and commercial field . . . to fill the gap between domestic and large industrial-type stokers."

In 1939 Krauss (7) discussed various aspects of the design and performance of underfeed (Skelly-type) stokers for anthracite and also developments being attempted to reduce the size and cost of traveling-grate stokers to adapt them to the use of anthracite, possibly down to barley size.

In 1940 Kerrick (6) described numerous commercial installations of anthracite-burning stokers of four types.

In 1949 Stein (13) described the developments since 1938 in both underfeed and traveling-grate stokers for burning anthracite and noted that more than 2,000 underfeed stokers had been installed.

In 1949 Mulcey (10) discussed the application of crossfeed combustion and described the development of retorts (grates) using this principle. The crossfeed principle, common to all large industrial stokers, was indicated as the movement of the fuel in a relatively thin bed along a substantially horizontal plane across tuyères that discharge the combustion air vertically upward through the fuel.

[6] Italicized numbers in parentheses refer to citations in the list of references at the end of this report.

In 1950 Miller (9) described auxiliary equipment for anthracite stokers to obtain the labor savings claimed for competitive fuels and technical improvements in stoker design to assure these savings.

In 1951 Mulcey (11) discussed progress in developing a new design for anthracite stokers, incorporating high burning rates and looking toward capacities of 100 to 400 pounds per hour. A compound feeder-distributor had been developed to bring in coal from a side hopper, spread it across the entire width of the grate, and give it an initial push toward the grate surface. It was designed to fit various commercially available boilers of different capacities.

In 1952 Loomis (8) described the development of an anthracite stoker with a recirculating twin-screw feeder and ram pushers for moving the fuel bed along the stationary-grate bars. Units for burning 300 pounds per hour were being marketed.

A Bureau of Mines report by Burdick and Morgan (2) described a series of tests with anthracites on a traveling-grate stoker under a 250-hp steam boiler. Heat efficiencies of 70 to 73 per cent were obtained on 4-hour runs with the better grades of barley.

A preliminary discussion (3) of the initial steps in the testing program described in this report was presented at the Tri-State Anthracite Conference in Elmira, N. Y., April 22-23, 1957.

The performance of fuel-burning equipment for hot-water and steam-boiler heating must be observed in operation with the types of apparatus for which they are designed. Only then can their effectiveness in producing both radiant and convective heat be evaluated and the various design characteristics and fuel properties compared. The two commercial 74-hp steam boilers at the Anthracite Experiment Station at Schuylkill Haven, Pa., are in the small industrial range. They have furnace settings in which two anthracite-burning stokers were originally installed, and one of these settings has been adapted to the installation of other stokers. The boilers are provided with special instrumentation for more extensive observations than a normal commercial installation.

The stokers investigated for this report were designs regularly marketed for boiler outputs in the intermediate or small industrial range. All were operated to conform with the procedures of the ASME Power Test Code for Stationary Steam-Generating Units (1). This code provides a standard procedure for acceptance tests on newly purchased equipment and is widely used for comparative tests of basic equipment designs, fuels, and special accessories. It specifies the data to be oberved, the formulas for computing the heat efficiency, and the items of heat loss. The code normally implies a continuous stabilized operation from beginning to end of the test-data period. For the test runs in this study, steam generation was maintained continuously by uninterrupted combustion-air input. The fuel feeds were as continuous as the stoker design or its condition permitted.

This operation differs from the intermittent or cyclic operation under automatic boiler-pressure control, where the stoker motor is on or off and there is no combustion-air input or fuel-feed movement during the off-period. Such on-off cycles are comparable to the automatic controls on liquid or gaseous fuel burners. Extra heat is lost during off-periods by air under natural draft through the setting and boiler flues. However, with stokers, part of this air comes through the fire bed and is warmed on the way into

206

the furnace; moreover, this air helps to keep the bed ignited and accelerates the return to efficient combustion.

Fifty 12- and 24-hour test runs were made on the stokers over the full range of inputs from minimum to maximum burning rates within the limitations of the equipment or the auxiliary testing apparatus.

ACKNOWLEDGMENTS

The extension of this program to include the testing of two pan-type stokers was made possible by the courtesy of Losch Boiler Co., Summit Station, Pa., and Electric Furnace-Man, Inc., Emmaus, Pa.

Cooperative agreements were executed by which these companies furnished the complete stoker equipment, supervised its installation, and advised on operation. The assistance of the officers and engineers of these companies contributed greatly to this study and is thoroughly appreciated.

EXPERIMENTAL PROCEDURES AND RESULTS

Description of Boilers and Accessory Operating Equipment

The steam plant at the Anthracite Experiment Station has two 74-hp steam boilers equipped with anthracite-burning stokers; fuel-weighing, ash-removal, feed-water, stack equipment, and instrumentation to provide complete performance data. Figure 1 [omitted] shows the boiler-room firing aisle, the boiler fronts, stoker feed hoppers and drive mechanisms, fuel-larry scales and chute, and instrument panel-board.

Steam Boilers

The two boilers are identical in design, construction, and installation. They were manufactured by Farrar & Trefts, Inc., Buffalo, N. Y., and cataloged as Boiler Series No. 570, "standardized firebox, up-draft, double-pass boiler with front smoke outlet and 3-inch tubes," and designed "for mechanical firing." They were built to the specifications of the Steel Boiler Institute (SBI), with capacities and dimensions as follows:

Total heating surface	608 sq ft
Working pressure	125 p s i g
Firebox volume enclosed in water legs	103 cu ft

Manufacturer's and SBI ratings were: Horsepower, 74; heat output, 2,479 kBtu per hr; steam radiation, 10,330 sq ft; hot-water radiation, 16,520 sq ft.

Figure 2 shows the essential design features and instrument connections of the boilers. The horizontal cylindrical shell has the firebox built into the lower half of its front end. The four walls of the firebox form a continuous water leg, with the upper part of the rear wall arranged as the tube sheet for the short, lower-pass tubes running to the back flue-box. The upper-pass tubes traverse the entire length of the boiler shell.

Both front and rear flue-boxes of the boiler have hinged doors which give access to the ends of the tubes for cleaning and removing flue dust. There is a manually operated damper in the breeching connection. A water-level float box with on-off switch to the feed-water pump is connected in parallel with the water column and a high-low water alarm. The steam connection

207

to the boiler-room header is fitted with a section of straightening vanes and an orifice plate. The feed-water inlet and the blowdown are not shown. All outside exposed surfaces of the boiler shell and the firebox and flue-box walls are insulated with 2 inches of magnesia fiber troweled on wire netting. The back flue-box door of No. 1 boiler also has a removable sheet-metal cover lined with 1½ inches of magnesia blocks.

Furnace Settings

Both boilers are elevated above the building floor, so the firebox water legs rest on brick walls 48 inches high.

No. 1 boiler furnace has walls under all four sides of the water leg. These walls are lined with firebrick and, as built for the Skelly stoker, gave a furnace 69 by 48 inches in inside dimensions. Only minor changes were made to accommodate the Losch and E.F.M. stokers. The furnace floor is sloped downward in a 12-inch strip along the right-hand wall to form a hopper for the ashes discharging from the stoker grate. This floor hopper has a gate at the bottom to retain the ashes for periodic removal.

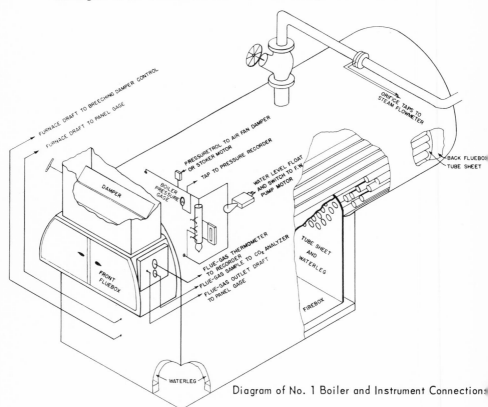

Diagram of No. 1 Boiler and Instrument Connections

No. 2 boiler furnace has the same two firebrick-lined sidewalls, but the walls are extended beyond the rear water leg for the special ignition arch over the Hazleton stoker. The front wall is also limited to an arch under the water leg. The floor hopper runs crosswise at the rear of the furnace extension below the ash-dumping edge of the grate.

208

Anthracite Fuel Handling

The station has two 25-ton elevated steel bins for boiler-fuel storage. One bin is used for barley-size and the other for rice-size anthracite. The fuel is unloaded by chute into a ground-level hopper and raised to the overhead bins by a bucket elevator. Anthracite from the storage bins is dropped into the 1,500-pound-capacity hopper of the weigh-larry for charging into the stoker hoppers. The larry carriage is suspended from track rails, which run overhead from the bins along the firing aisle in front of the boilers.

Ash Handling

A drag conveyor in a horizontal trough, which runs through a tunnel below the discharge gates of the two furnace hoppers, moves the ashes to the fuel elevator at the end of the boiler room. At the top of the elevator, a gate and chute are set to direct the ashes into a 15-ton vertical bin for storage. An opening in the conveyor trough near the elevator allows the ashes to be diverted for weighing and sampling during tests.

Feed-water Supply

A 120-gallon return tank collects the condensate from all the building heating units. It contains a float-valve connected to a metered make-up water supply to keep the tank at least half full. Two motor-driven centrifugal pumps below the tank deliver this feed-water into the respective boilers through individual disk-type displacement meters in increments of approximately 30 gallons, regulated by the boiler-water-level float-switch.

Boiler Steam Header

An 8-inch pipe header over the boilers takes steam from either boiler and, at one end, connects through pressure-reducing and pressure-regulating equipment to the heating and process steam lines of the station. At the other end is an overhead vent to the atmosphere through a 4-inch gate valve.

Stack, Breeching, and Damper

A square, brick stack is located inside the three-story pilot-plant bay next to the boiler room. It is 70 feet high and contains two separate flues, each 2 feet 10 inches square. A 34- by 40-inch, rectangular, insulated breeching extends across the two boiler flue-box outlets and into one flue of the stack. A butterfly-type damper inside the breeching near the stack regulates the firebox draft automatically.

Description of Plant Instrumentation

The boiler plant has the following instruments for operating control and performance records (the boilers are equipped alike as noted):

1. Outdoor temperature and barometric-pressure recorder; Bristol, model 2 LD 1 x 500-11-14 with 7-day chart; thermometer bulb in louvered weather guard above boiler-house roof.
2. Draft and stoker air gauges; Republic diaphragm-type with quadrant scales and Meriam-inclined liquid-type manometers.

THE HANDBOOK SECTION

1. Abbreviations
2. Capitalization
3. Compounding and Hyphenation
4. Spelling
5. Preferred Usage (Glossary)
6. The Handling of Numbers
7. Punctuation
8. Letter Form

NOTE: The numbering system used in this section is that recommended by the American Standards Association.

1. ABBREVIATIONS

General Principle

In business and industry the writer is permitted considerable freedom in using abbreviations. Even so, he must use only those recognized as standard by the dictionary, by the government, or by his industry or profession. And he must use them only when he is sure they save the reader time. Do not gamble: If in doubt, spell out.

Specific rules follow. The American Standards Association list of *Abbreviations for Scientific and Engineering Terms* is given on pages 214-21.

1.1 In text, do not use an abbreviation unless a quantity expressed in numeral form precedes it.

1.2 Do not abbreviate short words like *day, mile, rod, ton.*

1.3 Most abbreviations have no plural form [Exceptions: *pp.,* (pages), *mos.* (months), *nos.* (numbers), *vols.* (volumes) *yrs.* (years)]:

    15 in.   40 lb   110 mph   44 sq cm

1.4 Omit the period after technical abbreviations unless the resulting form constitutes a word:

    ft   hp   psi   Btu   *but*   in.   at. wt

1.5 Capitalize letters in abbreviations only when they represent proper nouns or adjectives [Exception: C for centigrade]:

    60-hp motor   *not*   60 HP or 60 H.P.
    1600 Btu   *not*   1600 BTU or B.T.U.

1.6 Generally omit both periods and spacing in abbreviating organization names:

    ASA   ASME   ASTM   ICC   TVA   *but*   U.S.   U.N.

1.7 Avoid exponents in text. They can be confused with footnote indexes and they are troublesome in typing and typesetting:

    40 lb per sq ft   *not* $40 \, lb/ft^2$

1.8 In street addresses spell out *North, South, East, West, Street, Avenue,* and so forth, but abbreviate sectional divisions of a city such as NW, SE [For street numbers see Section 6.2.11.]:

    439 West Prospect Avenue   33 Pennsylvania Avenue NW

1.9 Abbreviate compass directions:

    N   E   S   W   SW   NNW   12°N   25°W

1.10   Do not abbreviate *Brothers, Company, Corporation, Limited, Railroad,* and so forth unless the company itself abbreviates it.

1.11   Do not abbreviate city names:

WRONG: Phila.   L.A.   K.C.   N.Y.

1.12   Spell out May, June, and July. Abbreviate other months, *if at all,* only when the day is given:

August 1910   August 12, 1910   12 August 1910

1.13   Avoid abbreviating titles [Exceptions: *Mr., Mrs.,* and *Dr.* before a name, *Jr., Sr., Ph.D.,* and so forth after one.]:

Dr. William L. Nieman	Mr. John Truby, Sr.
President John A Hipple	Gen. Milton Bergstein *
Professor M. R. Cannon	Prof. Michael Cannon *

1.14   In abbreviating a compound word, retain the hyphen:

alternating-current motor	a-c motor
40-foot cut	40-ft cut

1.15   Use letter symbols (letters representing chemical terms or physical quantities) only in chemical or mathematical expressions; do not use abbreviations.

1.16   Practice differs in requiring or omitting the degree sign before C, F, K, and R, but do not use such symbols at all unless they are preceded by a numeral.

1.17   Avoid using conventional signs: # for *space or number,* ' for *feet* or *minutes,* / for *per* in text. [Exceptions: Intra-industry communications sometimes violate these rules. For example, B/D for *barrels per day* is widely used in the petroleum industry but should not be used for readers outside the industry. The percent and dollar signs are major exceptions when accompanied by a numeral, and *x* is often acceptable for *by* in giving dimensions.]:

50%   37½%   9 in.   10 ft   10 sec $63   4 x 6 x 12 in.

1.18   In text use the $\pm$ sign to express tolerances only when it immediately follows a number.

1.19   AMERICAN STANDARD ABBREVIATIONS FOR SCIENTIFIC AND ENGINEERING TERMS

This list is extracted from *American Standard Abbreviations for Scientific and Engineering Terms* (ASA Z10.1—1941) with the permission of the publisher, The American Society of Mechanical Engineers,† United

---

* Most authorities permit abbreviations when the given name is included.

† The American Standards Association has also published Bulletin Z32.13-1946, *Abbreviations for Use on Drawings.* The only significant difference in the two sets of abbreviations is that those for use on drawings are consistently capitalized throughout.

Engineering Center, 345 East 47 Street, New York, N.Y. 10017. It is sponsored by the following organizations:

> American Association for the Advancement of Science
> American Institute of Electrical Engineers
> American Society of Civil Engineers
> American Society for Engineering Education
> The American Society of Mechanical Engineers

"These [the following] forms are recommended for readers whose familiarity with the terms used makes possible a maximum of abbreviations. For other classes of readers editors may wish to use less contracted combinations made up from this list. For example, the list gives the abbreviation of the term 'feet per second' as 'fps.' To some readers 'ft per sec' will be more easily understood."

absolute	abs
acre	spell out
acre-foot	acre-ft
air horsepower	air hp
alternating current (as adjective)	a-c
ampere	amp
ampere-hour	amp-hr
amplitude, an elliptic function	am.
Angstrom unit	A
antilogarithm	antilog
atmosphere	atm
atomic weight	at. wt
average	avg
avoirdupois	avdp
azimuth	az or a

barometer	bar.
barrel	bbl
Baumé	Bé
board feet (feet board measure)	fbm
boiler pressure	spell out
boiling point	bp
brake horsepower	bhp
brake horsepower-hour	bhp-hr
Brinell hardness number	Bhn
British thermal unit	Btu or B
bushel	bu

calorie	cal
candle	c
candle-hour	c-hr
candlepower	cp
cent	c or ¢

center to center .... c to c
centigram .... cg
centiliter cl
centimeter .... cm
centimeter-gram-second (system) .... cgs
chemical .... chem
chemically pure .... cp
circular .... cir
circular mils .... cir mils
coefficient .... coef
cologarithm .... colog
concentrate .... conc
conductivity .... cond
constant .... const
continental horsepower .... cont hp
cord .... cd
cosecant .... csc
cosine .... cos
cosine of the amplitude, an elliptic function .... cn
cost, insurance, and freight .... cif
cotangent .... cot
coulomb .... spell out
counter electromotive force .... cemf
cubic .... cu
cubic centimeter .... cu cm, cm³ (liquid,
                                               meaning millili-
                                               ter, ml)
cubic foot .... cu ft
cubic feet per minute .... cfm
cubic feet per second .... cfs
cubic inch .... cu in.
cubic meter .... cu m or m³
cubic micron .... cu μ or cu mu or μ^3
cubic millimeter .... cu mm or mm³
cubic yard .... cu yd
current density .... spell out
cycles per second .... spell out or c
cylinder .... cyl

day .... spell out
decibel .... db
degree .... deg or °
degree centigrade C
degree Fahrenheit .... F
degree Kelvin .... K
degree Réaumur .... R
delta amplitude, an elliptic function .... dn
diameter .... diam
direct-current (as adjective) .... d-c
dollar .... $
dozen .... doz
dram .... dr

efficiency .... eff
electric .... elec
electromotive force .... emf
elevation .... el
equation .... eq
external .... ext

farad .... spell out or f
feet board measure (board feet) .... fbm
feet per minute .... fpm
feet per second .... fps
fluid .... fl
foot .... ft
foot-candle .... ft-c
foot-Lambert .... ft-L
foot-pound .... ft-lb
foot-pound-second (system) .... fps
foot-second (*see* cubic feet per second)
franc .... fr
free aboard ship .... spell out
free alongside ship .... spell out
freezing point .... fp
frequency .... spell out
fusion point .... fnp

gallon .... gal
gallons per minute .... gpm
gallons per second .... gps
grain .... spell out
gram .... g
gram-calorie .... g-cal
greatest common divisor .... gcd

haversine .... hav
hectare .... ha
henry .... h
high-pressure (adjective) .... h-p
hogshead .... hhd
horsepower .... hp
horsepower-hour .... hp-hr
hour .... hr
hour (in astronomical tables).................. h
hundred C
hundredweight (112 lb) .... cwt
hyperbolic cosine .... cosh
hyperbolic sine .... sinh
hyperbolic tangent .... tanh

inch .... in.
inch-pound .... in-lb
inches per second .... ips
indicated horsepower .... ihp

indicated horsepower-hour .... ihp-hr
inside diameter .... ID
intermediate-pressure (adjective) .... i-p
internal .... int

joule .... j

kilocalorie .... kcal
kilocycles per second .... kc
kilogram .... kg
kilogram-calorie .... kg-cal
kilogram-meter .... kg-m
kilograms per cubic meter .... kg per cu m or
                                                                kg/m^3
kilograms per second .... kgps
kiloliter .... kl
kilometer .... km
kilometers per second .... kmps
kilovolt .... kv
kilovolt-ampere .... kva
kilowatt .... kw
kilowatthour .... kwhr

Lambert L
latitude .... lat or ϕ
least common multiple .... lcm
linear foot .... lin ft
liquid .... liq
lira .... spell out
liter l
logarithm (common) .... log
logarithm (natural) .... log_e or ln
longitude .... long. or λ
low-pressure (as adjective) .... l-p
lumen l
lumen-hour .... l-hr
lumens per watt .... lpw

mass .... spell out
mathematics (-ical) .... math
maximum .... max
mean effective pressure .... mep
mean horizontal candlepower .... mhcp
megacycle .... spell out
megohm .... spell out
melting point .... mp
meter .... m
meter-kilogram .... m-kg
mho .... spell out
microampere .... μa or mu a
microfarad .... μf
microinch .... μin.

micromicrofarad .... μμf
micromicron .... μμ or mu mu
micron .... μ or mu
microvolt .... μv
microwatt .... μw or mu w
mile .... spell out
miles per hour .... mph
miles per hour per second .... mphps
milliampere .... ma
milligram .... mg
millihenry .... mh
millilambert .... mL
milliliter .... ml
millimeter .... mm
millimicron .... mμ or m mu
million .... spell out
million gallons per day .... mgd
millivolt .... mv
minimum .... min
minute .... min
minute (angular measure) .... ′
minute (time) (in astronomical tables) .... m
mole .... spell out
molecular weight .... mol. wt
month .... spell out

National Electrical Code .... NEC

ohm .... spell out or Ω
ohm-centimeter .... ohm-cm
ounce .... oz
ounce-foot .... oz-ft
ounce-inch .... oz-in
outside diameter .... OD

parts per million .... ppm
peck .... pk
penny (pence) .... d
pennyweight .... dwt
per .... spell out
peso .... spell out
pint .... pt
potential .... spell out
potential difference .... spell out
pound .... lb
pound-foot .... lb-ft
pound-inch .... lb-in
pound sterling .... £
pounds per brake horsepower-hour .... lb per bhp-hr
pounds per cubic foot .... lb per cu ft
pounds per square foot .... psf

pounds per square inch .... psi
pounds per square inch absolute .... psia
power factor .... spell out or pf

quart .... qt

radian .... spell out
reactive kilovolt-ampere .... kvar
reactive volt-ampere .... var
revolutions per minute .... rpm
revolutions per second .... rps
rod .... spell out
root mean square .... rms

secant .... sec
second .... sec
second (angular) .... ″
second-foot (*see* cubic feet per second)
second (time) (in astronomical tables) .... s
shaft horsepower .... shp
shilling .... s
sine .... sin
sine of the amplitude, an elliptic function .... sn
specific gravity .... sp gr
specific heat .... sp ht
spherical candle power .... scp
square .... sq
square centimeter .... sq cm or cm^2
square foot .... sq ft

square inch .... sq in.
square kilometer .... sq km or km^2
square meter .... sq m or m^2
square micron .... sq μ or sq mu or μ^2
square millimeter .... sq mm or mm^2
square root of mean square .... rms
standard .... std
stere .... s

tangent .... tan
temperature .... temp
tensile strength .... ts
thousand .... M
thousand foot-pounds .... kip-ft
thousand pound .... kip
ton .... spell out
ton-mile .... spell out

versed sine .... vers
volt v
volt-ampere .... va
volt-coulomb .... spell out

```
watt  .........................................w
watthour  .....................................whr
watts per candle  ..............................wpc
week  .......................................spell out
weight  ......................................wt

yard  .........................................yd
year  .........................................yr
```

2. CAPITALIZATION

General Principle

Too many writers capitalize indiscriminately, without real justification. Capitalization should serve a purpose, not a whim. It should distinguish the *particular* from the *general,* the *proper* from the *common:*

Senator Taft	a former senator
Switzerland	a country, a European country
the English language	any modern language
Essex Corporation	a closed corporation
Fig. 12, Figure 12	the figure

The following rules answer the most frequent questions about capitalizing.

2.1   Capitalize the first word of a sentence—including a sentence in quotation:

> The directors asked for a complete report.
> The doctor reported, "Four men suffered second-degree burns."

2.1.1   Capitalize the first word of a direct question whether or not it is part of another sentence:

> What should the report writer ask himself?
>
> The effective report writer asks himself, Who will read this report? What does he already know? What must he be told?
>
> To the question, What next? there are three answers.
>
> Three questions must be answered: Who? Where? When?

2.1.2   Do not capitalize a fragmentary quotation or the resumption of a separated quotation:

> The doctor reported (that) four men suffered "second-degree burns."
>
> "Four men," the doctor reported, "suffered second-degree burns."

2.1.3   Do not capitalize the first word following a colon when it begins a statement which amplifies, illustrates, or supports the preceding statement (see Section 7.3.1).

2.1.4   Do not capitalize the first word of an expression in parentheses unless the enclosed expression constitutes the entire sentence:

> Apply several coats of shellac (four is the usual number) before waxing.
>
> (Dr. J. A. Hipple was the first to attempt the experiment.)

2.2   Capitalize the principal words (including the first and last) in titles of publications, articles, speeches, and so forth:

> *The Theory of the Leisure Class*
> "Inexpensive Summer Vacations"
> "The Feasibility of Reclaiming Strip-Mined Land"

2.3   Capitalize names of persons, but not the common derivatives of these names:

Angstrom	angstrom (a unit of wave length)
Boycott	boycott
China	china (ceramic)
Diesel	diesel
Henry	henry (unit of inductance)
Macadam	macadamize
Pasteur	pasteurize

2.4   Capitalize titles used in place of specific names already identified:

the Senator (from Ohio)	*but:* one of the senators
the Mayor (of Troy)	any small-city mayor
the Director (of a particular laboratory)	a research director

2.5   Capitalize a title of honor or respect either immediately preceding or following a proper name:

> Professor E. J. Nichols
> Dean Perez
> Dr. John A. Hipple, Vice President, North American Phillips

2.6   Capitalize names of companies, organizations, or institutions— and their abbreviations, if any:

> Columbia Broadcasting System (CBS)
> Tennessee Valley Authority (TVA)
> American Society for Testing Materials (ASTM)
> University of Chicago
> Mellon Institute
> New York Yankees
> Rice Owls

2.7 Capitalize place names:

Allegheny Mountains	U.S. Highway 30	France
Inyo County	Tioga Street	Paris
Zion Canyon	Columbus Circle	the White House
Dust Bowl	Fifth Avenue	the Waldorf-Astoria

2.8 Capitalize points of the compass only when they designate specific areas:

the West	west of the Mississippi
the Middle West	six blocks south
the Far East	facing south
North vs. South	southeastern Utah

2.9 Capitalize historical, racial, and religious names:

Battle of the Bulge	Negro	Catholic
World War II	Caucasian	Lutheran
Treaty of Ghent	Mongoloid	Mohammedan

2.10 Capitalize days of the week, holidays, and months. Do not capitalize seasons:

Monday	Labor Day	Easter	September	fall

2.11 Capitalize registered trademarks:

Kodacolor	Sunoco	Mustang	Norelco

2.12 Capitalize *Fig., Table, No.,* and *Vol.* when they refer to a specific numbered item:

Fig. 5	Table I	No. 5	Vol. 24

2.13 Capitalize letters designating shapes:

T-square	I-beam	L-shaped

2.14 Capitalize abbreviations of academic degrees and similar distinctions:

M.D.	C.E.	Ph. D	M.P.

2.15 Capitalize names of genera, but not names of species:

	Genus	*Species*
man	Homo	sapiens
dog	Canis	familiaris
common lilac	Syringa	vulgaris

3. COMPOUNDING (USE OF THE HYPHEN)

The report writer neglects no tool more than the hyphen. His primary need for it is to show that two or more units (usually words) function as one. Its absence can slow, even stop a reader:

run down home	dual system of payment rule
no smoking signs	selected frost depth measuring points

general purpose insecticide	length to width ratio
slow breaking emulsion	vacuum tower bottoms cutter stock
break even point	the make-work rule attempts to . . .
low cost or free installation	operating experience statistics

Its presence can *change* the meaning:

a large scale map	[a large map drawn to scale]
a large-scale map	[a map drawn to large scale]
high temperature stability	[temperature stability is high]
high-temperature stability	[stability at high temperature]
five gallon containers	[five containers of one-gallon capacity]
five-gallon containers	[containers holding five gallons]
foreign car buyers	[foreign buyers of cars]
foreign-car buyers	[buyers of foreign cars]

The following rules illustrate the principal uses of the hyphen:

3.1   Hyphenate compound adjectives:

door-to-door canvass	alternating-current motor
oil-filled cable	never-to-be-forgotten experiment
ten-ton truck	a 2- to 100-kc peak signal
well-known engineer	induced-draft fan

In technical and business writing, the compound adjective formed from a quantity and a unit is extremely common:

eight-hour day	¼-hp motor	90-acre tract
one-man operation	12-quart pail	1500-degree range

NOTE: Instead of repeating the unit in a series of such compounds, it it included only in the last compound and a comma substituted elsewhere:

first-, second-, and third-effect heaters
4-, 8-, and 12-ft lengths

3.1.1   Adverbs ending in *-ly* do not form compound adjectives:

well-known engineer	*but:* widely known engineer
fast-moving belts	*but:* rapidly moving belts

3.1.2   Adjectives which should be hyphenated *before* a noun should *not* be hyphenated in the predicative position (where actually they become adverb and adjective, adjective and noun, and so on):

Dr. Sauer is a well-known physicist.
The device requires an alternating-current motor.

But: Dr. Sauer is well known as a physicist.
The motor for this device uses alternating current.

3.1.3   Chemical terms used as compound adjectives are not hyphenated:

carbon dioxide extinguisher   methyl chloride solution

3.2   Always use a hyphen after the prefixes *quasi-,* and *self-;* use a hyphen after *ex-* in the sense of *former:*

quasi-corporation   self-actuating   ex-manager

3.3   Hyphenate spelled-out compound numbers from twenty-one to ninety-nine whether used alone or in combination:

thirty-three   one hundred thirty-three   thirty-three hundredths

NOTE: See Section 6 for rules governing the use of numbers.

3.4   Hyphenate mixed numbers and spelled-out fractions:

1-3/16 (*not* 1 3/16)   five-eighths   one-fourth

3.5   Hyphenate *any* word to prevent confusion or awkward spelling:

cave-in	bull-like	re-treat
re-entry	micro-organism	re-cover
pre-empt	bird's-eye view	un-ionized
co-op	anti-inflationary	un-American

3.6   In general, do not hyphenate compound nouns:

book value	gas engine	view finder
living costs	pig iron	test stand
parking space	safety belt	toggle switch
textbook	horsepower	rollback
classroom	framework	eyepiece
roommate	workmen	dovetail

but:

degree-day	H-bomb	secretary-treasurer
light-year	I-beam	father-in-law
passenger-mile	U-turn	walkie-talkie

The treatment of compound nouns is so varied that the careful writer will consult a reputable dictionary when in doubt.

NOTE: All but one of the following compounds are written solid:

anybody	everybody	somebody	no one	myself
anyhow	everyday	somehow	nobody	yourself
anyone	everyone	someday	nothing	herself
anything	everything	someone	nowhere	himself
anytime	everywhere	something	whatever	itself
anyway		sometimes	whoever	ourselves
anywhere		somewhat	whichever	yourselves
		somewhere		themselves
				oneself

3.7   Use a hyphen when it is necessary to divide a word at the right-hand margin. Divide, of course, only between syllables.

4. SPELLING

Spelling is the writer's responsibility, not his secretary's. Though *mis*spelling seldom prevents communication, it can impair it:

> The operator used to much waist motion.
> All the streets had gentile slopes.
> The company advertised for lavatory personnel.

A misspelled word is a malformed symbol. If the reader notices the malformation, his mind no longer concentrates on the idea the symbol was meant to convey. The result is a loss in efficiency. There is also a loss in the reader's respect for the writer—if the writer is careless in this detail, he may be in others.

Few of us spell so well that we need no dictionary. Yet as useful as the dictionary is, some spelling problems are so common to business and technical writing that it is worthwhile to consider them here. See also Section 2, Capitalization, and Section 3, Compounding and Hyphenation.

4.1   *Forming Plural Nouns.* The plural of nearly all English nouns is formed simply by adding *s:*

alibi	alibis	bridge	bridges
dynamo	dynamos	curriculum	curriculums
zero	zeros	T-square	T-squares

Although exceptions continue to diminish in number, a few important ones remain:

4.1.1   Where an *s* would be unpronounceable add *es:*

gas	gases	church	churches	appendix	appendixes
tax	taxes	class	classes	index	indexes
box	boxes	loss	losses	waltz	waltzes

4.1.2   When common (but not proper) nouns end in *y* preceded by a consonant, change the *y* to *i* and add *es:*

but:

body	bodies	category	categories	tray	trays
city	cities	country	countries	buoy	buoys
ally	allies	carry	carries	Kennedy	Kennedys

4.1.3   For a few common nouns ending in *f* or *fe* substitute *ves:*

calf	calves	life	lives	self	selves
half	halves	wife	wives	sheaf	sheaves
leaf	leaves	knife	knives	loaf	loaves

4.1.4 A reasonable simplification of the involved rules for pluralizing compound terms would be "Use common sense." Preferably, add the *s* to the significant word or the last word:

commanders-in-chief	passers-by
assistant chiefs of staff	men-of-war
blocks and tackles	coats of arms
assistant directors	higher-ups
grants-in-aid	tie-ins

4.1.5 To form the plural of letters, symbols, figures, and abbreviations,* add *'s:*

A's   OK's   1900's   0's   Btu's*   psi's*

4.1.6 A few nouns have a common form for singular and plural or have no singular form at all. Typical examples:

deer	species	acoustics
apparatus	series	hydraulics
goods	pincers	tactics
means	pliers	politics
morals	scissors	economics
odds	trousers	mathematics

4.1.7 A number of foreign (or early English) words retain their original plurals—either because the plural form is solidly established in our language or because the anglicized plural would be displeasing in sound. Some of the troublesome ones:

alumnus	alumni	analysis	analyses	oasis	oases
axis	axes	basis	bases	paralysis	paralyses
bacillus	bacilli	crisis	crises	parenthesis	parentheses
criterion	criteria	diagnosis	diagnoses	synopsis	synopses
genus	genera	ellipsis	ellipses	synthesis	syntheses
larva	larvae	emphasis	emphases	thesis	theses
locus	loci	hypothesis	hypotheses	addendum	addenda
louse	lice	metamorphosis	metamorphoses	agendum	agenda
minutia	minutiae	neurosis	neuroses	datum	data
ovum	ova	series	series	erratum	errata
phenomenon	phenomena	species	species		
radius	radii	stimulus	stimuli		

* But see Section 1.3. Most abbreviations have no plural form except for reference to the abbreviations themselves:

In counting abbreviations he found 55 Btu's.
The process requires 1500 Btu.

4.1.7.1   A few of those foreign words whose plurals have been anglicized:

aquarium	aquariums	antenna	antennas	appendix	appendixes
curriculum	curriculums	dogma	dogmas	index	indexes
maximum	maximums	formula	formulas	vertex	vertexes
medium	mediums			vortex	vortexes
memorandum	memorandums	adieu	adieus		
minimum	minimums	beau	beaus	cactus	cactuses
sanatorium	sanatoriums	plateau	plateaus	focus	focuses
sanitarium	sanitariums			genius	geniuses
stadium	stadiums			octopus	octopuses

4.2   *Forming the Possessive Case (the Apostrophe):* Mistakes in forming (and failing to form) the possessive case are very common. Most result from carelessness, but an appreciable number are caused by ignorance of the following simple rules:*

4.2.1   If the noun, whether it is singular or plural, does not end in *s,* add *'s:*

John	John's	horse	horse's
child	child's	children	children's
owner	owner's	company	company's
man	man's	men	men's
someone	someone's	someone else	someone else's

4.2.2   If the noun ends in *s,* add only the apostrophe:

managers	managers'
boys	boys'
countries	countries'

4.2.3   In forming the possessive of inanimate objects, prefer the *of* phrase to the apostrophe:

the size of the plant	*not*	the plant's size
the face of the dial	*not*	the dial's face

4.2.4   Never use an apostrophe to show possession with the possessive pronouns *my, mine; your, yours; his, her, hers, its; our, ours; their, theirs;* or with the relative pronoun *whose.* An apostrophe used with these represents a contraction:

you're	you are
he's	he is, he has
it's	it is, it has
who's	who is, who has

NOTE: The apostrophe is used to indicate other contractions (*can't* for *cannot; don't* for *do not; '33* for *1933*) and, as indicated in 4.1.5, to pluralize letters, figures, or symbols:

A's   18's   #'s .

* For the report writer, the few minor exceptions are not worth inclusion here.

5. PREFERRED USAGE (GLOSSARY)

This text considers only those problems of grammar and diction found most troublesome by the business and technical writer.

a, an	Use *a* before all words beginning with a consonant sound (including *h*); otherwise use *an:*

a hotel	a history	a hydraulic press
an ending	an hour	an *n*th root

above	Do not use *above* as a noun ("the above proves"). Avoid it as an adjective ("the above statement"). Avoid it as an adverb ("as stated above"). Do not use the awkward *above-mentioned, aforementioned,* or other such phrases. Preferably, restate the subject or use a synonym.
affect, effect	*Affect* is always a verb meaning to *influence* ("Moisture does not affect its performance") or *to simulate* ("The foreman affected a gruff manner"). *Effect* is usually a noun meaning *result* ("These are the effects of exposure"), but is occasionally a verb meaning *to bring about* ("Adding cuprite effected a complete change in color").
agree	Agree *with* a person; agree *to* a thing.
agreement	In any clause, the verb must agree in number with its subject. Two special cases are worth noting:

1. In the pattern *one of those who, one of the plans which, one of those methods that,* the verb is plural:

   This is one of those plans that *look* good on paper.

2. In an *either-or* or a *neither-nor* sentence, the verb agrees with the nearer subject:

   Either his plan or those already discussed *are* suitable.

   Neither the plans already discussed nor this one *is* suitable.

all ready, already	*All ready* means *everyone is ready; already* means *by this time.*
all together, altogether	*All together* means *all in a group; altogether* means *completely.*
among	See *between.*

amount, number	*Amount* is used for things in bulk or mass, *number* for things which are countable (see *fewer, less*): a large amount of potash a large number of machines
and etc.	Because *etc.* means *and so forth,* drop the *and.*
and/or	Most authorities, including the American Standards Association, condemn this usage (see p. 52): *Not:* welding and/or riveting *But:* welding, riveting, or both
ante-, anti-	Sometimes confused: *ante-* means *before; anti-* means *against.*
as	Avoid using *as* for *since* or *because:* *Not:* The power was cut as men were working on the line. *But* (time sense): As oxygen was administered, his breathing improved.
as, like	See *like.*
as per	Meaningless. Use *according to* or a synonym.
as to	Do not use for *of* or *about:* *Not:* We are certain as to his reliability.
bad, badly	Be sure that you mean the adverb when you use it, especially after verbs like *seem, appear, taste, smell,* and *feel:* He feels bad. [He is unhappy physically or mentally.] He feels badly. [His ability to sense by touching is poor.]
balance, remainder, rest	*Balance* is used in the sense of equilibrium. Do not use it for *rest* or *remainder* in formal writing.
beside, besides	*Beside* means *next to; besides* means *in addition to.*
between, among	*Between* preferably implies only two objects; *among* implies more than two.
can, may	*Can* is generally acceptable for *may* in the sense of permission.
capacity, rating	Not interchangeable. A motor's *rating* may be lower than its *capacity.*

cite, quote;
   sight, site

The report writer uses *cite* or *citation* to mean a reference to another's work for illustration, explanation, or proof. Such a reference would be actually *quoted* only if the writer employed the original wording exactly. The homonyms *cite, sight,* and *site* are confused more in spelling than in meaning.

claim

Do not use *claim* for *assert or maintain* but only in the sense of *to demand as being due.*

common

See *mutual.*

contact

As a verb, *contact* is so vague that careful writers still avoid using it.

continual,
   continuous

Continual means *repeated frequently; continuous* means *repeated without interruption.* The distinction can be important.

contractions

Contractions (for example, *we're, you're, I'll, can't*) are seldom used in formal reports.

credible,
   credulous

See *incredible.*

data

Usage still demands, somewhat illogically, that *data* be considered a plural (singular *datum*):

   The data are convincing.

disinterested,
   uninterested

Disinterested means *unbiased, without selfish interest; uninterested* means *indifferent, without interest of any kind.* A *disinterested* witness would be impartial; an *uninterested* witness would be inattentive.

due to

The chief objection to *due to* is that it is overworked, particularly in technical writing. It is grammatically incorrect as an adverb in place of *because of:*

   Not: It expanded due to the heat.
   But: It expanded because of the heat.
   Or: Its expansion was due to the heat.

economic,
   economical

Economic refers to the science of economics (production, distribution, consumption); *economical* means *frugal, not wasteful.*

electric,
   electrical

Use *electric* to describe anything in which electricity is actually present (for example, electric motor, heater, control); use *electrical* in the abstract sense of *pertaining to electricity* (for example, an electrical engineer, the electrical industry) or in the figurative sense:

Response to the announcement was electrical.

factor   Not accurate for *consideration* or *part*. Webster defines it as *one of the elements that contribute to produce a result:*

Not: Financing is an important factor in industry.
But: Good financing was an important factor in establishing this industry.

fewer,
less   *Fewer* refers to countable objects; *less* refers to bulk or mass (See *amount.*):

less potash
fewer bags of potash

the field of   The phrase *the field of* is almost always deadwood:

Not: in the field of cryogenics
But: in cryogenics

flammable,
inflammable   Prefer the short form.

healthful,
healthy   *Healthful* means *good for one's health; healthy* means *having good health.*

healthy tree   healthful exercise
healthy body   healthful climate

imply,
infer   *Imply* means *to hint, to intimate,* or *to suggest;* but exactly used, *infer* means *to draw a conclusion from evidence.*

in, into   Generally *in* locates and *into* directs:

The trouble is in the supercharger.
The maintenance man had to go into the mud drums.

incredible,
incredulous   *Incredible* means *unbelievable; incredulous* means *unbelieving:*

an incredible feat   *but*   an incredulous onlooker

inside of,
within   Do not use *inside of* for *within* (for example, *within* a year; not *inside of* a year).

inter-,
intra-   Often confused. *Inter-* means *between* (for example, *inter*collegiate); *intra-* means *inside* (for example, *intra*company).

irregardless   A corruption of *regardless.*

is when, is where	Do not use these expressions to introduce a noun clause in a definitive statement: *Not:* Erosion is when. . . . *But:* Erosion occurs when. . . .
its, it's, (its')	*Its* and *it's* are very frequently and very improperly interchanged. *Its'* is an improper form, perhaps an attempt at the plural possessive of it (which is *their*). *Its,* of course, is the possessive pronoun and *it's* a contraction of *it is* or *it has.*
-ize	Though the suffix *-ize* in the sense *to make into* can be useful in saving words (for example, *pluralize* for *to form the plural of*), avoid awkward or unnecessary applications of it (for example, finalize, directorize, accountize).
kind of, sort of	Colloquial for *somewhat* or *rather.*
later, latter	Carelessly interchanged. *Later,* of course, means *after* in a time sense; *latter* means *the second of two.*
leave, let	*Leave* implies departure, *let* permission: Leave the valve open. [Don't close it.] Let the valve open. [Permit it to open.] Let him close the valve. [Permit him to close it.] Leave him close the valve. [Incorrect.] Leave him to his thoughts. [Correct.]
less	See *fewer.*
last, latest	*Last* means *final; latest* means *most recent.*
lay, lie	Perpetual troublemakers. *Lay* is transitive (requires an object) and means *to place; lie* is intransitive (can have no object) and means *to recline:* He lays the sample on the bench before. . . . He laid the sample on the bench before. . . . He had laid the sample on the bench. . . . The sample lies on the bench. The sample lay on the bench this morning. The sample has lain on the bench all day.
lightening, lightning	*Lightening* means *making lighter; lightning* is the companion of thunder.

like, as, as if	Formal English still rejects *like* as a conjunction: The gage behaved as (not like) we expected. It look as if (not like) there is internal thrust.
along the lines of, in the line of	Wasteful and usually meaningless: *Not:* what we have in the line of additives *But:* what we have in additives *Not:* along the lines of the Fox refinery *But:* like the Fox refinery
lots of, a lot of	Colloquial for *many, much, a great many, a large number,* and so forth.
maximum, optimum	Strong words. Use them with restraint. They are not interchangeable. Maximum (*greatest*) output is not necessarily optimum (*best*) output.
mil, mill	A *mil* is 0.001 inch; a *mill* is $0.001.
most, almost	Do not use the adjective *most* for the adverb *almost:* *Not:* most all the men *But:* almost all the men
mutual, common	Preferably *mutual* refers to two objects or persons, *common* to more than two.
number	See *amount.*
a number, the number	*A number* generally refers to several persons or things and thus requires a plural verb; *the number* generally refers to a total and takes a singular verb: There are a number of solutions. The number of leaks has increased.
-one	Write *-one* solid with *any, every,* and *some,* unless the *one* is stressed: Everyone must attend. Every one of us will attend.
only	Do not use for *but:* *Not:* We would have met our quota only the lines burst.
only, just	Misunderstanding can result from improper placement of these words in the word order. Better emphasis is obtained and possible confusion

avoided by placing them next to the word they describe or limit:

> They only stored the pyroborate. [No manufacturing.]
> They stored only the pyroborate. [Nothing else.]
> The mill just produced 200 tons. [Recently produced.]
> The mill produced just 200 tons. [Only 200 tons.]

optimum

See *maximum.*

party,
person,
individual

Except in legal language, do not use *party to* refer to a single person. Use *individual* in the abstract sense ("the rights of the individual").

percent (%),
percentage

Percent or its symbol % should be used only with a number—and in modern practice the symbol is much preferred. *Percentage* should never be used with a number.

99.44 percent   99.44%   a small percentage

personal,
personnel

Often confused, probably, through carelessness in spelling. A *personal* secretary attends to private, social, or nonbusiness affairs; a *personnel* manager selects new employees for a company.

practicable,
practical

Use *practicable* to describe what *could be* practiced. Use *practical* (opposed to *theoretical*) for *sensible* when applied to persons, for *efficient* when applied to things:

> Building a bridge across a large body of water would probably be practicable (it could be done), but it wouldn't be practical without enough traffic to pay for the construction.

principal,
principle

Principal, as either a noun or an adjective, always means *chief. Principle* is always a noun meaning *a general truth* or *a fixed rule:*

> The principle of this device is. . . .
> The principal method of obtaining fresh water. . . .

proposition

Colloquial for *proposal, offer,* or *plan.*

raise, rise
(verbs)

Raise is transitive (requires an object) and means *to lift. Rise* is *intransitive* (can have no object) and means *to get up* or *to go up:*

> Raise the level. The storm raised the level.
> The water is rising. The water in the lake rose.

real

In formal writing, avoid using *real* in the sense of *very* or *really.*

reason is because

Awkward and redundant. Use "The reason for . . . is that. . . ."

reason why

Also redundant. Drop one or the other:

> Here is the reason why it failed.
> This is the reason why it failed.

seasonable, seasonal

Seasonable means *suitable to the season; seasonal* means *pertaining to or dependent upon the seasons:*

> Bitter winds are not seasonable in May.
> Most seasonal work is performed by migrant workers.

respectfully, respectively

Embarrassing to the writer who confuses them. Both are overworked. *Respectfully* (meaning *with respect*) should be used as a complimentary close in a letter only when respect is justly due. *Respectively* (meaning *each in the order given*) requires the reader to backtrack in his reading.

said

As an adjective, suitable only in legal documents.

sewage, sewerage

Sewage is waste matter; *sewerage* is the disposal system.

set, sit

Set is transitive (requires an object) and means *to put or place down. Sit,* meaning *to be seated,* is intransitive (can have no object):

> Set the drums over there.
> He can sit as he works.

sort of

Colloquial for *somewhat* or *rather.*

specie, species

Specie means *coin. Species* (same form for singular and plural) means *variety* or *category.*

strata

Strata is the preferred plural of *stratum,* a layer of air, rock, or tissue.

their, there, they're

Confused through carelessness, but confused nevertheless:

> They are in their places. [Plural possessive.]
> They belong there. [Adverb of place.]
> They're not in the right place. [Contraction of *they* and *are.*]

split infinitive	There is no longer any objection to splitting an infinitive if the resulting construction is clearer or less awkward:

To better acquaint the public. . . . [Clear]
Better to acquaint the public. . . . [Awkward]

The Germans had failed seriously to halt the Allied offensive. [Ambiguous. Clarify by inserting *seriously* after *to*—splitting the infinitive.]

But: Entries are sufficiently informative to frequently obviate the necessity of going to the files. [Reword: Frequently entries are sufficiently informative to obviate, *or* Entries are often sufficiently informative to obviate. . . .]

these kind	*This* and *that* are the only adjectives in the language with plural forms. They must agree in number with the nouns they modify:

this kind, sort   these kinds, sorts
that kind, sort   those kinds, sorts

to, too, two	Be careful in spelling these words.
try (noun)	Acceptable for *effort* or *attempt* but such usage is not preferable in formal writing.
type, type of	Avoid *type* as an adjective:

Not: This type nozzle. . . .
But: This type of nozzle. . . .

verbal, oral	Strictly, *verbal* means *in words, written or spoken; oral* means *spoken.*
very	Be sure it is useful; it is often unnecessary:

Very is not of very much use as in intensive.
Sales were very much overestimated.

while	*While* should be used to express time relationships. Its use for *though* is weak and for *and* or *but* inaccurate:

Right: Don't oil the machinery while it is running.
Weak: Welding is best, while riveting is adequate.
Poor: Their work is completed, while ours is just begun.

unique	*Unique* means *having no like or equal;* it should not be compared. The same logic applies to optimum, maximum, square, circular, and so forth.

Not: The Trona process was very unique.
But: The process was very nearly unique.
Similarly: The figure was more nearly square.

6. NUMBERS

General Principle

In business and technical writing, prefer figures to spelled-out numbers. Sometimes, however, appearance, consistency, or clarity is better served by the longer form. The following specific rules often apply to ordinal as well as cardinal numbers.

6.1 *Spell Out:*

    6.1.1   Whole numbers under ten when used in text [Exception: 6.2.2]:

> The laboratory runs eight samples every hour.
> The eighth sample revealed foam contamination.

    6.1.2   Numbers beginning sentences, captions, or headings, and numbers related to and closely following them:

> Forty per cent is refunded.
> Twenty chemists will be needed.
> Twenty chemists and twenty-five engineers. . . .
> Fifty years of expansion. . . .
> *But:* 1960 Production Costs. [Large numbers in captions and headings are represented by figures.]

Suggestion: By rewording, move the number into the sentence:

> The job will require 20 chemists and 25 engineers.

    6.1.3   Numbers representing round-number approximations or indefinite expressions:

> two or three thousand units per day
> less than a thousand dollars a week
> the early thirties

NOTE: The words *about, approximately, nearly,* and so forth, are not usually considered introducers of indefinite expressions in this sense:

> nearly 12 years
> almost 40 hours
> approximately a thousand man-hours

    6.1.4   The first (sometimes the shorter) of two adjacent numbers not separated by punctuation:

> three 110-volt transformers   *but*   March 21, 1940
> The firemen were expected to work twenty 12-hour shifts.
> The order called for 126 forty-foot lengths.

    6.1.5   Fractions standing alone (see Section 6.2.5.1).

6.2   *Use Figures For:*

6.2.1   Numbers over nine [Exceptions: 6.1.2]:

10   439   1503   14,244

6.2.2   Related numbers in a sentence or consecutive sentences when one or more are larger than nine:

The crude came from 16 fields, 5 of them foreign.
The chemist takes 4, 8, or 12 samples daily.
The vehicles are designed for 8-, 10-, or 12-man crews.

6.2.3   Serial numbers and numbered objects:

Figure 5 (or Fig. 5)   Generator No. 4
Ohio Route 45   Part 23676593
Chapter 2   Pages 9-13

6.2.4   Decimals:

4.256   0.256   0.35 inch   11.35 inches   14.6 in.

NOTE: Prefer decimals to all but the commonest fractions except in businesses where fractions are customary (for example, the clothing and the construction industries). Decimals are simpler to read, type, or print.

6.2.4.1   Place a cipher before a decimal less than unity:

0.14   0.196   0.3487

6.2.4.2   Place ciphers after a decimal point or after the last figure to the right only when needed for exactness or consistency:

$75,000   *not* $75,000.00

But: at a unit cost of 0.004
at a unit cost of 0.0040 [If 4th place is significant.]
either $3.00 or $3.02 per thousand

6.2.5   Fractions and mixed numbers:

1/2-in. pipe   1-1/4 to 1-3/4 tons   3/4-hr intervals

6.2.5.1   Major exception: Fractions standing alone (not followed immediately by a unit) should be spelled out:

one-tenth as large
three-eighths of an inch
two-thirds rotation
three thirty-seconds (see Section 6.3.4.2.)

6.2.5.2   Use figures for fractions in compound modifiers:

1/4-hp motor   1/10-sec intervals

6.2.5.3   In typing mixed numbers, separate the integer from the fraction by a hyphen to prevent misreading:

    1-5/16   *not*   1 5/16 [which could be read 15/16]

6.2.6   Percentages, proportion, ratio:

    12.5%   87-1/2%   0.5%
    1:3 [often: 1 to 3]   1:3:5   1:50,000

6.2.7   Most numbers in compound modifiers (but see Section 6.1.4):

    60-cycle motor   3-ft radius *   8-hour shift

6.2.8   All numbers appearing in tables, diagrams, graphs. [Lower-case letters are used for footnote indexes in tabular matter to avoid confusion with exponents.]

6.2.9   Units of measurement, quantity, and time:

    9 by 12 inches   14 tons   63 cents   12 noon
    9 x 12 in.   20/20 vision 6 centimeters 8:50 P.M.
    $1450   *not* $1450 dollars   *or*   1450 dollars
    August 12, 1910   August 1910   12 August 1910
        August 12   12th of August
    4th of June   *but*   Fourth of July
    the 1st of June [Specific day]   *but*   the first [part] of June [General period]
    60 years old   14 years 6 months 5 days

NOTE: For large numbers in text use the words *million, billion,* and so forth.

    185 million persons $340 billion

6.2.10   To refer to numbers appearing on dials, scales, and so forth:

    Meter readings of 3.0, 3.5, and 4.1 were . . .
    When the needle drops below 0, recalibrate.

NOTE: Where misreading could result, spell out.

6.2.11   For house numbers (except one), and for street names requiring more than one word:

    439 West Prospect Avenue
    9 First Street NW
    502 East 101st Street
    70 Twenty-second Avenue

* In technical writing, standard abbreviations are often used in such compounds.

6.3   *Punctuation of Numbers:*

6.3.1   Omit the comma from a four-digit number:

2968   4352   6796   *but*   34,156

NOTE: For alignment, the comma is inserted in four-digit numbers appearing in columns containing larger numbers.

6.3.2   Commas are generally omitted from serial numbers regardless of length:

Part No. 1564734D   Engine 387456

6.3.3   Use a colon to express ratios (see Section 6.2.6).

6.3.4   Use a hyphen in mixed numbers, in spelled-out fractions, and in compound numbers 21 through 99 if they must be spelled out.

6.3.4.1   In mixed numbers:

44-3/4   1-5/16

6.3.4.2   In spelled-out fractions (unless part of the fraction already contains a hyphen):

three-fourths   seven-eighths   *but*
three thirty-seconds

6.3.4.3   In compound numbers from 21 to 99 if they must be spelled out:

ninety-nine   one hundred ninety-nine

6.4   *Miscellaneous Number Problems:*

6.4.1   Do not repeat units in a series unless they are represented by symbols:

loads of 6, 8, 12, and 14 tons
But: priced at $6, $7, $9, and $12

6.4.2   Use the singular form of a unit following fractions or decimals less than unity. Most abbreviations have no plural form (see Section 1.3):

0.14 mile   5/16 in.   3/4 lb   *but*   3.5 inches

6.4.3   Except in legal documents, do not repeat a spelled-out number in figures or vice versa:

$35,000   *not* $35,000 (thirty-five thousand dollars)
seven men   *not*   seven (7) men

6.4.4   Avoid roman numerals unless two numbering systems are required for differentation.

7. PUNCTUATION

Because a worthwhile treatment of punctuation requires a complex system of division and subdivision, an outline of the section is provided to expedite reference.

7.1 General Rules
7.2 The Full Stops: the Period, Exclamation Mark, the Question Mark
7.3 Strong Internal Punctuation:
      7.3.1 The colon
      7.3.2 The semicolon
7.4 Weak Internal Punctuation:
      7.4.1 The comma is used:
      7.4.2 The comma is NOT used:
      7.4.3 Parentheses
      7.4.4 The Dash
      7.4.5 Brackets
7.5 Special Marks
      7.5.1 Ellipses
      7.5.2 Quotation Marks
      The apostrophe (see Section 4.2)
      The hyphen (see Section 3.)

General Principle: The marks of punctuation were devised to help the reader, not to perplex the writer. Just as algebraic symbols mark off mathematical units or identify mathematical procedures, so punctuational symbols mark off grammatical units or identify rhetorical meanings.

7.1   *General Rules:*

    7.1.1   Punctuate functionally—punctuation should be useful, not whimsical.

    7.1.2   Punctuate sparingly.

    7.1.3   Do not use two or more marks of punctuation together.

    EXCEPTIONS:

    7.1.3.1   At the end of a quotation.

        The instructor said, "Place the period and the comma inside closing quotes." [And see Section 7.5.2.6].

    7.1.3.2   After a question, exclamation, or complete sentence enclosed in parentheses, brackets, or dashes [themselves marks of punctuation].

        . . . rockets using solid fuels (Only liquid fuels had been used before). [Note that

triple punctuation is not required here—
no period inside the parentheses.]

7.1.3.3   After an abbreviation occurring at a point
requiring a mark other than the period
[But *two* periods are not needed to end
a sentence ending in an abbreviation].

. . . gears, pulleys, levers, etc., which are
useful in. . . . They were taught to use
gears, pulleys, levers, etc.

7.1.4   Use common sense. If a statement can be misread
without punctuation, punctuate it.

Not: In drilling the men must learn to . . .
But: In drilling, the men must learn to . . .

7.2   *The Period and Other Full Stops:* None of the terminal marks
of punctuation (the period, the exclamation mark, and the
question mark) gives the average report writer much trouble.
Application is simple: use the period at the end of any sentence
that is neither an exclamation nor a question; use the other
marks as required:

The tools aren't here.   [A plain statement of fact.]
The tools aren't here!   [An expression of surprise.]
The tools aren't here?   [A question equivalent to: Aren't the
                            tools here?]

Also, use a period after:

7.2.1   Nontechnical abbreviations:

etc.   Mr.   U.S.   govt.   a.m.   vol.   Inc.

But do *not* use a period after any of the following:

7.2.2   Standard technical abbreviations:

psi   fbm   hp   Btu   cfm   kgps

7.2.3   Abbreviations of compound names of government
agencies, well-known Societies, and so forth:

TVA SEC FCC ASA ASEE ASTM ASME IRE

7.2.4   Chemical symbols:

Fe   Cu   Mg   NaOH   NaCl

7.2.5   Single letters, as used in:

L-shaped   T-square   I-beam   X-ray

7.2.6   Abbreviations of ordinal numbers:

1st   2nd   3rd   21st   99th   101st

7.2.7   Any heading not followed on the same line by text.

7.2.8   Items in list form unless they are complete sentences [7.2.7 and 7.2.8 illustrate this rule.]

7.3   *Strong Internal Punctuation:* Use the colon and the semicolon to indicate a break in grammatical continuity less sharp than that indicated by a period but sharper than that indicated by a comma.

7.3.1   Use the colon in the sense of *as follows* or *that is:*

7.3.1.1   To separate a statement (grammatically an independent clause) from another statement used to amplify, illustrate, or support the first:

> Two reasons for the breakdown were discovered: the filters had not been cleaned, and the temperature of the solution had not been kept high enough to prevent crystallization.
>
> The plan is impractical: it would be cheaper to buy the equipment outright.
>
> Stamp collecting is more than a hobby: it is a multimillion-dollar business.
>
> Good writing is like good golf: it requires practice.
>
> We have three other choices: (1)———, (2)———, and (3)———.

7.3.1.2   To introduce examples, lengthy quotations, or vertical enumeration. [Note the use of the colon in the first line of Section 7.3.1 and in introducing the examples under 7.3.1.1.] Long quotations thus introduced are customarily single-spaced and extra-indented from both margins.

7.3.1.3   After the salutation of a business letter (though some proponents of open punctuation omit punctuation there as well as after the complimentary close in order to be consistent).

7.3.1.4   Between the city of publication and the name of the publisher in a bibliographical entry for a book:

> Englewood Cliffs, N.J.: Prentice-Hall, Inc., 1965.
>
> New York: The Macmillan Company, 1963.

7.3.1.5   Between hours and minutes in numerical expressions of time:

7:38 p.m.   11:45 a.m.   *but*   12 noon

7.3.2   Use the semicolon to obtain more separative force than obtainable with a comma:

7.3.2.1   To separate two or more grammatically independent clauses so closely related in meaning that as a writer you do not wish to make separate sentences of them:

It is cold in his lab; wear heavy clothing.

The practice is worse than expensive; it is dangerous.

We ordered a carload; our experience had indicated that the material is remarkably resistant to abrasion.

NOTE: Use the semicolon, *not* the comma, between independent clauses whose relationship is expressed by such words as *accordingly, therefore, however, thus* (conjunctive adverbs). And to stress the separation, you may use a semicolon before *and, but, or, nor, for* [the coordinating conjunctions], particularly when the clauses are long:

He had not organized his ideas in his own mind; therefore his speech was ineffective.

Failure followed failure; but he kept on.

7.3.2.2   Between elements in a series when one or more of the elements contain lesser punctuation:

the procedure involved four steps: (1) —————————; (2)————————; (3)—————, —————, —————; (4)——————.

Chicago, Illinois; Cleveland, Ohio; New York, New York

[In this use, the semicolon bears the same relation to the comma as, in algebra, the bracket does to the parenthesis.]

7.3.2.3   As internal punctuation before independent clauses introduced by *that is, namely, for example, thus:*

Punctuating requires judgment; for example, a writer must choose between a colon and a semicolon when either is correct, but one is just a little more precise.

7.4   *Weak Internal Punctuation:* The comma, by far the most com mon and most difficult mark of punctuation, is used for great variety of purposes, but always to make the grammatica relationship of sentence elements clear to the reader.

7.4.1   The comma IS used:

7.4.1.1   To separate two independent clauses joine by a coordinating conjunction [*and, but, o nor, for*].

The building can be amortized over twenty-year period, or it can be purchase outright from cash reserves.

NOTE: When the clauses are short, you can usually omit the comma

The potash found a ready market but th borax didn't.

7.4.1.2   To separate introductory groups of word from the rest of the sentence:

The insulation having been applied, th building was ready for the experimen [An absolute construction.]
When the insulation had been applied, th building. . . . [An adverbial clause.]
In the underground gasification of coal, th basic problem consists of. . . . [A prep ositional phrase.]
Realizing how important to the compan this contract was, he flew to Los Angel [A participial phrase.]

NOTE: Use a comma after short introductory elements only when the would be misread without punctuation:

For this reason he flew home. [Comm unnecessary.]
After the sludge had been dried the heavi salts were. . . . [Comma optional.]
Although hydrogenation plants did succee in meeting Germany's fuel needs durir the war, their operation was prohibitive expensive. [Comma necessary.]
Soon after they joined, the corporation di solved. [Comma necessary.]

7.4.1.3   To set off nonrestrictive elements, elemen *not essential* to the intended meaning:

This company, which has been in oper tion since 1870, ...

Consolidated Steel, in operation since 1870, ...

[The elements marked off are simply added information; they do not identify the company, do not restrict it from being some other company.]

Ebaugh, the chief chemist, stated. . . .

[Ebaugh is restricted by his own name. If the commas were omitted, the writer would be distinguishing Ebaugh the chemist from some other Ebaugh with whom the reader could confuse him.]

IPORTANT NOTE: It is equally important *not* to set off restrictive elements with commas:

Not: The company will buy anything, *guaranteed by Truby.*

Not: The company will buy anything, *that is guaranteed by Truby.*

[The italicized elements are essential to the meaning and *must not* be set off by a comma.]

We need the plans *he brought yesterday.*

The break was not discovered *until the plant was shut down.*

No equipment *made of steel* is suitable.

No equipment *that is made of steel* is suitable.

The flowmeter *second from the left* needs calibrating.

In these last seven examples the sentences would have a different eaning (or no meaning at all) without the italicized elements, which, erefore, are essential to the sentences and must not be set off by mmas.

7.4.1.4   To set off parenthetical, interrupting, or displaced elements:

By all those who ever knew his work, Beese was considered an excellent photographer.

Production, *usually down in the summer months,* continued to increase in July.

In July 1945, *before Hiroshima,* Vannevar Bush submitted his report, *Science, the Endless Frontier,* to President Truman.

Production schedules must be cut, *at least in the soda products plant.*

The major problems, *concerned primari*
with installation, were solved by 1964.
That this is not proof, we realize, but. . .

7.4.1.5   To set off three or more elements of
series:

NOTE: Though the comma is often omitted between the last two item
of a series (that is, before the *and* or the *or*), it is sound
practice to include it.

The company contemplates new plants
Troy, Utica, and Syracuse.
The coordinating conjunctions are *an*
but, or, nor, and *for.*
The plan is not feasible because of the hig
initial investment, the small quantity
benzene that can be produced, and th
excessive competition.
In the years 1938-1943, according to th
CAA, an average of one in every 11
civilian planes was involved in a fatal acc
dent, one in every 49 was demolished
an accident, and one in every 6 or 7 w
in an accident causing major damag
[NOTE: If one or more of the clauses co
tained internal punctuation (commas
then semicolons should have been subst
tuted for the commas.]

7.4.1.6   To separate two or more adjectives prece
ing a noun—but *only* when the adjectiv
separately modify the noun. When the fir
adjective of the two modifies the combin
tion of the following adjective-plus-nou
no comma should be used.

NOTE: Do *not* insert a comma between the last adjective in the seri
and the noun:

a risky, borderline venture
the obvious, existing market
a tall, imposing building

but:

bright red paint
current political trends
boiler feed water

7.4.1.7   To separate adjacent numbers (particular
in dates) or identical words:

April 14, 1964 [But prefer 14 April 196

That he didn't know what it was, was evident.

There was a total of 42,216, 33,000 of which were obsolete [Even better, reword.]

7.4.1.8 To separate name from title, surname from inverted given name or initials:

E. F. Osborn, Vice President for Research
Osborn, E. F. [Inverted for alphabetizing.]

7.4.1.9 To separate units of three digits in numbers of more than four digits, and in four-digit numbers if they occur in columns containing larger numbers:

13,000 111,564 41,221,300 *but* 1651

[In tables it is often preferable to separate each three digits by a space.]

7.4.1.10 To separate a quotation from the rest of the sentence:

"These filters," he explained, "require constant checking."
The manager asked, "When are . . . ?"
[For placement of quotation marks see Section 7.5.1.]

7.4.2 The comma IS NOT used:

7.4.2.1 To set off restrictive elements. [See IMPORTANT NOTE under Section 7.4.1.3.]

7.4.2.2 To separate independent clauses—unless they are joined by one of the five coordinating conjunctions (*and, but, or, nor,* and *for*). [See Section 7.4.1.1.]

Not: The generator was operated until it failed, then it was junked. [Use a period and new sentence or a semicolon.]

Not: Earnings were double those of the year before, therefore the dividend was increased. [A semicolon is needed before such words as *therefore, however, accordingly, thus, then,* and *also* (conjunctive adverbs) when they introduce independent clauses. Actually, in the above sentence, the relationship of the two ideas could be more exactly expressed by subordinating

one of the clauses: "Because earnin
were double those of the year befor
the dividend was increased."]

Not: Efficiencies were low, a typical boil
operated at only 60 per cent of 1
rated capacity. [Use a colon, sem
colon, or a period and a new se
tence.]

7.4.2.3   To separate a subject from its verb or
verb from its complement, unless an inte
polated, parenthetical, or transposed el
ment requiring punctuation intervenes:

Conclusions from this first series of inve
tigations, *made before antibiotics we.
known,* are of doubtful value. [Th
commas are needed to set off the inte
polated, nonrestrictive phrase.]

Not: The data indicate, that friction
negligible. [The complement, here
direct object, is separated from i
verb.]

Not: To terminate this research, would t
to endanger our development. [Th
subject is separated from its verb

7.4.2.4   To separate the last adjective in a seri
from its noun [see Section 7.4.1.6.]:

Not: This is a fine, healthy, specimei
[Omit second comma.]

Not: Successful planning requires n
speed, but careful, unhurried, inte
ligent, work. [Omit the last comma

7.4.3   Parentheses are used to set off an explanation, illustra
tion, or reference that is inserted in a sentence t
which it is not necessarily grammatically relate
Since parentheses have more separative force tha
commas, they should enclose only supplementar
information:

This was the second attempt (the first was made i
1910) to remove the water from the mine.

The death rate from children's diseases (measle
diphtheria, whooping cough, and scarlet fever) ha
been cut 87 per cent.

The author states (p. 181) that his investigation wa
completed in 1964.

7.4.4   The dash is properly used to indicate a sharp break in the thought or in the grammatical structure; it is seldom useful in technical writing.

> The process—we used it once before—is not efficient for small batches. [The inserted independent clause is a kind of "aside" which is unrelated grammatically to the sentence.]

The dash, as in the following excerpt from *Fortune,* is sometimes useful in securing emphasis:

> "Dr. Urey . . . drew the top Willard Gibbs Medal and Nobel Prize for the isolation of 'heavy hydrogen'— research landmark in chemistry and nuclear physics."

7.4.5   Brackets. In technical writing brackets are useful for inserting comment, correction, or explanation in quoted material. Infrequently they are used for parentheses within parentheses:

> The [coal] industry needs an economic shot in the arm.

> Magnesium [obviously a typographical error for manganese] makes an even more satisfactory alloy.

> Stevens observed (Transistors in Communications [summarized in *Business News,* pp. 157–58, November 1953]) that transistors would make this possible.

7.5   Special marks: *apostrophe* [see Section 4.2], *ellipsis, hyphen* [see Section 3], and *quotation marks.*

7.5.1   Ellipses. Ellipses (. . . or . . . .) are used, as in the second example under 7.4.4. to indicate the omission of a part of the quotation, a part believed by the writer to be unnecessary for the purpose at hand. [The marks themselves are called suspension points, three of which are used for an ellipsis inside a sentence, four for an ellipsis at the end.]

7.5.2   Quotation marks:

7.5.2.1   Use quotation marks to set off the words of another writer or speaker when you exactly reproduce them.

7.5.2.2   Long quoted passages are usually introduced by a colon, *unmarked* by quotation marks, indented from both margins, and either reduced in type size or single-spaced.

7.5.2.3   Do *not* set off indirect statements with quotation marks:

He telegraphed that the shipment had no arrived.

The exact words were, "The shipment ha not arrived."

The foreman admitted the operator wa careless.

The foreman said, "He's careless."

7.5.2.4 In bibliographical reference, use quotatio marks to enclose the name of an articl in a periodical or a chapter in a book.

7.5.2.5 Use quotation marks to enclose a technica word used in a special sense if it is likel to be unfamiliar to your reader—but onl the first time you use it.

7.5.2.6 Placement of quotation marks:

7.5.2.6.1 Place a period or a comm inside closing quotes:

Roethke said the Universit had "the edifice complex."

"This trend," the chemis pointed out, "is significant."

7.5.2.6.2 Place a colon or semicolo outside closing quotes:

The plan involves four "cal culated risks": (1) . . . . (2)

7.5.2.6.3 Place the question mar (and, similarly, the exclama tion mark) where its positio indicates how much of the sen tence it controls.

7.5.2.6.3.1 If only the quotation itself i a question, place the questio mark *inside* the closing quote

"What *is* a catalyst?"
His next question was, "Wha does a catalyst do?" [Not that no period follows th quote.]

7.5.2.6.3.2 If an entire sentence constitutes a question and ends
with quoted matter, place the
question mark outside the
closing quote:

> Did he plead "no defense"?
>
> What reason did he give for
> claiming, "Service is unpre-
> dictable"?
>
> NOTE: The last example—and
> almost any sentence in which
> both quotation *and* the con-
> taining sentence are questions
> —can be more efficiently
> written as an *indirect* ques-
> tion:
>
> What reason did he give for
> claiming (that) service is un-
> predictable?

8. LETTER FORM

Good letter form must do more than please the eye. It must minimize typing costs and must place identifying information where the reader expects to find it. Since the predominantly used block style performs both of these functions efficiently, only it and some of its modifications are discussed or illustrated in this text. Note particularly the examples on pages 255, 256.

Paper

Paper should be white, opaque, of good quality, and standard in size (8½ by 11). Half sheets or executive sizes are sometimes used, but their use poses an awkward filing problem. For intracompany correspondence, paper of various colors permits easy identification of originating department, division, or plant.

Color of Ink

Though a few reputable companies use other colors, a black typewriter ribbon is still preferred. For the signature—or for the rare occasion when the entire letter must be handwritten—only black, blue, or blue-black ink is generally accepted.

Margins and Spacing

The width of all margins depends, of course, on letter length, but it is usually better to use two pages than to crowd one. Minimum side margins of one inch are suggested for the average letter. The bottom margin should be preferably more than one inch. An even ("justified") right-hand margin is impossible on the ordinary typewriter, but there should be as little variation as possible in the length of the lines, and no line should noticeably exceed the established margin. When this principle requires the division of a word at the end of a line, the word can be divided only between syllables. (Never divide a very short word, and never separate a one-letter or two-letter syllable from the rest of the word.) A hyphen must, of course, be used to indicate the division.

The appearance of the letter depends upon intelligent spacing. Generous use of space has much to do with making the letter attractive. A good letter should give the effect of being framed on the page, with its center slightly above the center of the page.

Format

Though the modified block (Figure 25) or a slight variation of it has for many years been a big-margin favorite, the full block (Figure 26)

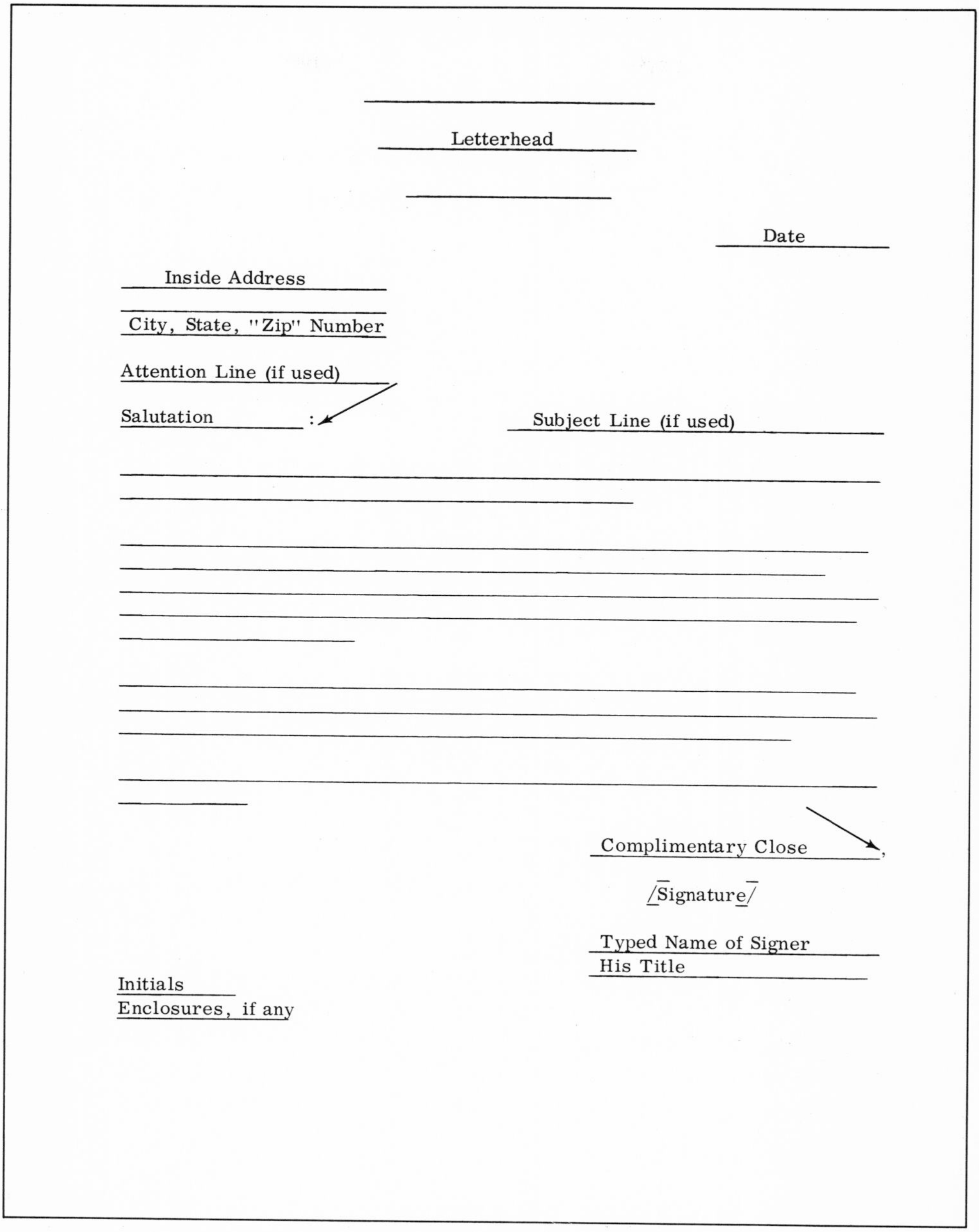

Letterhead

Date

Inside Address

City, State, "Zip" Number

Attention Line (if used)

Salutation   :

Subject Line (if used)

Complimentary Close   ,

/Signature/

Typed Name of Signer
His Title

Initials
Enclosures, if any

FIGURE 25. MOST COMMON POSITIONING OF LETTER ELEMENTS.

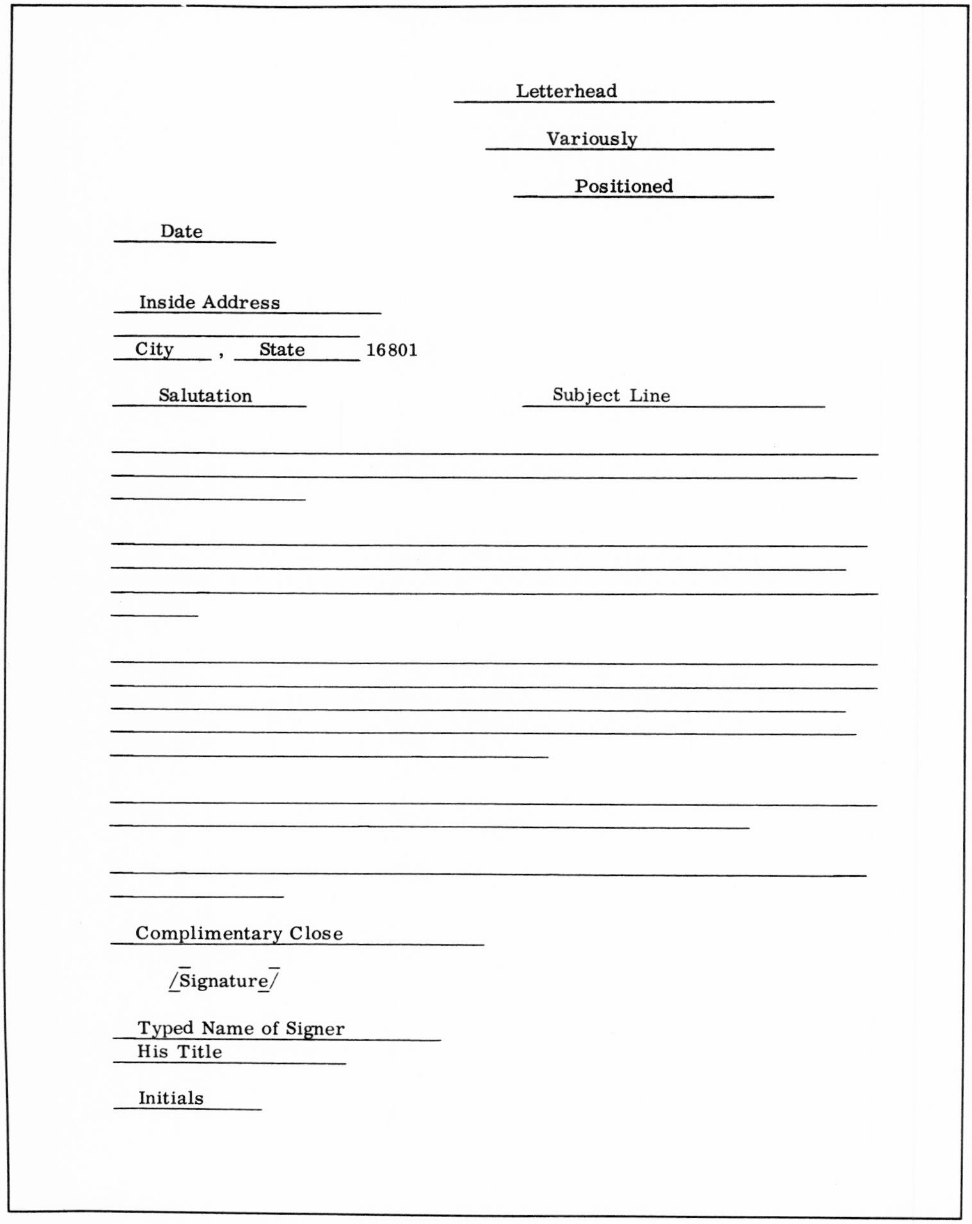

Letterhead

Variously

Positioned

Date

Inside Address

City , State 16801

Salutation   Subject Line

Complimentary Close

/Signature/

Typed Name of Signer
His Title

Initials

FIGURE 26. THE EFFICIENT FULL BLOCK.

Letterhead

Date

Inside Address

City , State 09432

SUBJECT LINE (in capitals)

/Signature/
Typed Name of Signer , His Title

cc: Persons receiving copies

FIGURE 27. THE "SIMPLIFIED LETTER" RECOMMENDED BY THE NATIONAL OFFICE MANAGEMENT ASSOCIATION (NOMA). [Full block. Open punctuation. No salutation or complimentary close. More space between formal parts.]

and the "Simplified Letter" (Figure 27) advocated by the National Office Management Association (NOMA) are gaining popularity. From the standpoint of typing they are certainly more efficient, but many consider them less attractive. Both of these modern forms oppose the inertia of tradition, and the NOMA must also contend with a general reluctance to surrender the gestures of courtesy, however stereotyped, which are provided by the salutation and complimentary close.

For a comprehensive grasp of letter spacing examine the skeletal mock-up on page 255. It represents what is probably the commonest variety of the block style. A popular variation indents each paragraph; a modernization of this form speeds typing by beginning *every* element at the left margin (see the example on page 256).

A good rule of thumb is to double-space between the parts of the letter, double-space between paragraphs, and single-space everywhere else. This rule should be tempered by good judgment in several instances:

1. When a letterhead is used, the date line may be variously placed to produce the best appearance.
2. In short letters the inside address is dropped more than two lines below the date line, and the complimentary close more than two below the letter body.
3. In all letters, sufficient space should be provided for the hand-written signature.
4. The subject (or reference) line is generally placed on the same line as the salutation—with a minimum of five spaces between.
5. The supplement (for example, identifying initials) is placed on the same line as the typed name of the signer or a few lines below it.

Conventional Letter Elements

Most of the formal parts of the letter (for example, heading, date, inside address, and signature) convey information obviously indispensable to both the receiver of the letter and to anyone reading the carbon copy. Two parts (the salutation and the complimentary close) are largely traditional concessions to courtesy. One (the initials of the dictator and the typist) is useful only to the sender—and for this reason sometimes appears only on the carbon copy. Practice in both the form and placement of these elements has become quite well established.

The Heading

Because the first page of most business letters bears a printed letterhead, only a date line is commonly required. This is sometimes placed directly below the letterhead, more often below it and to the right so that it just reaches the right-hand margin (see the example on page 255). If no printed letterhead is available, the heading appears in the upper right-hand corner, just over the date, with the end of its longest line establishing the right-hand margin:

> 1041 Fifth Avenue
> Pasadena, California
> 12 August 1970

If the date line is arranged in the more common but less logical order, a comma is needed between day and year:

> August 12, 1970

The Inside Address

The inside (introductory) address includes the name and complete address of the person, group, or company to which the letter is directed. It should be consistent with the address on the envelope. The individual or the company name must agree in spelling and abbreviation with that used by the owner (in a letterhead, for example). To preserve a neatly blocked appearance some rearrangement of the lines is often desirable:

	Mr. Hubert Engle
Mr. Hubert Engle	Vice President
Vice President for Underground Operations	Underground Operations
Thanatopsic Engineers	Thanatopsic Engineers
413 Nimitz Avenue	413 Nimitz Avenue
Rebersburg, Ohio 23401	Rebersburg, Ohio 23401
UNATTRACTIVE	IMPROVED

The Attention Line

When the individual's name is known, he is usually addressed directly. Occasionally, however, the writer wishes a prompt response from the *company,* not necessarily from a particular person in it (who may be out of town, or perhaps no longer employed there). Then the attention line is useful. If the person named in the attention line is available, he can answer the letter; if not, someone else can accept the responsibility. When used, the attention line is placed against the left-hand margin, two lines below the inside address and two above the salutation. Note the example on page 255: the word *attention* is followed directly by *Mr.* with neither *of* nor a punctuation intervening.

The Salutation

The salutation is the polite form of address introducing nearly all business letters. Usage is very strongly in favor of addressing a known individual by his or her name, an unknown individual by *Dear Sir,* and a group or company by *Gentlemen.* In every case, the salutation must address the individual or organization appearing in the first line of the inside address—even when an attention line is used (see the example on page 255). The salutation is placed against the left-hand margin two lines below the inside address, or, if one is used, below the attention line.

Subject or Reference Line

The subject line—really a heading for the letter—is becoming increasingly common, especially when frequent correspondence between two organizations involves a variety of subjects. It should be placed to the right of the salutation and should be underscored for easy recognition.

To facilitate filing—and file searching—more and more organizations are using a code or reference number for important correspondence. In response to a letter bearing such a number, it is only courteous to include this reference number just to the right of the salutation instead of using a subject line. If both a subject line and a reference number are used, place the latter at the right, three to five spaces below the date:

14 June 1964

Your Ref. 23.2410
Our file 1910-D

The Body of the Letter

The text of the letter is centered on the page, in the white space below the letterhead, and divided into relatively short paragraphs for easy comprehension. The first paragraph begins two lines below the salutation. All paragraphs are normally single-spaced, with double-spacing between. Though some styles indent paragraphs, most begin them at the left-hand margin.

If a second (or third) page is necessary, it should maintain the same side margins used on the first page, but its text is begun at the top, two lines below the second-page indentification. This identification, necessary since multipaged letters are seldom stapled, includes the name of the addressee, the page number, and the date:

Mr. Walter Carney   2   21 March 1971

or, if necessary,

Mr. Walter Carney   2   March 21, 1971
Stanton & Dill
Upland, Oregon

The Complimentary Close

It is customary to close a letter with a conventional *Yours truly, Respectfully yours, Sincerely yours, Cordially yours,* or the like. The phrase selected should have a genuine relationship to the message of the letter or with the writer's attitude toward his reader. *Sincerely yours* is relatively friendly and informal, *Yours truly* is proper but impersonal, and *Respectfully yours* should be reserved for occasions actually justifying a show of respect.

The complimentary close is placed two lines below the letter body and on a line by itself. It usually begins at the center of the page or the plumb line established by the heading or date line.

The Signature

Every letter should be signed—and proofread—by the writer. The writer, not his secretary, is responsible for both content and presentation. If the secretary *must* sign for a writer, her initials should appear below his handwritten name. Even when the signer is an executive whose name appears in the letterhead, his name, and usually his title, should be typed below the signature. Occasionally the company name precedes the signature, occasionally it follows; more often, however, it is omitted entirely, because it appears in the letterhead. Note the examples on pages 10-11.

A woman can avoid uncertainty by inserting her proper title before her typed name:

/signed/ Anne Christy   /signed/ Anne Christy
(Mrs.) Anne Christy   (Miss) Anne Christy

The Supplement

A supplement reveals who dictated the letter and to whom. A number of forms are in reputable use. All are typed against the left margin, on the same line, or a little below the last line of the signature. Some companies type the supplement on the carbon copy only, since its information is useful only to the sender. A few of the acceptable styles follow:

          Very truly yours,
          BOWMAN & NICHOLS, INC.
          /signature/
          Michael Cannon
MC:eb   General Manager

          Sincerely yours
          /signature/
          (Mrs.) Betty Cannon
BC/eb   General Manager

          Yours truly,
          /signature/
Michael Cannon: eb   General Manager
Enclosures 2

The fact that a letter contains an enclosure should be noted just below the supplement. More than one should be indicated with an arabic numeral. Important items are customarily identified.

RPM;gch	RPM/GCH	RPM–GCH
Enclosure	Encl. 3	Encl. Check $1400
		Easement agreement

The Envelope

The envelope and inside address should match (though the Post Office Department prefers city and state on separate lines). Note the placement of special directions in the example below:

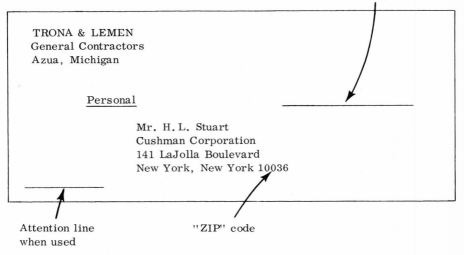

Special Delivery
Certified Mail
Registered Mail
Air Mail

TRONA & LEMEN
General Contractors
Azua, Michigan

Personal

Mr. H. L. Stuart
Cushman Corporation
141 LaJolla Boulevard
New York, New York 10036

Attention line
when used

"ZIP" code

Punctuation

The formal parts of the letter require no end punctuation except a colon after the salutation and a period after an abbreviation. Internal punctuation follows the general rules of punctuation.

Some specific practices are the following:

1. No colon is used after *Attention* in the attention line.
2. A colon *is* used after *Subject* in the subject line.
3. A colon or slant (virgule) separates the initials in the supplement.
4. A comma is used between city and state, between day and year, and (when on the same line) between name and title.
5. No marks surround the postal zone number in a city address or the "ZIP" number following the state name.

Capitalization

Capitalization presents no difficulty peculiar to the letter, but it is worth noting that the *dear* in *My dear Sir* or *My dear Mr. Simes* is not capitalized, and that only the first word in the complimentary close is capitalized. Capitalize all important words in the subject line.

Abbreviations

In the best modern correspondence, abbreviations of all kinds are usually avoided. To preserve the block appearance in the formal parts of the letter, some secretaries abbreviate the name of a state when both city and state are long names (for example, State College, Pennsylvania); others use two lines. Words like *company, corporation, limited,* and *incorporated* are abbreviated in titles *only* when abbreviated by the firm itself in its legal name. In addresses, spell out numbered streets unless their numbers require more than two words. If abbreviations are used at all (as in interoffice or intracompany correspondence), they should be used consistently. When in doubt, spell out.

Some Notes on Style

A good business letter states its business courteously but directly, without trite or stereotyped expressions (see pages 23, 29). Modern letters use the language of speech, avoiding the letter-writing jargon of the last century. The following rules should be observed in all letters:

1. Do not write the entire date in figures (5/8/64); always use the conventional form (May 8, 1964) or the modern form (8 May 1964).
2. Use figures for house numbers except *One.*
3. Write out street numbers unless they require more than two words:

   10 Fifth Avenue   910 West 125 Street   420 Forty-fifth Street

4. Omit *-st, -nd, -rd, -th* after the day of the month.
5. Avoid the participial conclusions *Hoping this will, Trusting you will,* and so forth. Conclude with a firm statement: *I hope this will please you,* or *We are sure you will find our service satisfactory.*

The

Letter

of

Application

The letter of application is usually an important first step toward eventual employment. It seldom brings an immediate offer, but if it creates genuine interest it should lead to an interview. The interview may result in the kind of job you want.

Every letter of application competes for a reader's attention with other letters, sometimes hundreds of them. Personnel directors develop their own criteria for sorting out the applicants who look most promising. The suggestions that follow derive largely from information supplied by men who have read many application letters.

WHAT THE READER LOOKS FOR

The busy executive with a pile of application letters usually begins by throwing out those that seem least promising. There is wide agreement about the kinds of letters quickly tossed aside—often without being read:

1. *The careless letter*: Misspelled words, erasures and strikeovers, worn ribbon or dirty type, bad centering, cheap quality of paper—any of these things can keep your letter from receiving a fair reading.

   "We assume the applicant is writing us the best letter he knows how to write. If he's careless about this, when could we ever trust him to be careful?"

2. *The vague letter:* Often it is not clear what kind of job the applicant wants, or why, or when. His statements are general, not specific. He includes no dates, names, places, specific duties connected with jobs he has held, courses of study, or records.

   "Without specific evidence we can't make even a preliminary judgment."

265

3. *The negative or timid letter:* An apologetic, doubtful tone suggests that the writer lacks normal self-confidence.

> "If he doesn't have *any* faith in himself, why should we have more faith?"

4. *The pompous or egotistical letter:*

> "This man just sounds like a stuffed shirt."
> "Nothing in this fellow's data sheet backs up the boasts he makes in his letter."
> "This man seems to know too much to learn anything more. We prefer a man who knows he doesn't know everything."

5. *The unorganized letter:* Letter and accompanying data sheet are too hard to read.

> "It just takes too long to find what's here."
> "A disorderly mind—not for us."

6. *The stereotyped letter:*

> "A canned letter—probably out of some textbook."
> "Nothing to distinguish this fellow from a thousand others."
> "Clichés and business gobbledygook—no hint that a human being wrote this letter."

What, then, are some of the *positive* qualities that cause such men to give an application special consideration?

1. *Efficient organization:* These readers appreciate any plan of letter and accompanying data sheet or any scheme for displaying evidence that will save their time.

2. *Distinctive facts:* These readers look closely for evidence that may distinguish one candidate from all the others. They search for something unusual.

3. *Personality:*

> "We like a letter that's natural and direct—not clever, not cute, but still individual."
> "We think we can usually tell whether the tone of a letter is genuine or phony. If it reads like a real man talking, we usually take an interest. If it reads like all the other letters in the pile, we lose interest."

WHAT YOU HAVE TO OFFER

The real basis of a good letter of application is not style, form, or make-up, however important these eventually may seem. The real basis is the kind of evidence about yourself that shows your potential worth to an employer. Once you find that kind of evidence you are in a position to sit down and plan an effective way to present it. Until you find it, you are wasting your time worrying about how to write a good letter.

First, suppose you jot down on paper all the facts about yourself and your experiences that seem at least remotely relevant:

> EDUCATION: Grad. Glover H.S.—4 yrs math—physics, chem., biol.— honor roll 3 terms—State U, B.S. in industrial eng.—Dean's list 2 semesters—etc.
>
> WORK EXPERIENCE: Part-time asst. mechanics lab., jr. year—driving truck for Worthley's summer '63—etc.
>
> HOBBIES and ACTIVITIES: Sailing—cycling—bridge—reading science fiction—secy. Traffic Club—etc.
>
> NAMES OF PERSONS WHO KNOW YOU—H.S. physics teacher—Prof. Busby-Worthley trucking—etc.
>
> PERSONAL DETAILS: Born Augusta, April 17, 1943—married, 1 son— etc.

Of course not everything you jot down may be worth including, but it is better to put down too much than too little. *Somewhere* among these jottings you should be able to find *something* which really distinguishes you from every other applicant and which may be worth emphasis in an application.

What you list should be verifiable fact. Feelings are hard to communicate, especially in a written application. Exaggeration or misrepresentation can serve no useful purpose whatever, and vague generalizations count for nothing ("very active in Boy Scouts"—"much interested in minerals"—"engaged in intramural sports").

When you apply to a specific company or agency, you should learn as much as possible about it in advance. What you learn can surely help you write a more effective letter, and the knowledge becomes especially useful if you get an interview. The corporation's annual report is one good source of information. Other sources are Standard & Poor's manuals and Moody's manuals, which include information about company histories, products and services, number of employees, number of plants, financial structure, and other matters. Articles in *Fortune* magazine about specific companies are especially enlightening.

The final step before you begin writing the application is to sort out all the details about yourself that seem worth inclusion *somewhere,* and to give double checks to those that deserve real emphasis. Naturally the applicant with a truly distinguished record ought to present a better case than the applicant with a mediocre record. Nevertheless, every applicant is expected to present his own case in the most effective way he knows how. He owes that much to himself and to his reader.

THE LETTER ITSELF

A letter of application is ordinarily accompanied by a data sheet (or résumé) which includes, for quick reference, specific information about education, experience, personal characteristics, and references. If the evidence in the data sheet is striking—and well displayed—the applicant is fortunate indeed; but the accompanying letter must arouse the reader's interest by highlighting unusual qualifications. The letter, moreover, demonstrates something of the applicant's individuality and attitudes.

The first essential is simply good taste. Paper, typing, attractive format with good margins and proper centering—all these are important because such a letter is assumed to represent the best you know how to produce. Conventional usage is expected: the proper form for heading, inside address, complimentary close, signature; normal punctuation and spelling; good idiomatic writing. Good taste, too, includes respect for the reader's intelligence: it avoids the clever or bizarre.

Generally the letter includes three main elements: a *contact* to state the business of the letter and to get attention; the *evidence* to prove that this applicant is worth more attention than others; and the *close*—to suggest action, usually a definite date for an interview. Each of these elements deserves careful attention.

The Contact

The opening paragraph must at least state the business of the letter. It may also suggest some need that this applicant can satisfy, or it may establish a favorable first impression and stimulate the reader's curiosity to learn more. The first paragraph must be comparatively short, because in busy offices mail is first classified according to subject or purpose, and your letter of application must get into the right pile of mail.

Ask yourself this: "If I were a busy personnel director, what would get *my* attention?" Then think of possible statements about yourself that might be interesting. Here are a few opening paragraphs that try to connect the applicant's wants with the wants of an employer:

> "Your sales representative in this area, Mr. James Durkee, suggests that I apply for acceptance in your Technical Sales Training Course. He thinks I meet specifications."

> "*Fortune*'s article last month about Muncy's interesting new programs suggests that you will be hiring a few graduating seniors in Labor Relations. The Stratton course I am completing in June ought to be about the right preparation for such a job."

> "The Stratton University Placement Bureau tells me you regularly hire a number of our graduating seniors in Chemical Engineering—that

they generally do well and like to work for Cordon. I am interested and believe I can qualify."

"The recent news of Muncy's new plant in West Orange leads me to believe I can be useful there in your Engineering Division."

"The two months I spent last summer in your Accounting Department were so happy and profitable that I hope you will feel as I do about a continuation. With my degree in Accounting from Stratton University in June, I should like to be considered for a permanent position."

"Your advertisement in last Sunday's *Tribune* for twenty young chemists to work in Brazil appears to be directed at me. Stratton University will give me a B.S. in Chemistry in June, and as a third-generation Portuguese-American considered good in languages, I ought to get along in Brazil."

Emphasis in your opening paragraph should be on something the reader wants and not on what you want. It ought to be confident in tone, but not boastful.

Evidence

Significant evidence to show your qualifications belongs in the middle of the letter. Since you have a data sheet that includes numerous details, there is no need to put all the facts in the letter. The letter should not be mere repetition of the data sheet. In the body of your letter you should highlight and emphasize your most impressive evidence. Here are a few paragraphs that illustrate how various applicants tried to call attention to their special qualifications:

"Last summer's job in your East Karthaus plant—ten weeks in three different departments—introduced me pretty well to the demands and methods of National Electric. I liked it, and Mr. Cartman can tell you how well I did. Now that I am expecting my degree from Stratton in Industrial Engineering next month, I believe I can do a job for you that will please us both."

"Besides carrying my course work successfully in Transportation, I have been very active in numerous organizations on campus that seem to me good preparation for what lies ahead: I have been Vice-president and House Manager of the Gamma Psi Rho fraternity, Circulation Manager of the monthly undergraduate magazine *Sights,* and campaign manager of the Progress Party that won a majority of offices in last spring's elections."

"Your consultant Dr. Gunthere gave me a job as lab assistant at the end of my sophomore year. For two academic years I have by this means earned part of my college expenses while observing Dr. Gunthere's approach to problems. That job must have had considerable influence when I came to the advanced course in Laboratory Methods under him this year. At any rate, I was one of the few undergraduates who got better than a C in that course."

"One of my most valuable college experiences has been the kind of assignment where I had to find a problem, dig out material to answer it, and then write a paper supporting my conclusions. I had such a problem in Sociology, where I wrote a term paper on 'Social Relationships of Technical and Nontechnical Students.' Another came in an Insurance course, ending with a paper on 'Insuring the Personal Loan.' Another more extensive assignment, in Report Writing, led to a report entitled 'Comparative Premiums and Dividends of Ten Life-Insurance Companies.' These assignments required a planned investigation, careful selection of evidence, and some original thinking. It seems to me that they ought to be good introductions to the kind of work you expect."

Close

The final paragraph should assume that the preceding elements of the letter have been moderately successful; you therefore shift attention to some kind of action. If you feel you have stimulated your reader's interest and provided enough evidence to justify real consideration for your application, then obviously the next step is an interview—or, if an interview is for some reason impossible, at least a definite step in the direction of employment. You should shift now from "reasons why" to "how." The best strategy is to give the reader some choice of alternatives. Here are some possibilities:

"If my qualifications seem promising, could I come to Chicago for an interview some Friday between now and mid-May?"

"From April 20 through 25 I expect to be in New Orleans for a visit with friends. Could you find time during that period when I might come to your office for an interview?"

"An interview to discuss my qualifications in detail would certainly be desirable, but perhaps not feasible. If you write to some of the references listed in my data sheet—especially Mr. Bartson—perhaps they will provide the information about me that you need."

"Since you, or another of your representatives, will be here to talk with graduating seniors next month, I wonder if you could assign me a half hour on a Thursday. That happens to be the day when I can devote the most time to interviews. I look forward to talking with you."

On page 271 we demonstrate how a weak and ineffectual letter might be revised.

The letter in the left-hand column is vague, general, verbose, and a little pompous. It tells the reader almost nothing about the applicant except that he will graduate (where?) and that he has worked (at what?). In contrast, the revision at the right is specific, concise, and informative.

Here is a checklist that should be useful in testing your letter of application:

1. Is it neat, attractive, and generally appealing to the eye?

2. Does it follow accepted usage for business letters?

INEFFECTUAL	IMPROVED
Edmund West, Power Engineer Western Salt Company Trona, Calif.	Mr. Edmund West, Power Engineer Western Salt Company Trona, California
Dear Sir:	Dear Mr. West:
I would like to be considered an applicant for a position with your firm.	Professor Larker, Head of Stratton University's Mechanics Department, says he thinks I meet the requirements for the Training Program in your Testing Division. I am available in June.
Since I am especially desirous of residence in California, and since I shall be graduated in June after two summers' employment in work related to your line of production, I possess the qualifications you require of trainees in your Testing Division.	Of this year's graduates in Mechanical Engineering, I am one of four in Professor Larker's Special Problems course who had individual testing assignments and completed a senior thesis. He knows me pretty well from the three years I served him as an assistant, and he can tell you what he thinks of my promise.
You will find me very ambitious, capable of assuming major responsibilities, and adaptable in human relationships. I enclose a data sheet which supplies numerous information concerning my education, experience, and personality, together with the names and addresses of three references who can testify regarding my character, intelligence, diligence, and personality.	The accompanying data sheet supplies information about me that you will want to have: my record at Stratton, places where I worked and at what, my activities, and names of men who know my work and have agreed to testify.
I should greatly appreciate the opportunity of a personal interview if you are at all interested.	If my qualifications seem promising, could I come to your New York office for an interview? The week of April 24–30 would be especially convenient, since I plan to visit friends in that locality at the time.
Respectfully,	Sincerely yours,
INEFFECTUAL	IMPROVED

3. Does the opening paragraph clearly state the purpose of the letter? the kind of work you want? when?

4. Will the opening paragraph catch attention and get a hearing?

5. Does the letter contain any specific evidence about yourself that will be at all convincing? Is this the most impressive evidence you can use? Does it help set you apart from other applicants?

6. Does the concluding paragraph tactfully suggest action?

7. Is the style economical, businesslike but natural, simple and direct?

8. Have you eliminated exaggerations, signs of boastfulness, unverifiable assertions, vague generalizations?

9. Have you eliminated clichés, trite expressions, every sign of the stuffed shirt?
10. Finally, is this letter *different* in a way that should attract favorable attention? Does it exhibit a decent and restrained confidence in your ability to handle the job?

THE DATA SHEET

A data sheet accompanying the letter of application has distinct advantages. In some ways it has an advantage over the application form which many companies provide, because here you have a chance to display *your* evidence in a way most effective for yourself. Naturally, if you have been given an application form to fill out, that is what you use—for that is what the prospective employer requires. But with a first letter, before you have any regular application form to restrict you, your own data sheet can be very useful.

A good data sheet permits the reader to tell in a few moments whether you have at least the minimum requirements. It helps you emphasize, without any hint of egotism, the truly impressive evidence about your qualifications. It provides a quick reference guide when the employer wants to check particular details at a later time.

Naturally, the applicant with the most impressive record ought to have the most impressive data sheet. Your aim should be to make your own qualifications stand out as clearly as the facts permit. The data sheet sticks to the facts, but you ought to make sure that all significant facts are there, and that facts that weigh most in your favor will not be missed.

Personnel directors usually expect a data sheet to include everything an application form would include, and perhaps a bit more. They expect full information about these things:

EDUCATION: School or college, degree, major and minor, rank in class (or some equally good means of measuring scholastic standing), special scholastic honors if any, relevant courses.

You may add: names of distinguished professors, unusual assignments, original studies of any kind.

Dates are always important.

WORK EXPERIENCE: Where employed? By whom? What duties? When? Immediate superior?

Most personnel directors are interested first in work closely related to the job the applicant wants, but when there is no such experience they want to know whether the applicant *ever* worked at *anything*, and if so, where and when and at what.

EXTRACURRICULAR ACTIVITIES: Names of organizations (clearly identified as to nature if the name itself is not sufficiently indicative), specific offices held and assignments carried out (not a vague "Dramatics" but "parts in four plays" or "lighting technician for five plays"); off-campus activities such as work with a Boy Scout troop or campaigning in a local election.

PERSONAL DETAILS: Date and place of birth, marital status, number of children and other dependents, possibly height and weight and any physical disabilities (if these have any relevance for the job you want), citizenship, and so forth.

For certain jobs, religious affiliation is relevant, but not for all. Sometimes race or political affiliation is relevant. But don't list things that are *not* relevant. Hobbies and special interests may deserve mention. If some of them seem particularly interesting, they should be included.

MILITARY SERVICE: Certainly dates of service, branch, grade, and kind of discharge, plus anything of interest to the prospective employer: special training or assignments, schooling, travel, and official recognition of merit.

Usually the *draft status* is essential information.

The data sheet on p. 274 illustrates good form and suggests possibilities for your own adaptations.

KENNETH R. SELVING — Data Sheet

Photograph	5173 Berkshire Avenue Danbury, Connecticut ZU 8-5656	**College address** Alpha Psi House Albany 17, New York DN 7-7686

PERSONAL DETAILS

Born Gary, Indiana, Dec. 18, 1944
Unmarried, no dependents
No military service

Good health, no physical defects
Height 5 ft 11 in. Wt: 172 lbs
Interests: science fiction, choral
  singing, bowling, golf

EDUCATION

Stratton University: B.S. in Mechanical Engineering, June 1965
  Rank in class: second fifth   Epsilon Nu (engineering society)
  Major study: Power-plant operation

Important courses (and credit hours)

Mathematics (18)	Thermodynamics (9)	English (12)
Physics (15)	Machine Design (9)	Economics (6)
Chemistry (6)	Eng. Materials (6)	Psychology (3)
Drawing (5)	Special M. E. Problems (6)	Report Writing (3)

Danbury High School, graduated 1961

ACTIVITIES AND ORGANIZATIONS

Alpha Psi (social fraternity), Chapter Secretary 1964-65
Cabinet representative, College of Engineering, junior year
Glee Club, Varsity Choir, three years
Intramural bowling, Alpha Psi team, two years
Contributor to Engineer (undergraduate quarterly)
Epsilon Nu (upper-class engineering society)
ASME, Junior member

WORK EXPERIENCE

Part-time, academic year 1964-1965   Summers 1962, 1963
  Shop Asst. to Prof. Max Croft   Parts inspector, Arvin Meter Co.
  Stratton University   Hartford, Conn.
                   Superior: Mr. C. L. Jameson
Summers 1960, 1961
  Truck driver, Carmel Lumber Co.
  Employer: Mr. Stephen Cornell, Carmel, N.Y.

REFERENCES (by permission)

Prof. Max Croft, Head   Mr. C. L. Jameson, Head
Department of Mechanical Engineering   Inspection Department
Stratton University   Arvin Meter Company
Albany, New York   Hartford 17, Connecticut

Bibliography

of

Abstracts

and

Indexes

EACH year the world production of technical articles, bulletins, and published reports numbers in the millions. One of a researcher's greatest problems is to utilize the information reported by other investigators. A thorough search of the literature may enable him to avoid waste motion—faulty procedure, false trails, overlap, possibly even complete duplication—and it may acquaint him with new materials, processes, and techniques, or with fresh points of view.

Without such indexes and abstracts as are listed in the following bibliography, a thorough search of the literature would be impossible. Automation will undoubtedly continue to improve present methods of information retrieval. (Lists of "keywords" or "descriptors" already accompany many articles and abstracts.) But until automated information retrieving approaches data-processing in practical usefulness, the researcher must depend on established indexes and abstracts.

In the following bibliography only the most important entries will be annotated beyond indicating the frequency of publication and the first year published. Entries marked with an asterisk are British publications. The list includes only a limited selection of English-language publications useful in business and technology. For others, and for the new ones constantly being added, consult the latest edition of Winchell's *Guide to Reference Works.*

1. *Accountants' Index*   Monthly   1921
2. *Aeronautical Engineering Review*   Monthly   1942
3. *Aerospace Engineering Index*   Monthly   1947
4. *Agricultural and Horticultural Abstracts* *   Quarterly   1950
5. *Agricultural Index*   Monthly   1919
   An important cumulative (annually and triennially) subject index to agricultural bulletins and periodicals.

6. *Air University Periodical Index*	Quarterly	1948
7. *Animal Breeding Abstracts* *	Quarterly	1932
8. *Annotated Bibliography of Economic Geology*	Semiquarterly	1928
9. *Applied Mechanics Reviews*	Monthly	1948
10. *Applied Science and Technology Index*	Monthly	1958

      Formerly part of the *Industrial Arts Index*. An important subject index, accumulated quarterly and annually.

11. *The Art Index*	Quarterly	1929
12. *ASM Review of Metal Literature*	Monthly	1944
13. *Astronautics Information Abstracts*	Monthly	1958

      Reports areas not covered by other indexes.

14. *Bibliography and Index of Geology Exclusive of North America*	Annual	1933

      Indexed by author. Maps by country. Comprehensive.

15. *Bibliography of North American Geology*	Annual	1919

      Includes Alaska, Hawaii, Guam, Greenland, and the West Indies.

16. *Bibliography of Scientific and Technical Reports*	Monthly	1946

      An index of reports received from civil and military agencies of the U.S. Government and cooperating foreign governments.

17. *Biological Abstracts*	10 yearly	1926

      Includes *Botanical Abstracts* and *Abstracts of Bacteriology*.

18. *Book Review Digest*	Monthly	1905

      An index and digest of book reviews appearing in British and American periodicals. Cumulative annually and semiannually. General.

19. *Books in Print* and *Subject Guide to Books in Print*	Annual	1948
20. *Business Education Index*	Annual	1940
21. *Business Periodicals Index*	Monthly	1958

      Formerly part of *Industrial Arts Index*. The most important index in accounting, advertising, banking and finance, general business, insurance, labor and management, public administration, and taxation. Subject index, cumulative annually.

22. *Ceramic Abstracts*	Monthly	1922
23. *Chemical Abstracts*	Biweekly	1907

      The most important index in chemistry and related sciences. Indexes and abstracts (in

English) over 8000 periodicals. Indexed by author, subject, numerical patent, and formula. Cumulative annually, semiannually, and decennially (1917, 1926, 1936, 1946, 1956, 1966).

24. *Chemical Titles* A current author and keyword index for selected chemical journals (about 600).	Semimonthly	1962
25. *Cumulative Book Index* A world list of books in English. Cumulative frequently but irregularly; permanent five-year accumulation.	Monthly (except August)	1898
26. *Current Contents* Actual tables of contents from journals in space, electronic, and physical sciences. Tear sheets available. Worldwide, but not translated.	Weekly	1961
27. *Current Geographical Publications*	Monthly	1938
28. *Education Index* Cumulative author and subject index to a selected list of educational periodicals, books, and pamphlets. Cumulative annually and triennially.	Monthly	1929
29. *Electronics and Communications Abstracts*	6 yearly	1961
30. *Engineering Index* Briefly annotated subject index, international in coverage.	Monthly (annually until 1962)	1884
31. *Excerpta Medica* Abstracts every article from every medical journal in the world, comprising fifteen comprehensive sections and covering the whole field of clinical and experimental medicine.	Monthly	1947
32. *Fire Research Abstracts and Reviews*	3 yearly	1959
33. *Forestry Abstracts*	Quarterly	1940
34. *Geoscience Abstracts* Formerly *Geological Abstracts*. Indexes and abstracts significant literature in geology, solid earth geophysics, and related areas. Comprises material dealing with or published in North America.	Monthly	1953
35. *Guide to Reference Books* Based on Mudge's *Guide to Reference Books, 6th Ed.* Supplements approximately every three years. Comprehensive annotated index and classification to references (including abstracts and indexes) in all languages	Irregularly	1951

36. *Highway Research Abstracts*   Monthly   1930
                                                     (except August)

37. *Index Chemicus*   Semimonthly   1957
    Useful index of new chemical compounds.
    Author and molecular formula index.

38. *Index Medicus*   Monthly   1960
    An important index by the U.S. Department
    of Health, Education, and Welfare (Public
    Health Service).

39. *Index of NASA Technical Publications*   Irregularly   1915
    An important specialized author and subject
    index formerly published by the National Ad-
    visory Committee for Aeronautics. Superseded
    by #66.

40. *The Industrial Arts Index*   Monthly 1913-1958
    A selective index to engineering, trade, and
    business periodicals. Now separated into #10
    and #21.

41. *International Aerospace Abstracts*   Monthly   1961

42. *International Index to Periodicals*   4 yearly   1907
    Cumulative author and subject index, world-
    wide in coverage, but chiefly concerned with
    humanities and science.

43. *Journal of the Institute of Petroleum Abstracts* *   Monthly   1912

44. *Keywords Index*   Semimonthly   1962
    Permuted title index for U.S. Government re-
    ports. Includes reports of AEC, NASA, ASTIA,
    and others.

45. *Mathematics Reviews*   Monthly   1940

46. *Metallurgical Abstracts* *   Monthly   1934

47. *Meteorological and Geoastrophysical Abstracts* Monthly   1950
    Formerly *Meteorological Abstracts and Bibliog-
    raphy*. Abstracts in English important literature
    of the field in every language.

48. *Mineralogical Abstracts*   Quarterly   1920

49. *New Serial Titles*   Monthly   1949
    A Library of Congress list of world periodicals
    which were first published after December
    1949. Cumulative annually and every five
    years.

50. *New Technical Books*   Bimonthly   1915
    Acquisitions by the New York Public Library.

51. *The New York Times Index*   Semimonthly   1913
    Classifies and summarizes news alphabetically
    by subject, person, or organization. Cumula-
    tive annually.

52. *Nuclear Science Abstracts*	Semimonthly	1947

Each issue includes subject, personal and corporate author, and report number indexes. Cumulative quarterly, semiannually, and annually. Published by the Division of Technical Information of the U.S. Atomic Energy Commission. Covers reports of USAEC and its contractors; technical reports of government agencies, universities, and independent research organizations in the U.S. and abroad; also book, patent, and journal literature (and translations) on a worldwide basis.

53. *Plant Breeding Abstracts* *	Quarterly	1932
54. *Population Index*	Quarterly	1935

Annotated. Worldwide. Cumulative annually. Index by author and country.

55. *Psychological Abstracts*	Monthly	1927

An important index of author and subject by the American Psychological Society.

56. *Public Affairs Information Service (PAIS)*	Weekly	1915

Index to all kinds of material concerning political science, government, economics, sociology, and law. Cumulative five times a year and annually.

57. *Quality Control and Applied Statistics—Abstract Service*	Monthly	1956
58. *Quarterly Cumulative Index Medicus*	Quarterly	1879

Formerly *Index Medicus* and *Quarterly Cumulative Index to Medical Literature*. Worldwide author and subject index by the American Medical Association.

59. *Readers' Guide to Periodical Literature*	Semimonthly	1900

The most important nonspecialized index. Cumulative at irregular intervals and annually.

60. *Refrigeration Abstracts*	Quarterly	1946
61. *Reviews of Modern Physics*	Quarterly	1929
62. *Science Abstracts* *	Monthly	1898

Section A: Physics Abstracts
Section B: Electrical Engineering Abstracts
Each section cumulated and issued separately. Monthly author index, but classified by subject. Worldwide and translated.

63. *Scientific and Technical Aerospace Reports (STAR)*	Semimonthly	1963
64. *Sociological Abstracts*	6 yearly	1953

65. *Technical Abstract Bulletin*   Semimonthly   1953
    Published by the Armed Services Technical
    Information Agency (ASTIA). Subject index.
    Descriptors included.

66. *Technical Book Review Index*   10 yearly   1935
    Useful guide to reviews. Sometimes annotated.

67. *Technical Publications Announcements*   Biweekly   1961
    NASA list of releases.

68. *Technical Translations*   Semimonthly   1957
    Index and abstracts by U.S. Department of
    Commerce (Business and Defense Administra-
    tion, Office of Technical Services).

69. *Monthly Catalog of U.S. Government Publica-*   Monthly   1895
    tions
    Indexes all nonclassified government publica-
    tions by government author (issuing agency,
    administration, bureau, or office). Cumulative
    annually.

70. *U.S. Government Research Reports (USGRR)* Semimonthly   1946
    Formerly *Bibliography of Technical Reports*.
    Announces material available through the Of-
    fice of Technical Services (OTS). Descriptors
    included with abstracts.
    > *Section 1: Subject Index*
    > *Section 2: Technical Abstract Bulletin*
    > *Section 3: Military and Nonmilitary Research*
    > *Papers*

71. *The U.S. Quarterly Book List*   Quarterly   1945
    A selective bibliography, descriptively anno-
    tated, of books currently published in the
    United States.

72. *U.S. Patent Office Official Gazette*   Weekly   1872
    Used with the *Patent Office Manual of Classi-*
    fication and *Index to Classification Subject*
    Headings. A complete reference to patents (de-
    scriptions, patentees, patent suits, and so forth).

73. *Zoological Record* *   Annual   1864

Index

A

ABBREVIATIONS:
 American Standard list, 215-20
 in letters, 263
 rules for, 213-14, 223
Abbreviations for Scientific and Engineering Terms, 213
Abstracts, 33, 100-102, 274-80
Accuracy, 5, 27, 31-32, 48, 73
Address, 259
Adjective compounds, 46, 224
Advisability of action, subjects for reports, 8
American Potash and Chemical Corp., monthly report, 182-86
American Standards Association, 54, 125, 144, 213, 214
Analogies, 71
Analyzing the problem, 60-62
Andre, David J., 101
Annual report outlines, 86-87
Answer to inquiry, 12-15
 specimens, 13, 14-15
Anthracite-burning stokers, report, 204-209
Apostrophe, 228, 251
Appearance:
 of letter, 265, 268
 of report, 119
Appendix of report, 27, 129, 151
Application, letter of, 265-74
Armstrong Cork Co. outline, 83-84
Arrangement (*see* Organization)
Arthur D. Little, Inc., 32
Art of Readable Writing, 29
Assignments for reports, 6-8
Atlantic Monthly, 30
Attention line, 259
Authorization, 18, 93, 96

Automation in trucking industry, proposed policies, outline, 91

B

BAR CHART, 152
Battelle Memorial Institute, outlines, 83, 89
Bell Telephone Co., 146
Bibliography, 129-31
 of abstracts and indexes, 274-80
 specimen references, 132
 working, 64
Binding, 120
Body of letter, 260
Body of report, 126-27
Brackets, 251
Brief, 78
 exercise, 91
Bureau of Mines, 102, 146, 147
 report, 199-209
Bureau of Standards outline, 83

C

CAPITALIZATION, 54, 130, 213, 221-23, 263
Captions (*see* Headings)
Cards, use of, 73
Careless modifiers, 39
Careless reference, 40-42
Cause and effect, 7, 71
Central thesis and support, 77-78
Charts (*see* Mechanical aids)
Chemical Abstracts, 101, 276-77
City plan outline, 86
Civil Service Commission, 140
Clarity, 26, 27-28, 37-42, 112
Climactic order, 36, 104
Close of letter, 260-61, 270
Collecting data, 60-76
Colon, 244-45
Comma, 246-50
Communications consultants, 29
Comparison of values, subjects, 7
Complimentary close, 260-61
Compounds, 46, 223-25
Computer Control Company, 110
Conciseness, 28-29, 42-49

Conclusions and recommendations, 33, 103, 125-26
Condensation (*see* Summary)
Confirmation report, 21-22
Consistency, 27, 35, 36
Construction progress, Wilson Dam, 177-81
Contact paragraph, 9, 12, 18, 268-69
Contents (*see* Table of Contents)
Cover letters, 95, 96
Curves (*see* Mechanical aids)
Cuts, 137

D

DANGLING MODIFIERS, 38-39, 40
Data:
  collecting, 60-76
  evaluating, 113
  interpreting, 111-14
  recording, 68, 72-76
Data sheet, 272-74
Dates, style for, 240
Deadwood, 23, 26, 29, 43-49, 100
Decimals, 239
Definitions, 28, 97, 106-109
  examples, 97-98, 108, 109
  of object and scope, 16, 97-98
Demand for reports, 1-8
Detroit Edison Company report plan, 82
Diagrams, 142
Diction, 30, 31, 32, 229-37
Digest, 98, 105
Digital systems, 111
Direct observation and experiment, 64-65
Documentation, 72-76, 131-35
DuPont de Nemours & Company outline, 83

E

ECKERD, J. W., 204
Economy, 5, 23, 26, 42-49
Editorial departments, 3
Ellipses, 251
Emphasis, 35
Employers' complaints, 1
Employment statistics, 117, 118
Endnotes, 135
Engineering, abbreviations for, 215-20
Engineering and Scientific Graphs for Publication, 144
Engineer's Annual Report of Power Plant outline, 87
Envelope for letter, 262

Epitome, 77, 78, 98, 99-100
"Escalator" sentence, 36
Evaluating the data, 113
Evidence, 62-70, 71-72
  for applications, 269-70
  direct observation and experiment, 64-65
  evaluating, 113
  from interview and questionnaire, 67-70
  from reading, 62-64
  sampling, 65-67
Exaggeration, 31-32
Examination of a mine, outline, 88
Examination report (*see* Investigative reports)
Executive, 1, 3, 4, 12, 22, 28, 60, 265-66
Exhibits, 151
Experiment, observation, 64-65
Explanation of mechanisms, processes, and organizations, 110-11
Exposition, 2, 92 (*see also* Rhetorical elements)

F

FACTS (*see* Data)
Faulty predication, 35
"Feasibility of Using Radioisotopes to Measure Catalyst Circulation Rates in the Catalytic Cracking Unit of the Sungei Gerong Refineries," 154-76
Figures (illustrations) 129, 142-52
Figures (*see* Numbers)
Final summary (*see* Terminal)
First principles, 5-6
Flesch, Rudolph, 29, 49
Flow sheets, 150
"Fog Index," 29-30
Footnotes, 133-35
  examples, 134
Foreign words (plurals), 226-28
Foreword (*see* Introductions)
Form and style in letters, 22-23, 254-63
Format, 119-52
  for letters, 254-58
Form of report, 2, 79
Fortune, 51, 74, 115, 141, 144
Fractions, 238, 239

G

GENERALIZATIONS (*see* Sampling)
General Motors Corporation, 102
Glossary of usage, 229-37

Goodyear Tire and Rubber Company, 83
Graphs, 143-49
Guiding principles for report writing, 5-6
Gunning, Robert, 29, 49

H

HANDBOOK SECTION, 211-64
Headings, 18, 104, 121-25, 126-27, 128
   in letters, 258-59
   specimen page, 128
"Hedging," 32, 47
"How NSF Got Lost in Mohol," 51
HRB-Singer, Inc., 149
Hyphenation, 54, 223-25

I

ILLUSTRATION GUIDE, U.S. BUREAU OF MINES, 147
Indexes, 63, 100, 274-80
Industrial development of region, outline, 90-91
Informative abstract or summary, 99, 101-102
Inquiry:
   answer to, 12-15
   letter of, 9-12
Inspection report subjects, 7
Instructions, letter (memo) of, 12-17
   exercises, 23-25
Interoffice communication, proposals to improve, outline, 89-90
Interpretation of data, 111-14
   exercises, 115-18
Interrogation, 67-70
Interviews, 67-70
   exercises, 76
Introductions, 92-98, 125
Introductory summary, 103-104
Investigation, 2, 16 (see also Collecting data)
Investigative reports:
   outlines, 82-85, 88-89
   subjects for, 7
   U.S. Bureau of Mines, 199-209
Irrelevancies, 22, 35
Issues, 5, 60-62

K

KIRCH, J. H., et al., 101

L

LAYOUT (see Format)
Length:
   of letters, 16
   of paragraphs, 32-33
   of reports, 2, 4-5, 79
   of sentences, 29, 30, 49-50
Letter and memorandum, 9-24
Letters:
   answers to inquiry, 12-15
   of application, 265-73
   cover, 95, 96
   exercises, 23-25
   form, examples, 254-63
   of inquiry, 9-12
   of instructions, 12, 16-17
   reports, 16-22
   of transmittal, 93-95
Library indexes, 63-64
Library investigation, 62-64
Life expectancy tables, 116, 117
Literature search, subjects, 8
Little, Arthur D., Inc., 32
Logic, 70-72, 113-14

M

MANUSCRIPT, PREPARING, 92-152
Maps, 142
Margins:
   of letter, 254
   in reports, 136-37
Mechanical aids, 138-52
Mechanical considerations, style, 53-55
Mechanics in letter-writing, 254-62
Mechanisms, explaining, 110-11
Memorandum, 9, 16, 17, 18-22, 23, 95, 96
Methods of investigation, 16, 64-65
Metropolitan Life Insurance Co., 116
Mine, examination of, outline, 88
Modifiers, 39-42
Monthly report, research and development, 182-86

N

NATIONAL OFFICE MANAGEMENT ASSOCIATION (NOMA), 257
N/C Control Compared to Other Systems, table, 141
New York Central System, report, 189-98
New York Times, The, 148, 152
Nonrestrictive elements, 246-47

Note-taking, 68, 72-76
  specimens, 74
Nuclear Science Abstracts, 101
Numbering system for subdivisions, 125, 211ff.
Numbers, use of, 55, 101, 225, 238-42, 263
  in bibliography, 130, 131
  page, 137

O

OBJECTIVITY, 2, 5, 65
Observation and experiment, 64-65
Organization, 77-92
Organization charts, 149-51
Organizations, explaining, 110-11
Outlines for reports:
  investigative reports, 82-85, 88-89
  periodic reports, 80-81, 86-87
  preliminary, 60-62, 73
  progress reports, 81-82, 87
  proposals and recommendation reports, 85-86, 89-91
Owens-Corning Fiberglas Corporation, outline, 83

P

PAGE NUMBERING, 137
Paper, 136
Paragraphs, 32-34
  "contact," 9, 12
  exercises, 58-59
  in letters, 9, 12, 18, 268-70
  length, 32-33
  for recommendations, 103
  topic sentences for, 33, 34
Parallel construction, 36-37, 52-53
Parentheses, 250
Parks and Recreation Dept. chart, 150
Participial ending, 263
Passive voice, 38-39
Percent, percentage, 235, 240
"Performance of Small Industrial-Type Anthracite-Burning Stokers," 199-209
Period, 243-44
Periodic reports, 6, 182-86
  plans, 80-81, 86-87
Personnel directors, 265-66, 272
Photographs, 142, 143
Pictographs, 146
"Pie" diagram, 148
Planning the report, 77-92
Plant manager's report outline, 81

Plurals, 226-28
  in abbreviations, 213
Population statistics, 116
Possessives, 228
Preciseness, 28
Prefaces, 92-95
Preferred usage, 229-37
Preliminary report, 18-19
Preparing the manuscript, 92-152
Primary reader, 4
Principles, guiding, 5-6
Printed forms, 79
Printer, submitting manuscript to, 137
Problem, analyzing a, 5, 60-62
Processes, explaining, 110-11
Progress reports:
  epitome, 77
  exercises, 25
  plans, 81-82, 87
  specimens, 177-81
  subjects for, 6-7
Proposals, 20, 85, 89-90
Punctuation, 55, 242-53
  in bibliography, 130-31
  in letters, 262
  in numbers, 241
Pure Oil Company outline, 86-87

Q

QUALIFICATIONS OF REPORT WRITER, 5
Qualifying judgments, 32
Questionnaire, 67-70
  exercises, 76
Questions and answers in letters, 10-15
Quotation marks, 106, 251-53
Quotations, 131-33, 249

R

RADIOISOTOPES, REPORT, 154-76
Random sample, 65-67
Raytheon Manufacturing Company, outline, 86
Readability, 27, 29-31
Reader adaptation, 2, 3-5, 28
Reader's Digest, 28
Reading for evidence, 62-64
Recap sheet, 75
Recommendation reports:
  epitome, 78
  N. Y. Central System, 189-98
  outlines, 85-86, 89-91
  subjects for, 7-8
Recommendations, 2, 103
Recording data, 72-76

Reference abstracts and indexes, 274-80
References in reports, 129-35
Relevance, 22, 35
Responsibility, 2, 16
Restraint, 31-32
Restrictive elements, 249
Rhetorical elements, 92-118
Rockefeller Panel Reports, 75

S

SALUTATION IN LETTER, 259-60
Sampling, 65-67, 71
  exercise, 76
Scientific American, 28
Scientific terms, American Standard
    abbreviations, 215-20
Scientific writing, 32
Scope, 16, 97, 98
Search of the literature, subjects, 8
Secondary readers, 4
Selection of materials, outline, 89
Selection of sites, subjects, 8
Semicolon, 245
Sentences:
  accuracy, 53
  clarity, 37-42
  completeness, 37
  direction, 51-52
  economy, 42-49
  exercises for revision, 55-58
  length, 29, 30, 42-49
  readability, 49-53
  topic, 33, 34
  unity, 34-37
  variety, 50-51
Siefert, H. S., 105
Signature in letters, 261
Simplicity, 23, 27, 29-31
Simplification, 111-12
Simplified letter, 27, 258
Solow, Herbert, 51
Sources, 62-70, 129-31, 274-80
Spacing, 136-37
  in letters, 254, 258
Specimen reports, 153-210
Spelling, 54-55, 226-28
Statistical Abstract of the U.S., 140
Statistics, 111-14, 138-42
  for interpretation, 115-18
Status report, 187
Stereotypes, 23, 29
Stratified sample, 65, 66
Style:
  of a good report, 26-59
  in letter and memo, 22, 23

Subject line, 260
Subjects for reports, 6-8
Submitting manuscript to printer, 137
Subtitles (*see* Headings)
Sumantri, Raden B., 154
Summaries, 18, 19, 33, 81, 82, 83, 84,
    85, 93, 98-106, 111-12, 125
  of conclusions, 18, 19, 33
  of evidence, 105-106
Supplement in letter, 261-62
Synopsis, 98

T

TABLE OF CONTENTS, 121-25
  specimen, 123-24
Tables, 129
  rules for, 138-42
  specimens, 139, 140, 141
Technical abbreviations, 213-20
Technique of Clear Writing, 29
Telegraphic style, 37
Tennessee Valley Authority:
  outline, 83
  report, 177-81
Tenney, R. F., 204
Terminal summary, 104-105, 127, 129
Thesis, 27
  and support, 77-78
Title page, 120-22
  specimen, 121
Titles:
  of reports, 120-22
  of tables, 138
Tone of report, 2, 27
Topical summary or abstract, 99, 101-
    102
Topic sentences, 33, 34
Transitions, 34
Transmittal, letter of, 93-95
Triteness, 23
Trucking industry, proposed policies to
    meet automation in, 91
Types of mechanical aids, 138-52

U

"ULTRASONIC PROOF TESTING OF SPARK
    PLUG CERAMIC BODIES," 88-89
Unity, 26, 27-28, 30, 33
Usage, 55, 229-37
U.S. Bureau of Mines, report, 199-209
U.S. Department of the Army, status re-
    port, 187

V

VOLUNTARY SUPPORT OF AMERICA'S COL-
LEGES AND UNIVERSITIES, FIGURES,
148

W

WALL STREET JOURNAL, 30
Waste, 26, 42-49

Western Union, outline, 83-84
Westinghouse Research Laboratory Re-
port, 105
What Is a Report, 2
White Collar Employees in Federal
Government, table, 140
Wilson Lock, report, 143, 177-81
Winchell's *Guide to Reference Works,*
274